RECENT DEVELOPMENTS IN THE

CHEMISTRY OF NATURAL
PHENOLIC COMPOUNDS

RECENT DEVELOPMENTS IN THE

CHEMISTRY OF
NATURAL
PHENOLIC COMPOUNDS

Proceedings of the
Plant Phenolics Group Symposium

Edited by

W. D. OLLIS

Department of Organic Chemistry
University of Bristol

SYMPOSIUM PUBLICATIONS DIVISION

PERGAMON PRESS

OXFORD · LONDON · NEW YORK · PARIS
1961

PERGAMON PRESS LTD
Headington Hill Hall, Oxford
4 & 5 Fitzroy Square, London W.1

PERGAMON PRESS INC
122 East 56th Street, New York 22, N.Y.
1404 New York Avenue N.W., Washington 5, D.C.
Statler Center 640, 900 Wilshire Boulevard
Los Angeles 17, California

PERGAMON PRESS S.A.R.L.
24 Rue des Écoles, Paris V^e

PERGAMON PRESS G.m.b.H.
Kaiserstrasse 75, Frankfurt am Main

Library of Congress Card Number 61–10648

Set in Monotype Times 10 on 12 pt
and printed in Northern Ireland at The Universities Press, Belfast.

173181

PREFACE

THIS volume is based on the lectures which were given at the Symposium held in April 1960 by the Plant Phenolics Group at its Third Annual General Meeting. The contributions to the Symposium were selected in an endeavour to cover most of the current investigations on the chemistry of naturally occurring phenolic compounds. Although it was not possible at a meeting of this type to provide a comprehensive coverage, reference was made to most of the more important and interesting recent developments in the subject.

When the Committee of the Plant Phenolics Group invited me to act as editor of this publication it was felt that rather than provide a record of the lectures and the discussions, it would be much more rewarding to encourage the authors to expand their contributions and review their subjects in relation to the general context of current research in natural product chemistry. I should like to thank all the authors for their co-operation in providing contributions of this type. As much of the work described by Professor R. D. Haworth and Dr. E. Haslam is awaiting publication, a full account of their lectures is not given. However, they both very kindly agreed that summaries of their talks should be included and I should like to thank them for making this possible.

The book may be divided into two parts which are concerned with the biosynthesis and the determination of the structure of phenolic natural products.

The first three chapters are concerned with various aspects of biosynthesis and include a detailed account of recent contributions by the Manchester school, a broad survey of the structural and biogenetic relationships among a large number of natural products, and a review of the biosynthesis of flavonoids with particular reference to the isoflavones. Recently there has been considerable interest in the variety of structures shown by phenolic compounds containing terpenoid substituents and this is reviewed in Chapter 4. The following chapter deals with the recent syntheses of various natural products by methods involving oxidative coupling of phenolic precursors. These methods are of interest because of their relationship to natural biosynthetical routes.

Recently there has been a revival of interest in the chemistry of the tannins. This is covered by Chapters 6, 7, and 8 and it is clear that other interesting developments in this field may be expected shortly. The rest of the book deals with structural investigations which have led to the recognition of several new classes of natural products. The discovery of the families of related compounds illustrates one of the fascinating aspects of natural product chemistry.

The Plant Phenolics Group is an informal group of scientists which meets several times each year with the object of promoting "the advancement of the knowledge of phenolic and related constituents of plants in respect of their chemistry, function, biosynthesis, effect on plant and animal physiology and pathology, and the application of such knowledge in agriculture and industry." Membership is open to all and application may be made to the Hon. Secretary, Dr. T. Swain, Low Temperature Research Station, Downing Street, Cambridge.

Special thanks are due to the Pergamon Press and to the Committee of the Plant Phenolics Group for their advice in the preparation of this book and to the Sub-Committee, Dr. E. C. Bate-Smith, Dr. T. Swain, Professor R. D. Haworth, Professor E. J. Bourne, and Dr. J. B. Pridham, who arranged the Symposium. I should also like to thank Miss J. M. Bovett for her valuable assistance in the preparation of typescripts for this publication.

W. D. OLLIS

Bristol, 1960

CONTENTS

LIST OF CONTRIBUTORS

W. BAKER, Department of Organic Chemistry, The University, Bristol 8.

A. S. DREIDING, Organisch-Chemisches Institut der Universität Zürich, Zürich, Switzerland.

H. GRISEBACH, Chemisches Laboratorium der Universität Freiburg, Freiburg i. Br., Germany.

E. HASLAM, Department of Chemistry, The University, Sheffield 10.

C. H. HASSALL, Department of Chemistry, University College of Swansea, Singleton Park, Swansea.

R. D. HAWORTH, Department of Chemistry, The University, Sheffield 10.

L. HÖRHAMMER, Institut für Pharmazeutische Arzneimettellehre der Universität München, Germany.

W. D. OLLIS, Department of Organic Chemistry, The University, Bristol 8.

R. W. RICKARDS, Department of Chemistry, The University, Manchester 13.

A. I. SCOTT, Chemistry Department, The University, Glasgow, W.2.

O. Th. SCHMIDT, Chemisches Institut der Universität Heidelberg, Germany.

I. O. SUTHERLAND, Department of Organic Chemistry, The University, Bristol 8.

H. WAGNER, Institut für Pharmazeutische Arzneimittellehre der Universität München, Germany.

W. B. WHALLEY, Department of Organic Chemistry, The University, Liverpool.

CHAPTER 1

THE BIOSYNTHESIS OF PHENOLIC COMPOUNDS FROM ACTIVATED ACETIC ACID UNITS

R. W. RICKARDS

University of Manchester

Two major biosynthetic routes leading to aromatic compounds are now established, one based on shikimic acid, the other on acetic acid. Recognition of the former route (Fig. 1) by Davis and his associates[1] depended chiefly on

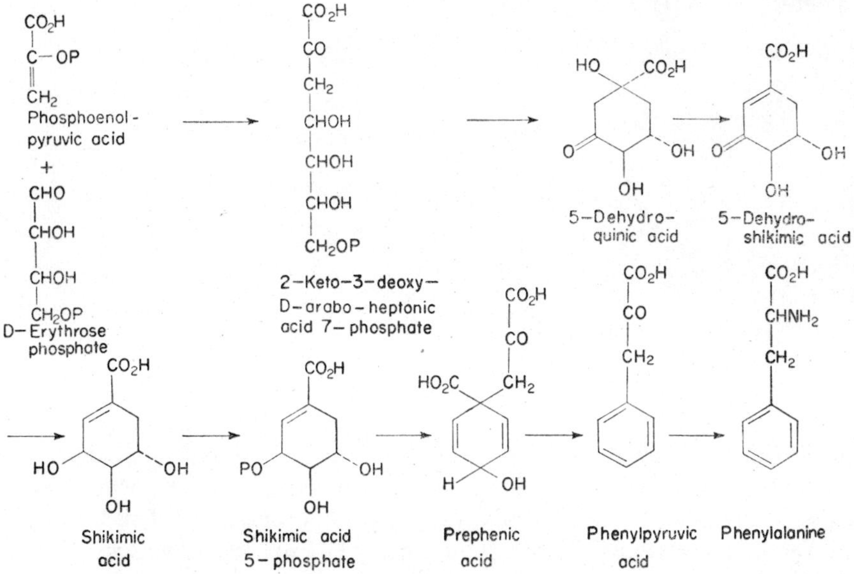

FIG. 1

the use of mutants of micro-organisms (mainly *Escherichia coli* and *Aerobacter aerogenes*) deficient in the ability to produce certain essential metabolites, including phenylalanine, tyrosine, tryptophan and *p*-aminobenzoic acid.

The acetate route was recognized initially by Collie,[30,31] and later independently and on different grounds by Birch[2] as the result of inductive reasoning from structural comparisons of a large number of natural products, chiefly phenols. Acetic acid, of known importance in the biosynthesis of fats and terpenoids, was revealed as a structural unit in phenolic compounds by the presence of "marker" oxygen atoms, just as the structural units in isoprenoid compounds are delineated by carbon atoms, and in alkaloids by carbon and nitrogen atoms.

Phenolic biosynthesis from acetic acid can conveniently be considered at two levels: first, generation of the main carbon–oxygen skeleton from acetate units, and secondly, subsequent structural modifications of this skeleton, including the introduction and removal of certain substituents.

THE HYPOTHESIS—GENERATION OF THE CARBON–OXYGEN SKELETON

Hypothetically, acetic acid units (biologically activated for acylation as their thiolesters with coenzyme-A) are joined by formal elimination of water in head-to-tail linkage with each other or with naturally occurring carboxylic acids to form β-polyketomethylene-acids. Ring closure by aldol condensation or C-acylation would then produce phenols of the orcinol or acylphloroglucinol type, respectively (Fig. 2). The terminal acid, RCO_2H,

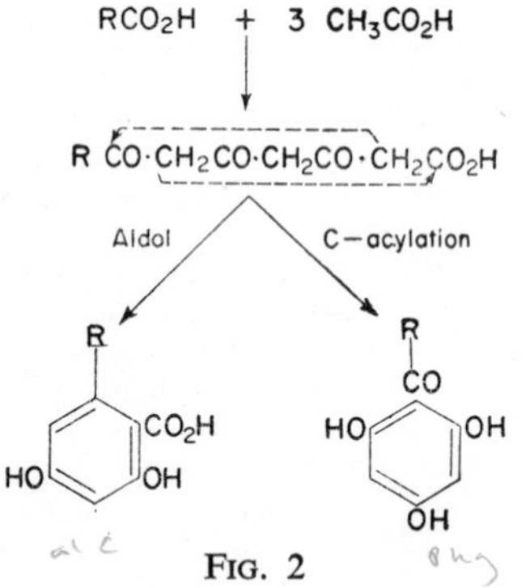

FIG. 2

could be any natural acid, but is frequently a fatty acid, a branched chain acid related to the terpenes or amino-acids, or a cinnamic acid. Known natural products provide many illustrations of the possible operation of such routes.

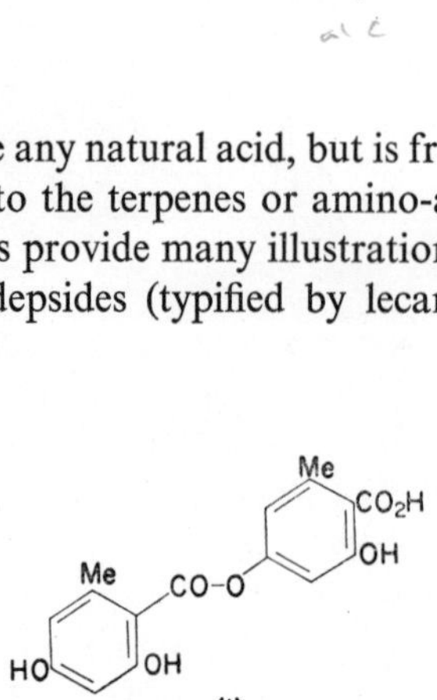

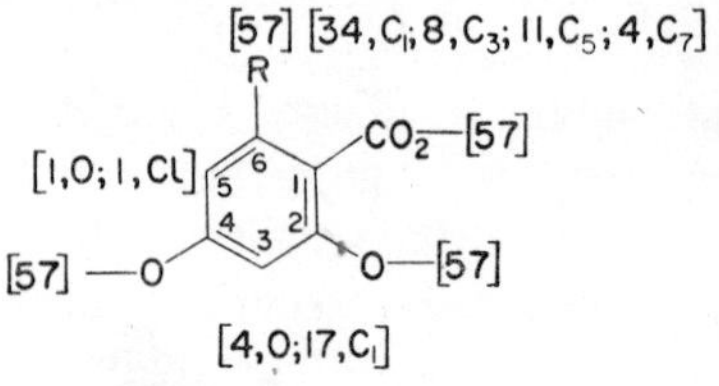

The depsides (typified by lecanoric acid, 1) from the lichens provide a particularly convincing example of the orcinol-type route.[3] Formula (2) summarises the frequencies of occurrence of substituents in the unit nucleus of known depsides (described in a review by Nolan[4]), in which two of these units are joined by an ester group.

It is clear that a common factor represented by structure (2) is present: the side chain (R) always has an odd number of carbon atoms in accord with its benzyl carbon originating in the methyl group of acetic acid; substituents at the 3- or 5-positions of the ring are less numerous, and unlike those at the

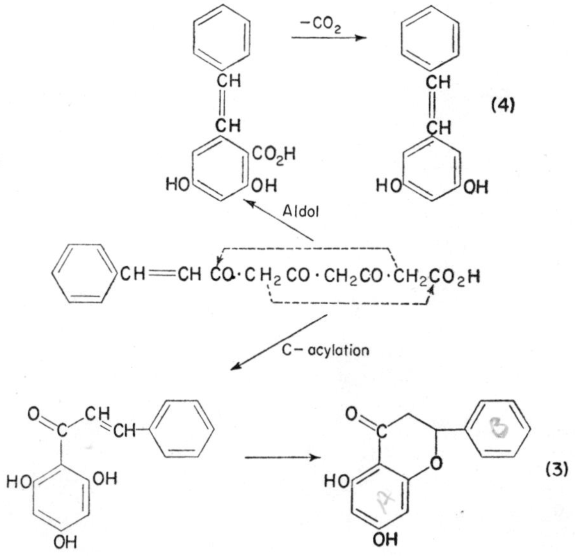

FIG. 3

1-, 2-, 4-, and 6-positions can be either one-carbon or oxygen substituents. The co-occurrence of derivatives of flavanoids (e.g. 3) and pinosylvin (4) in pine heartwoods[5] is indicative of the simultaneous operation of both types of ring closure, the terminal acid being here a cinnamic acid (Fig. 3). Cinnamic acid itself has been found in pines.[6]

THE HYPOTHESIS—MODIFICATION OF THE CARBON–OXYGEN SKELETON

Carbon–oxygen skeletons generated from acetic acid by processes of these types can undergo secondary structural modifications, occurring either before or after cyclization. These modifications include principally the introduction and removal of oxygen, alkylation notably with methyl and isoprenoid groups, and halogenation, and enable extension of the acetate hypothesis to many natural substances not directly within its scope.

(i) *Modification by Introduction and Removal of Oxygen*

Oxidation of phenols at their *o*- or *p*-positions is chemically facile, and similar biological introduction of oxygen is indicated notably by the frequent co-occurrence of anthrones with the related anthraquinones [e.g. (5) and emodin (6) derived by decarboxylation of a β-polyketo-acid precursor which is probably related structurally to the naturally occurring endocrocin, emodin-2-carboxylic acid (7)]. *p*-Quinones in general provide many examples of skeletal modifications of this type [e.g. flaviolin, (8)].

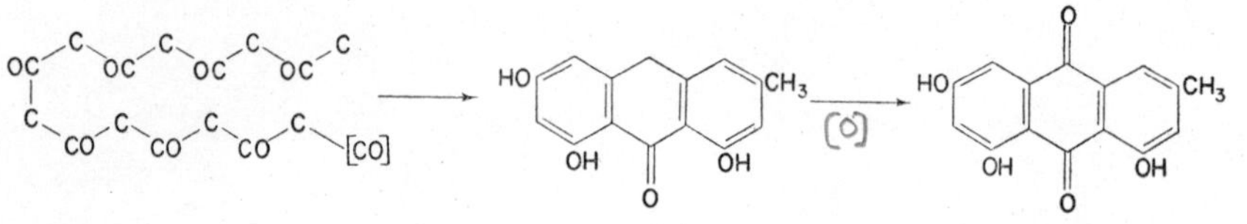

(5)   (6)

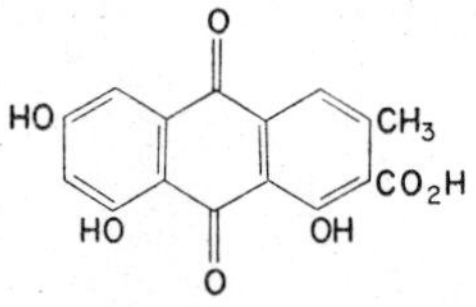

(7) 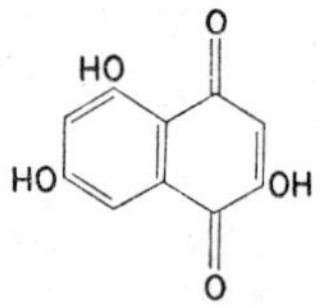   (8)

Oxidation may also occur at methyl groups, whether derived from the acetate skeleton itself or "introduced". Stages in this oxidation process can be discerned in many cases, for example the pigments physcion (emodin-6-methylether, 9; R = CH_3), fallacinol (9; R = CH_2OH) and fallacinal (9; R = CHO) of the lichen *Xanthoria fallax*, and ω-hydroxyemodin and emodic acid (10) which occur in *Penicillium cyclopium*.

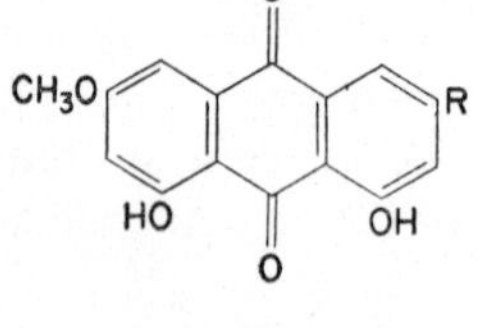

(9) 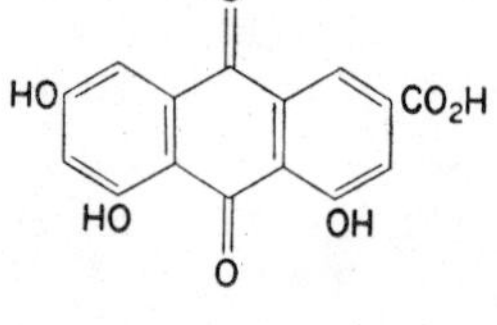   (10)

A number of natural phenols lacks one or more of the "marker" oxygen atoms delineating the original acetate units. Such removal of oxygen probably involves reduction of a carbonyl group to hydroxyl in a non-aromatic intermediate, followed by dehydration, as occurs in the biological formation of crotonic acid from acetoacetic acid. In some cases intermediate stages in this oxygen removal process are found: both flavoskyrin (11) and its dehydration product, chrysophanic acid (12), have been isolated from

Penicillium islandicum, and may be compared with emodin (6) and helmin-thosporin (13) in which both removal and introduction of oxygen have occurred.

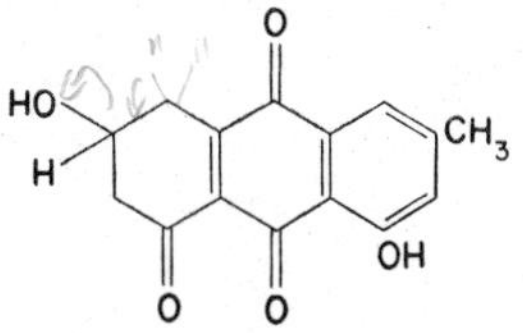

(11) 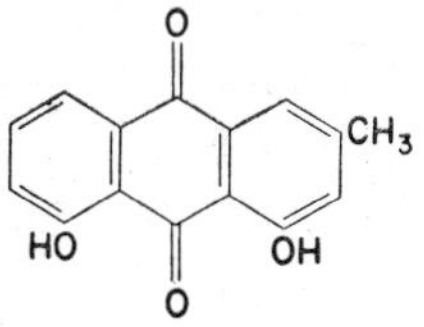   (12) 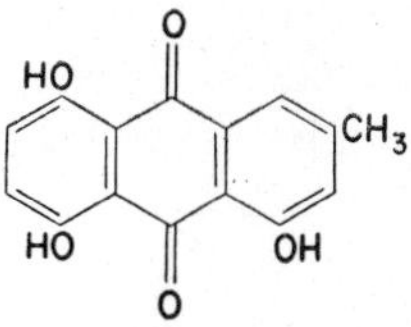   (13)

(ii) *Modification by Alkylation*

Alkylation of the carbon skeleton may occur at positions of anionoid reactivity, either before cyclization at the methylene groups of β-polyketone intermediates, or after cyclization at the methine groups of a phenolic ring. The alkyl groups thus introduced are commonly methyl, isopentenyl, and multiples of the latter. The enzymic C-alkylation probably occurs via the cations CH_3^+ [donated from methionine $CH_3SCH_2CH_2CH(NH_2)CO_2H$, or choline $HOCH_2CH_2\overset{+}{N}(CH_3)_3$] and $(CH_3)_2C{=}CHCH_2^+$ (generated from iso-pentenyl pyrophosphate) in processes analogous to S-, N-, or O-methylation.

Consideration of several series of compounds [e.g. the series xanthoxylin (14), baeckeol (15), butanofilicinic acid (16), tasmanone (17), and leptosper-mone (18); and the hop "phenols" humulone (19) and lupulone (20)] in which the individuals differed essentially only in the degree of biological alkylation of a common carbon skeleton indicated that such alkyl groups were introduced independently of the formation of the basic skeleton.

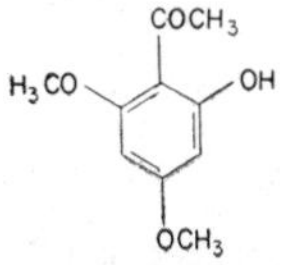

(14) 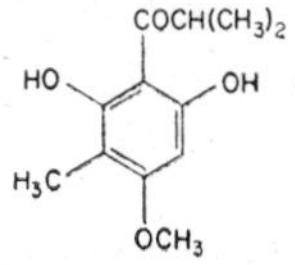   (15) 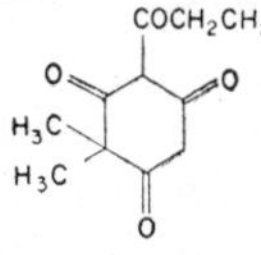   (16) 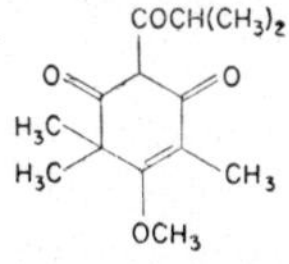   (17) 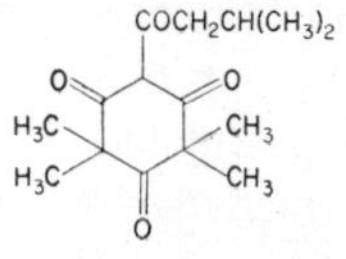   (18)

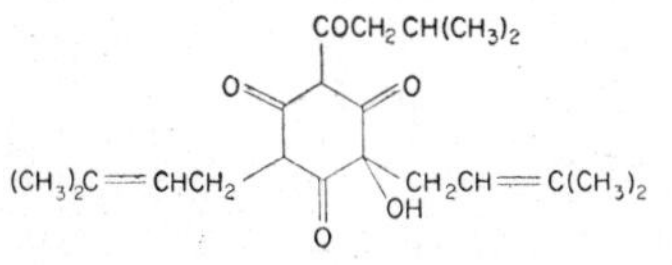

(19) 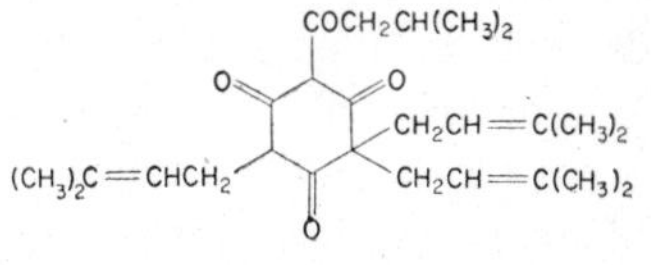   (20)

BIOCHEMICAL EVIDENCE FOR THE HYPOTHESIS

Abundant biochemical evidence on the general validity of these aspects of phenolic biosynthesis has now accumulated, mainly through the use of isotopic carbon-14 tracers in biological systems.

(i) *Evidence for the Origin of the Skeleton, its Oxidation, and its Reduction*

The first phenolic compound investigated by Birch[3] was 2-hydroxy-6-methyl-benzoic acid, metabolized by *Penicillium griseofulvum* in the presence of [1-^{14}C] acetate ($CH_3{}^{14}CO_2H$). Degradation confirmed the predicted isotope distribution [as in (21)] in this case where removal of a "marker" oxygen atom has occurred. Another strain of the same mould produces griseofulvin (23), of particular importance since it was shown[7] using $CH_3{}^{14}CO_2H$ to arise by simultaneous operation of both aldol and C-acylation types of ring closure of a polyketonic precursor [as in (22)]. Supplementary work with [2-^{14}C] acetate ($^{14}CH_3CO_2H$) as substrate[8] has verified the circumstantial, but nevertheless convincing, evidence on the origin of the alternate unasterisked carbons in the skeletons of these compounds; these atoms, previously completely unlabelled from $CH_3{}^{14}CO_2H$, now carry isotope, while the presence of slight radioactivity in the carboxyl-derived positions is indicative of some redistribution of label in the incorporated units produced by participation of acetic acid in the tricarboxylic acid cycle. The O-methyl groups of griseofulvin arise from the usual biological C_1-donor systems (experimentally [methyl-^{14}C] choline was used[9]), and the secondary, non-essential nature of the chlorination stage is evidenced by the production of the corresponding dechlorinated and brominated analogues of griseofulvin by *Penicillium* strains.[10]

Gatenbeck and Mosbach[11] have studied the biosynthesis of orsellinic acid itself (24), the unmodified prototype of the orcinol-type ring closure, from doubly-labelled acetate, $CH_3{}^{14}CO^{18}ONa$, in *Chaetomium cochliodes*. The distribution of radio-carbon in the orsellinic acid was as expected, and isotopic oxygen was also incorporated, the ^{18}O content of the carboxyl group being half that of each hydroxyl group. This elegantly confirms the postulated direct condensation of activated acetate units to β-polyketo-methylene-acid intermediates and precludes a pathway involving successive β-oxidations of fatty acids. Furthermore, condensation of acetate units, activated as their coenzyme-A derivatives, to orsellinic acid would conclude with hydrolysis of the terminal thiolester group introducing non-isotopic oxygen, in agreement with the observed ^{18}O distribution.

Alternariol (26) from *Alternaria tenuis* provides a further example of the genesis of an unmodified carbon–oxygen skeleton (25) from seven acetate units by aldol ring closures and lactonization.[12] Similar processes, coupled with extensive reductive removal of oxygen, give rise [as in (27)] to the phenolic and twelve-membered lactone rings of curvularin (28) from a species of *Curvularia*.[13] The culture medium of *P. urticae* contains 2-hydroxy-6-methyl-benzoic acid (21), 2-hydroxy-6-formyl-benzoic acid, and 3-hydroxy-phthalic acid (29).[14] Stimulation of the phthalic acid production by addition of exogenous 2-hydroxy-6-methyl-benzoic acid indicates utilization of the latter by stepwise oxidation through the formyl-compound. 3-Hydroxyphthalic acid (29) produced by *P. islandicum* from $CH_3{}^{14}CO_2H$ carried an isotope distribution compatible with a variation of the 2-hydroxy-6-methyl-benzoic acid (21) route involving oxidation at some stage, although formation of the phthalic acid (29) by oxidative fission of the co-occurring anthraquinone islandicin (40) is also possible.[18]

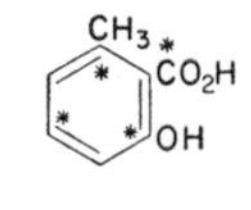

(21) 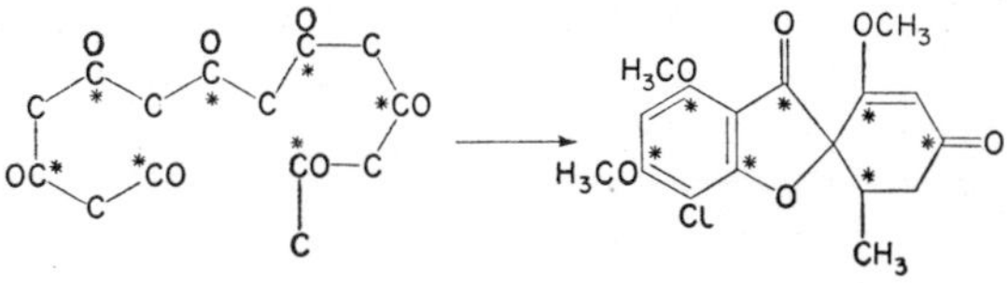　　　　　　　　(22)　　　　　　　　(23)

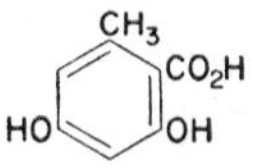

(24) 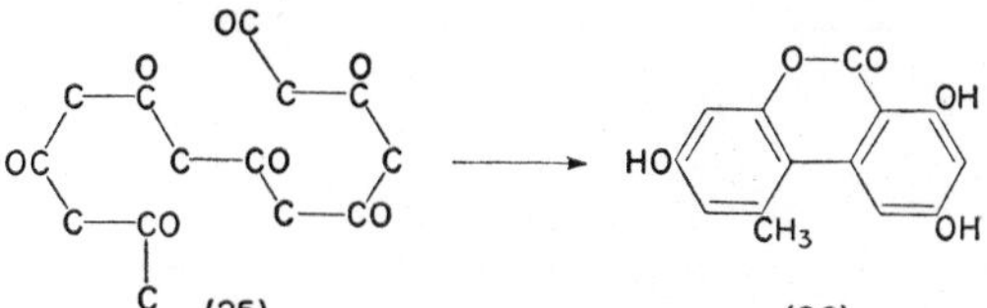　　　　　　　　(25)　　　　　　　　(26)

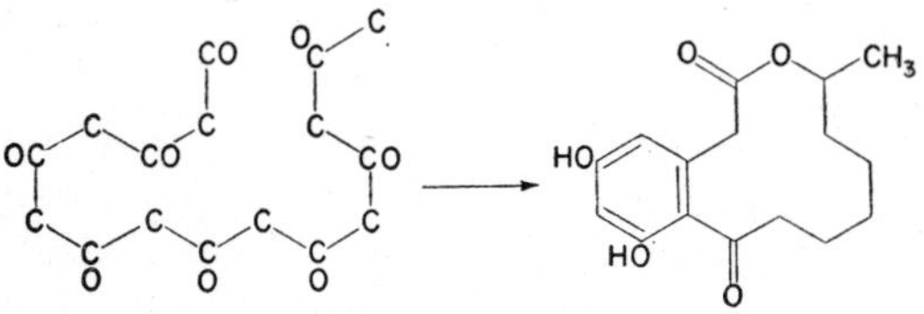

(27)　　　　　　　　(28) 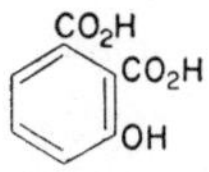　　　　　　　　(29)

The phloroglucinol rings of the flavonol quercetin (30) produced by buck-wheat,[15] and cyanidin (31) from red cabbage[16] arise from acetate in the expected[2] fashion, the 3,4-dihydroxycinnamic acid moieties originating in the shikimic acid route to phenylpropane-type compounds. Related to the acyl-phloroglucinol system is the acylresorcinol nucleus of 2-methyl-5-hydroxy-chromanone (32) investigated by Bu'Lock[17] in *Daldinia concentrica*. The co-metabolites of this heterocycle include the corresponding chromone (33), the naphthols (34; R = H, R′ = CH₃; R = R′ = CH₃), and the acyl-resorcinols (35–38), and illustrate the variety of compounds which can arise from a common precursor derived from acetate units. The processes which are involved include cyclisation on to either carbon or oxygen and reductive removal of oxygen.

The structures of many natural polyhydroxyanthraquinones are consistent with a skeletal biosynthesis by acetate condensation and cyclization, modifications occurring in decarboxylation, reduction, and oxidation stages. The

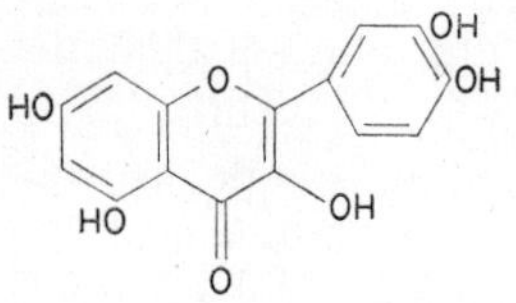

(30) 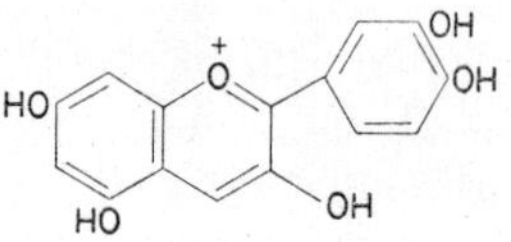　　　　　　　(31) 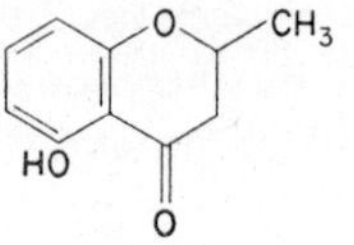　　　　　　　(32)

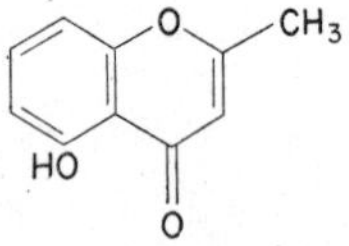

(33) 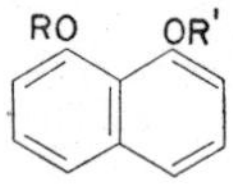　　　　　　　(34) 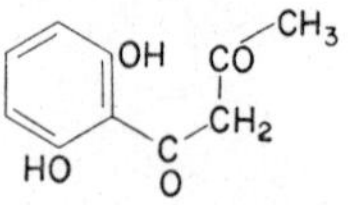　　　　　　　(35)

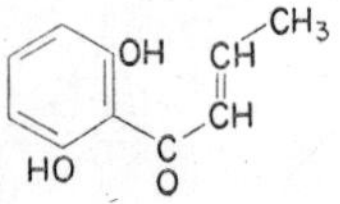

(36) 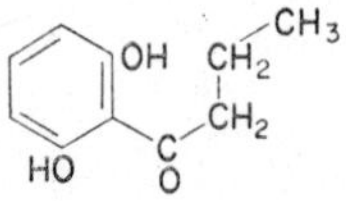　　　　　　　(37) 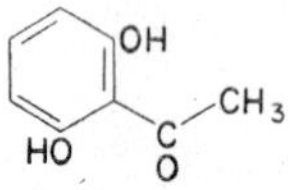　　　　　　　(38)

anthraquinone acid endocrocin (7) represents this scheme in its least modified form, one quinone oxygen atom having been introduced. The origin of emodin (6) [obtained chemically by reductive cleavage of the dianthraquinone skyrin (43)], in which an additional decarboxylation stage is involved, from acetate in *P. islandicum* has been demonstrated by Gatenbeck,[18] and it is significant that a mutant of this organism produced by ultraviolet irradiation yields endocrocin (7), and catenarin (39) in which hydroxylation has occurred at the 1-position. Helminthosporin (13) in *Helminthosporium gramineum*[19] and islandicin (40) in *P. islandicum*[18] are derived from eight acetate units with reduction, oxidation, and decarboxylation stages.

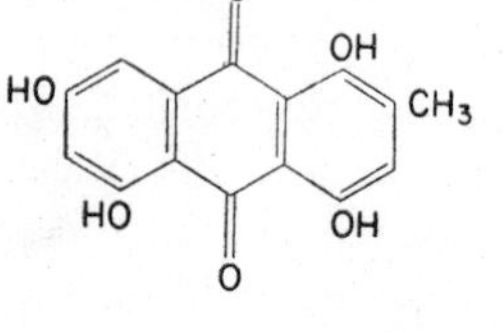

(39) 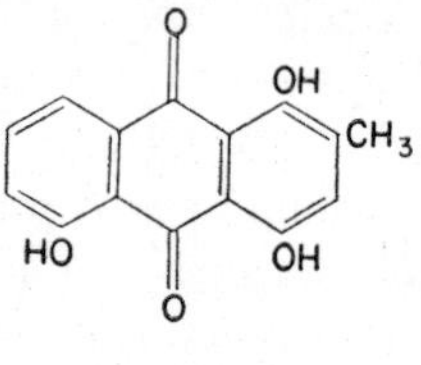　　　　　　　(40)

Gatenbeck, incorporating doubly-labelled acetate $CH_3{}^{14}CO^{18}ONa$ in *P. islandicum* fermentations,[18] has verified the postulated introduction of oxygen, and reductive removal of oxygen. Of the five oxygen substituents in emodin (6) and islandicin (40), four and three atoms respectively were derived from the isotopic carboxyl oxygen of the condensing acetate units. Incorporation of the isotopic oxygen into the secondary alcoholic groups of the dianthraquinone rubroskyrin (41) confirmed them to be reduced carbonyl groups of acetate units. It is of interest that analysis of the specific radio-activity/time curves for the pigments islandicin (40), rubroskyrin (41), iridoskyrin (42), and skyrin (43), produced by *P. islandicum* in the presence of radio-acetate, indicates that they are biosynthesized completely independently of each other and are not interconvertible *in vivo*; in particular, the immediate precursor of the dianthraquinone iridoskyrin (42) is neither its monomer islandicin (40) nor its hydrated form rubroskyrin (41), while as expected skyrin (43) is not a precursor of iridoskyrin (42).

(41)   (42)   (43)

Throughout this discussion it has been convenient to regard acetyl-coenzyme-A itself as the fundamental, condensing unit generating the carbon–oxygen skeleton. Recent work by Lynen[20] on the early stages of carbon chain biosynthesis in fatty acids is of interest in this connection. In the utilization of acetic acid units for fatty acid synthesis, the monomer unit which polymerizes is not in fact acetyl-coenzyme-A itself, but its carboxylation product, malonyl-coenzyme-A. Malonyl-coenzyme-A units, ideally activated for acylation, condense together with concomitant decarboxylation, the successive reduction of the β-keto-groups thus formed yielding fatty acids. In biological systems synthesizing phenolic compounds, carboxylation of acetyl-coenzyme-A to malonyl-coenzyme-A, which then polymerizes with omission of the carbonyl reduction stages, could lead to β-polyketomethylene skeletons.

(ii) *Evidence for Alkylation of the Skeleton*

The *in vivo* biochemical proof of the occurrence of C-alkylation reactions in an acetate-derived carbon–oxygen skeleton involves in general two stages; first, verification of the origin of the skeleton itself by use of isotopic acetate, and secondly, demonstration of the origin of the alkyl substituents from alkyl-cation donor systems by the use of tracers such as labelled methionine,

2

choline or formate for introduced methyl groups, and mevalonic lactone for isoprenoid groups.

The C-methylation reaction was first demonstrated in the case of myco-phenolic acid (62),[21] the biosynthesis of which is discussed in detail later. The dihydroxyphthalide nucleus of this compound carries methyl groups introduced on to oxygen and on to carbon, both of which were provided efficiently and specifically by transmethylation from the S-methyl group of isotopic methionine, $^{14}CH_3SCH_2CH_2CH(NH_2)CO_2H$.

Formate is known[22],[23] to be a carbon source for the labile methyl groups of the C_1-donors methionine and choline, and consequently the readily available [^{14}C] formate can frequently be used as a substitute for [$^{14}CH_3$] methionine

(44)   (45)

in biochemical studies. Sclerotiorin (45), a metabolite of *P. multicolor*, contains an acetate-derived skeleton which has undergone methylation at three positions, chlorination, oxygenation and O-acetylation, reduction, dehydration, and ring closure on to both carbon and oxygen; $H^{14}CO_2H$ in the culture medium was incorporated specifically into the introduced methyl groups, while the use of two isotopic acetates, $CH_3{}^{14}CO_2H$ and $^{14}CH_3CO_2H$, proved the biosynthetic origin of the remainder of the molecule [as in (44)].[24] Feeding experiments with *Aspergillus candidus* confirmed the genesis (46) of citrinin (47) from five acetate units and three introduced C_1 units, one of which has been oxidized to carboxyl.[24] Schwenk[25] arrived independently at similar conclusions, and in particular demonstrated that [$^{14}CH_3$] methionine was a more efficient C_1-donor than [^{14}C] formate, while neither [2-^{14}C] propionate nor [^{14}C] bicarbonate was utilized in the biosynthesis. A notable feature of the biosynthesis of both sclerotiorin (45) and citrinin (47) is the reduction of the carboxyl group of a terminal acetic acid unit to the methynyloxy state in the pyran rings.

The distribution of isotope in the *p*-benzoquinone aurantiogliocladin (49), produced by *Roseum gliocladum* in the presence of $CH_3{}^{14}CO_2H$ and $H^{14}CO_2H$, is in agreement with oxidation, C- and O-methylation, and decarboxylation of a skeleton derived from four acetate units as in (48),[26] and additional support for an acetate pathway to such benzoquinones was provided by study of *p*-methoxytoluquinone (51) biosynthesis [represented in (50)] in *Lentinus degener*.[27] Confirmatory evidence resulted from the incorporation into the toluquinone (51) of biosynthetically ^{14}C-labelled 2-hydroxy-6-methyl-benzoic acid and the non-incorporation of synthetic

[5-^{14}C] orsellinic acid (71). Unexpected, however, was the similar behaviour of both these labelled compounds in *R. gliocladum* cultures producing aurantiogliocladin, inferring that reductive removal of a "marker" acetate oxygen is common to the biosynthesis of both these quinones, and that in the case of aurantiogliocladin this oxygen is replaced at a post-aromatic stage by "introduced" oxygen.

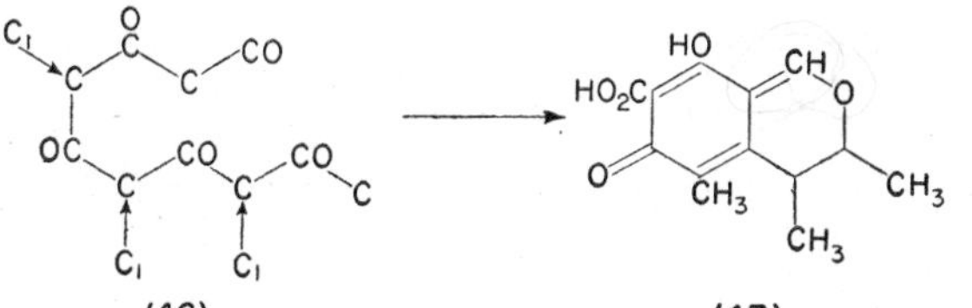

(46)   (47)

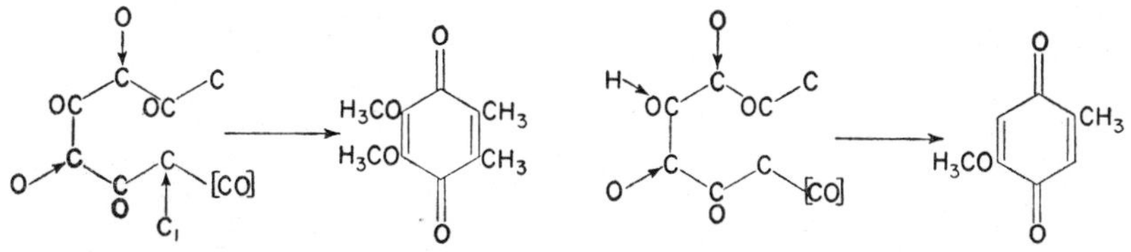

(48)   (49)   (50)   (51)

The incorporation of [1-^{14}C] acetate into auroglaucin (52) by *Aspergillus novus* cultures indicated the presence of an acetate-derived skeleton modified as in (53) by both removal and introduction of oxygen, reduction of a

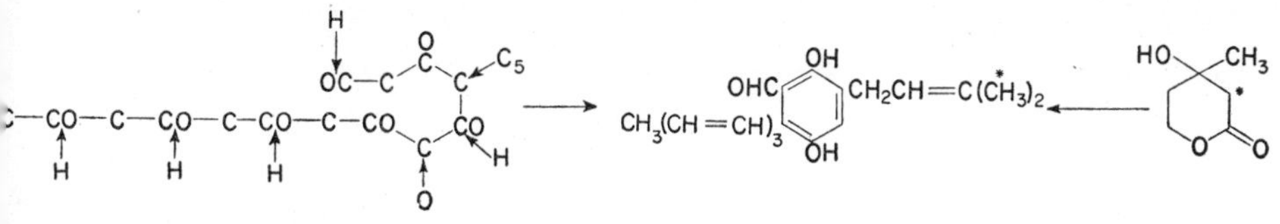

(53)   (52)   (54)

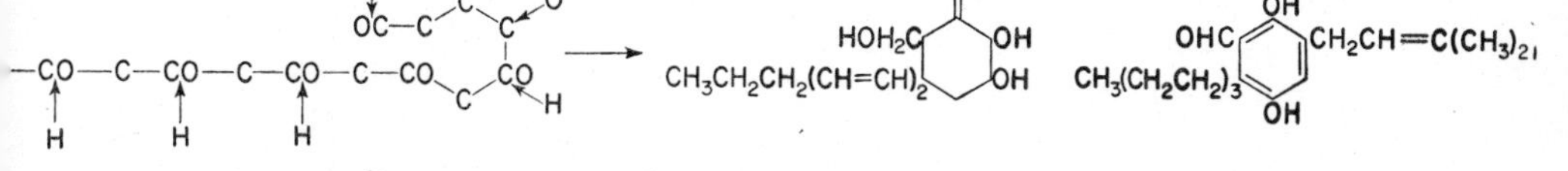

(56)   (55)   (57)

carboxyl to an aldehyde group, and isopentenylation by a C_5-unit generated from the established isoprenoid precursor mevalonic acid (which itself originates in acetate by the known route).[28] This alkylation stage was confirmed by the specific incorporation of isotope from [2-^{14}C] mevalonic lactone (54) into the *gem*-dimethyl group of auroglaucin. Structural similarities between auroglaucin (52) and the non-aromatic C_{14} compound palitantin (55) investigated in *P. cyclopium*[29] are indicative of biogenetic variations [represented in (53) and (56)] of a common scheme. A notable similarity is that reduction of an acetate carbonyl group accounts both for the removal of an expected oxygen *meta* to the C_7 side chain in auroglaucin (52) and for the presence of a hydroxyl group at this position in palitantin (55). Co-occurring with auroglaucin is the related flavoglaucin (57), in which saturation of the C_7 side chain is complete.

Inspection of the formula of fuscin (58) indicates possible modes of biosynthesis involving either the shikimate or the acetate routes to aromatic compounds. A C_6–C_3 skeleton generated from shikimic acid may have under-

(59)   (58)   (60)

gone degradation to a C_6–C_2 fragment followed by addition of C_2 (acetate) and C_5 (isopentenyl) units (59). Alternatively an isopentenyl unit may have been introduced into a penta-acetate skeleton (60). This latter route was verified[36] by fermentation of *Oidiodendrum fuscum* in media containing [1-^{14}C] acetate, which produced the typical β-polyketonic and isoprenoid patterns in the metabolite, and [2-^{14}C] mevalonic lactone which labelled only the *gem*-dimethyl group of the isoprenoid substituent.

THE BIOSYNTHESIS OF MYCOPHENOLIC ACID

Examination of the structure of mycophenolic acid (62), a metabolite of *Penicillium brevi-compactum*, indicates the presence of a dihydroxyphthalide nucleus, derivable from acetate units by an orcinol-type ring closure and lactonization, which at some stage in its genesis [represented in (61)] has undergone methylation on carbon and on oxygen, and C-alkylation with a terpenoid group. Initial tracer studies[32] using $CH_3{}^{14}CO_2H$ in the culture medium gave rise [as in (63)] to the typical acetate pattern of phenolic labelling in the phthalide nucleus and the typical acetate terpenoid distribution in the side-chain (the quantitative degree of labelling in these two discrete systems is not necessarily the same), while [$^{14}CH_3$] methionine provided both introduced methyl groups with high specificity and efficiency (77% incorporation of isotope).[21]

Confirmation of the isoprenoid origin of the C_7 side chain was obtained from the specific incorporation into the expected position (65) of isotope from the established terpenoid precursor, [2-^{14}C] mevalonic lactone (64).[32] Recent work[34] has verified that this C_7 acid substituent is in fact the remnant of a geranyl substituent, derived from two isopentenyl units, oxidized at the isopropylidene double bond [as in (61)], and is not the result of the condensation of an isopentenyl unit with a two-carbon fragment. Fermentation of *P. brevi-compactum* in the presence of [4-^{14}C] mevalonic lactone (66) produced

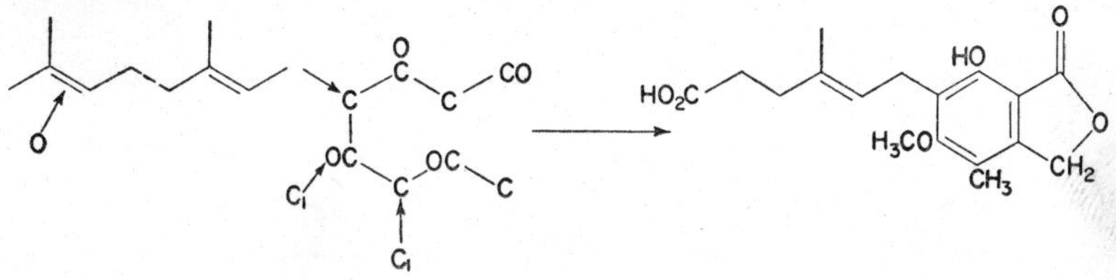

(61)   (62)

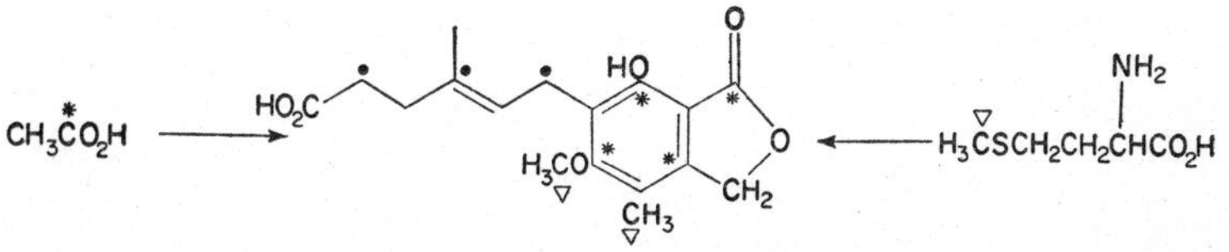

(63)

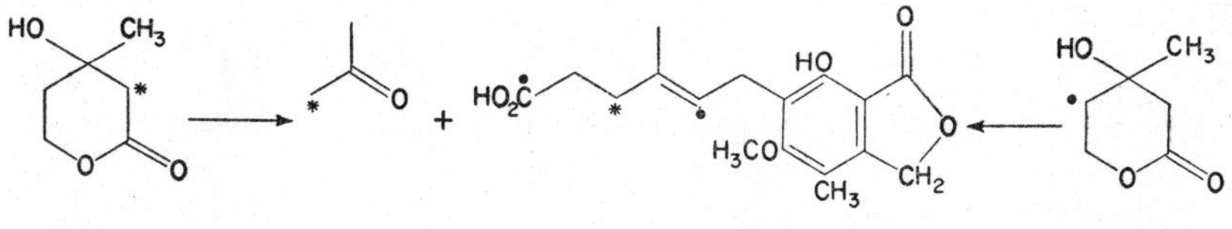

(64)   (65)   (66)

specific, equal labelling at the two positions expected in an isoprenoid-derived chain (65). Furthermore, steam distillation of the culture filtrate from a fermentation involving [2-^{14}C] mevalonic lactone (64) gave acetone (isolated as its 2,4-dinitrophenylhydrazone), equimolar in quantity with the mycophenolic acid isolated, and of equal molar activity. This result demonstrates that the isoprenoid chain involved in the biosynthesis is, in fact, geranyl and not a higher isoprenoid system. It also implies that oxidative degradation of the geranyl unit to acetone and the carboxylic acid occurs after introduction into the carbon-skeleton, rather than oxidation prior to what must then necessarily be quantitative alkylation.

Some evidence is available as to the stage at which the methyl and geranyl introductions occur on to the carbon–oxygen skeleton generating the phthalide ring. Raistrick[35] isolated the phenols (67–70), co-metabolites of mycophenolic acid in *P. brevi-compactum*, and observed that the compounds (67) and (68) were produced early in the growth of the mould, but reached a maximum concentration which then decreased with continued growth. This may indicate formation of the phthalide nucleus by initial condensation of five acetate units rather than the minimum four required, followed by oxidation at the benzyl position, lactonization, and deacetylation. Alkylation would then occur after aromatization.

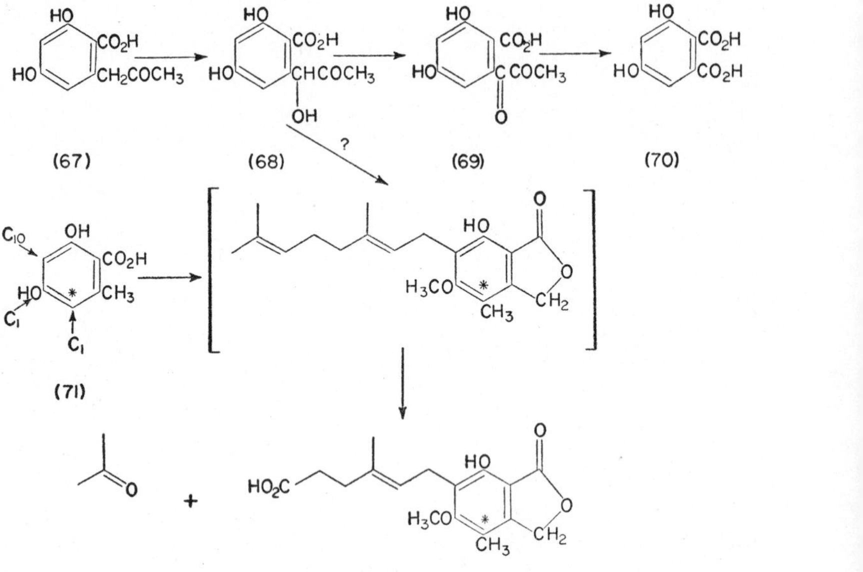

(67)   (68)   (69)   (70)

(71)

(72)

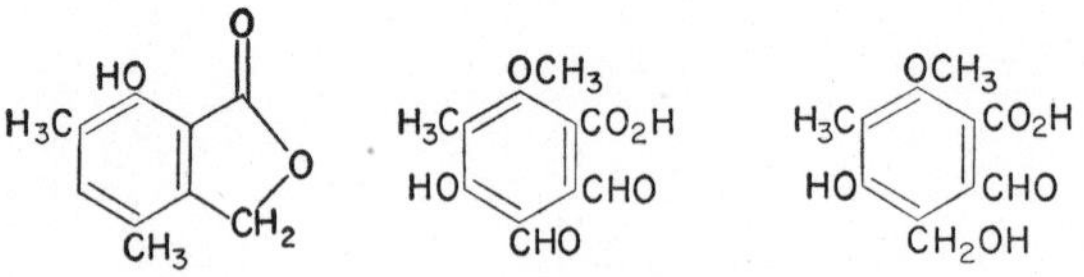

(73)   (74)   (75)

More definite evidence for this view of the alkylation stage has resulted from feeding experiments with synthetic [5-^{14}C] orsellinic acid (71).[36] Isotope incorporation into mycophenolic acid was low, and some degradation of the specifically labelled substrate into small units had occurred with random incorporation resulting to some extent, but 28% of the total activity of the mycophenolic acid resided at the 4-position of the phthalide nucleus (72). This indicates some incorporation of the preformed aromatic ring of orsellinic acid as a unit. The poor incorporation may be due to relative inability of the enzyme systems to utilize orsellinic acid itself in preference to phenols of the acetyl-orsellinic acid type, (67) and (68), or to problems of permeability and activation associated with the added substrate.

Biosynthetically related to mycophenolic acid are the metabolites 7-hydroxy-4, 6-dimethylphthalide (73) of *P. gladioli*, and cyclopaldic acid (74), which occurs together with cyclopoldic acid (75) in *P. cyclopium*; here methylation has replaced the geranylation stage.[33],[29]

THE BIOSYNTHESIS OF THE TETRACYCLINE ANTIBIOTICS

The formulae of the tetracycline antibiotics, for example 5-hydroxytetra-cycline (77), suggest a biosynthetic origin (76) from an acetate-derived skeleton which has undergone secondary modifications including the intro-duction and removal of oxygen, and alkylation on both carbon and nitrogen.

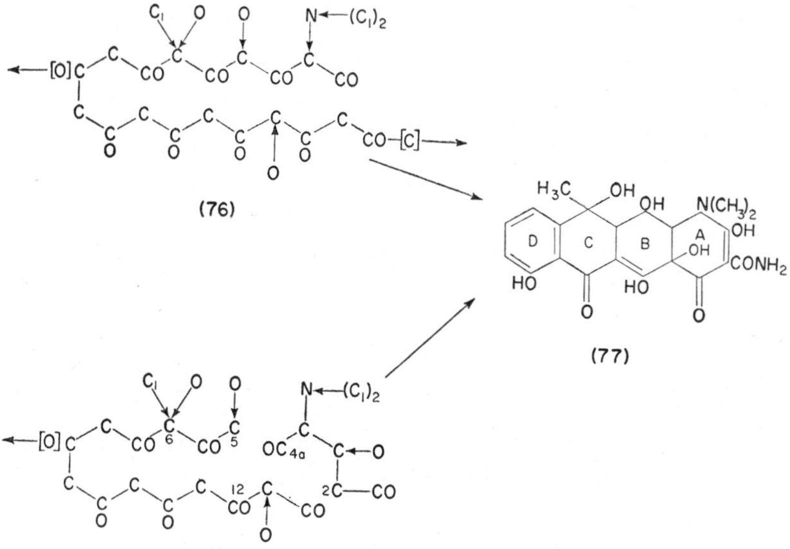

(76)

(77)

(78)

Fermentation in the presence of isotopic acetate of *Streptomyces rimosus*[37] and *S. aureofaciens*[38] demonstrated that acetate was a precursor of both 5-hydroxytetracycline (77) and 7-chlorotetracycline (84). Degradation of the 5-hydroxytetracycline showed a deficiency of activity in ring A as compared to rings B, C, and D.[39] Synthetic media studies suggested glutamic acid, $HO_2CCH(NH_2)CH_2CH_2CO_2H$, glutamine, $HO_2CCH(NH_2)CH_2CH_2CONH_2$, or a closely related compound as a precursor of ring A, and in confirmation isotope from $(\pm)$-[2-^{14}C] glutamic acid in the culture medium was incor-porated into the antibiotic, which was now, moreover, labelled preferentially in ring A.[39]

Detailed degradation[40] of 5-hydroxytetracycline (77) biosynthesized from [2-^{14}C] acetate has confirmed that the molecular skeleton at least from C_5 to

C_{12} is derived from acetic acid units in head-to-tail linkage, as in (78). It is likely that glutamate provides the A-ring fragment extending from the amide group through C_2 to C_{4a}, but adequate chemical degradations of this region of the molecule are lacking. [$^{14}CH_3$] Methionine contributes equal labelling to both the C_6-methyl and each of the N-methyl groups, verifying their expected introduction from the C_1-donor system.

The variations produced in the tetracyclines by natural genetic differences in the *Streptomyces* species, and artificial mutation of the species, provide an interesting illustration of secondary enzymic modifications occurring in an acetate-derived carbon–oxygen skeleton. These variations range from the 6-demethyl compounds, (79) and (80), tetracycline itself (81) and its 5-hydroxy (82) and halogeno analogues, (83) and (84), to 7-chloro-5a(11a)-dehydrotetracycline (85).

(79) R_1=H , R_2=H , R_3=H

(80) R_1=Cl, R_2=H , R_3=H

(81) R_1=H , R_2=Me, R_3=H

(82) R_1=H , R_2=Me, R_3=OH

(83) R_1=Br, R_2=Me, R_3=H

(84) R_1=Cl, R_2=Me, R_3=H

(85)

(86)

These compounds result from complex sequences of biological reactions, and represent the effect of enzymic blockages at certain secondary stages of the biosynthesis.

The 5a(11a)-dehydro-compounds, in which the double bond may represent the dehydrated remnant of an aldol ring-closure generating the B/C ring junction, may perhaps be the immediate precursors of the saturated tetracyclines; two mutants of *S. aureofaciens* normally producing the chlorotetracyclines (80) or (84) can reduce the chloro-dehydro-compound (85) to 7-chlorotetracycline (84)[41]. The total production of tetracycline itself (81) and its 7-bromo- and 7-chloro-analogues (83) and (84) by three *S. aureofaciens* mutants is independent of the bromide and chloride concentration in the medium, while withholding halide or inhibiting halide utilization with thiocyanate results in biosynthesis of equivalent amounts of tetracycline itself. This indicates the secondary, non-essential nature of the halogenation step, which must occur after the overall rate-limiting stage.[42] It is also of interest that 12a-deoxytetracycline (86) can be hydroxylated to tetracycline (81) both chemically and microbiologically by several organisms (*Curvularia* and *Botrytis* species), although *Streptomyces* mutants capable of effecting this transformation have not yet been found.[43]

BIOSYNTHETIC APPROACHES TO STRUCTURE DETERMINATION

The initial applications of the acetic acid hypothesis to the structure determination of phenolic compounds were similar, in principle, to the familiar uses of biogenetic relations based on the isoprenoid and C_6-C_3 routes in the terpenoid, flavanoid, and alkaloid groups. Considerable degradative evidence bearing on the structure was required in order to indicate whether or not an origin from acetic acid units was probable. If this were so, then the hypothesis could be used to predict the biosynthetically most probable structure. The accuracy of such predictions lent strong support to the hypothesis.[2]

The abundant biochemical evidence accumulated for the validity of the hypothesis and its extensions now permits a different approach—the assistance of structure determination by the use of isotopic tracers *in vivo*, in conjunction with proven biosynthetic theories. In biological systems adaptable to tracer techniques, it should, for example, be possible to obtain information about the nature of the carbon skeleton by use of isotopic acetate, to detect the presence of introduced C_1 substituents by use of formate or methionine, and of isoprenoid substituents by mevalonic lactone, and even to utilize oxygen-18 techniques to investigate the nature of oxygenation (derived from acetate carboxyl, or "introduced") in unknown compounds. The two following examples illustrate the potential value of this type of approach.

Degradation of curvularin, $C_{16}H_{20}O_5$, a metabolite of a *Curvularia* species, demonstrated the presence of either one or two C-methyl groups, together with the dihydroxybenzoyl system (87) which indicated that at least part of the molecule was derived from acetate units. If the skeleton were wholly acetate-derived, then the presence of two C-methyl groups would indicate biosynthesis by introduction of a methyl group into an octa-acetate skeleton with decarboxylation [as in (88)]. This possibility was eliminated by Kuhn-Roth oxidation of labelled curvularin obtained by fermentation in the presence of $CH_3{}^{14}CO_2H$, when acetic acid was obtained carrying in its carboxyl group one-eighth of the total activity of the curvularin. This indicated that curvularin (C_{16}) was derived from eight acetate units, without introduction of a methyl substituent which would have given rise on oxidation to unlabelled acetic acid, diluting that obtained from the terminal unit of the polyketomethylene chain. Confirmation of the absence of a transmethylation stage resulted from the low, non-specific incorporation of isotope from [^{14}C] formate into curvularin. This information assisted the ultimate elucidation of the structure (28) for curvularin.[13]

Previous investigations by Quilico (cf. 44) on the structure of echinulin from *Aspergillus glaucus* had led to the tri-alkylated indole formulae (89) or (90) for this substance. Of these possibilities, (89) contains three isoprenoid groups while (90) contains only one. The incorporation of isotopic acetate and mevalonate from the *Aspergillus* culture media occurred specifically into the alkyl chains and not into the amino-acid derived indole and diketo-piperazine systems. Ozonolysis of the echinulin produced from $CH_3{}^{14}CO_2H$,

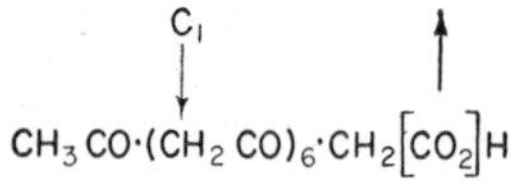

(88)

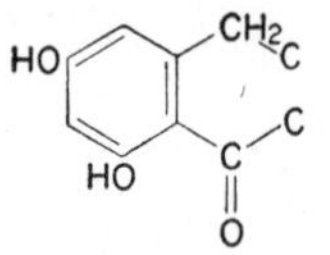

(87)

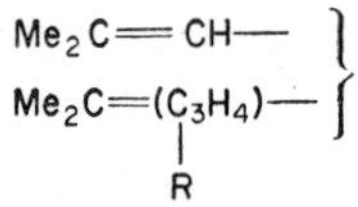

(90)

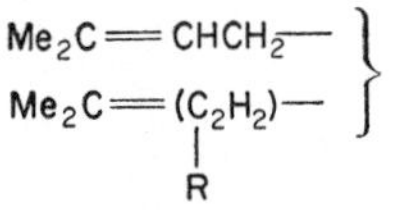

(89)

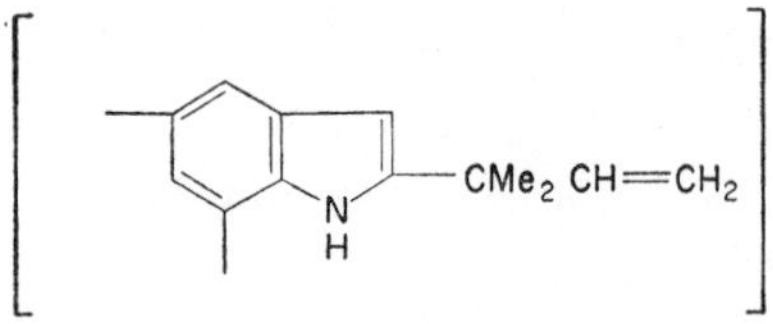

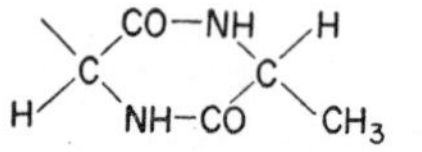

which would be expected to yield a doubly-labelled isoprenoid unit ($Me_2\overset{*}{C}{=}C{-}\overset{*}{C}$) by the known route, gave rise to acetone and formaldehyde each containing molar activity equivalent to one-sixth of the molar activity of the metabolite. Similar degradation of material derived from [2-${}^{14}C$] mevalonic lactone, which yields a singly-labelled isoprenoid unit ($Me_2\overset{*}{C}{=}C{-}C$), gave inactive formaldehyde and acetone with a molar activity one third of the echinulin activity. These results clearly indicate the presence of three isoprenoid units in echinulin and the correctness of formula (89), a conclusion which has been verified chemically by Quilico.[44]

The author is indebted to Professor A. J. Birch, F.A.A., F.R.S., for helpful discussions and permission to quote unpublished results.

REFERENCES

1. B. D. DAVIS, *Arch. Biochem. Biophys.* 1958, **78**, 497, and references cited therein.
2. A. J. BIRCH and F. W. DONOVAN, *Austral. J. Chem.* 1953, **6**, 360. For reviews see A. J. BIRCH, *Fortschr. Chem. org. Naturstoffe* 1957, **14**, 186; A. J. Birch and H. Smith, *Chem. Soc. Special Publ.* 1958, **12**, 1.
3. A. J. BIRCH, R. A. MASSY-WESTROPP and C. J. MOYE, *Austral. J. Chem.* 1955, **8**, 539.

4. T. J. NOLAN, *Thorpe's Dictionary of Applied Chemistry* Longmans Green and Co., London, 1946, **7**, 293.
5. G. LINDSTEDT and A. MISIORNY, *Acta Chem. Scand.* 1951, **5**, 121.
6. H. ERDTMAN, *Perspectives in Organic Chemistry*, Interscience, New York, 1956, p. 453.
7. A. J. BIRCH, R. A. MASSY-WESTROPP, R. W. RICKARDS and H. SMITH, *J. Chem. Soc.* 1958, 360.
8. A. J. BIRCH, P. W. HOLLOWAY, R. W. RICKARDS and Z. VANEK, unpublished work.
9. D. J. HOCKENHULL and W. F. FAULDS, *Chem. and Ind.* 1955, 1390.
10. J. MACMILLAN, *J. Chem. Soc.* 1953, 1697; 1954, 2585.
11. S. GATENBECK and K. MOSBACH, *Acta Chem. Scand.* 1959, **13**, 1561.
12. R. THOMAS, *Proc. Chem. Soc.*, 1959, 88.
13. A. J. BIRCH, O. C. MUSGRAVE, R. W. RICKARDS and H. SMITH, *J. Chem. Soc.* 1959, 3146.
14. S. W. TANENBAUM and E. W. BASSETT, *Biochim. Biophys. Acta* 1958, **28**, 21.
15. T. A. GEISSMAN and T. SWAIN, *Chem. and Ind.* 1957, 984; E. W. UNDERHILL, J. E. WATKIN and A. C. NEISH, *Canad. J. Biochem. Physiol.* 1957, **35**, 219, 229.
16. H. GRISEBACH, *Z. Naturforsch* 1957, **12b**, 227, 597; 1958, **13b**, 335.
17. D. C. ALLPORT and J. D. BU'LOCK, *J. Chem. Soc.* 1960, 654.
18. S. GATENBECK, *Svensk kem. Tidskr.* 1960, **72**, 188, and references cited therein.
19. A. J. BIRCH, A. J. RYAN and H. SMITH, *J. Chem. Soc.* 1958, 4773.
20. F. LYNEN, *J. Cell. Comp. Physiol.* 1959, **54**, suppl. 1, 33. cf. P.K. Stumpf, *Ann. Revs. Biochem.* 1960, **29**, 282.
21. A. J. BIRCH, R. J. ENGLISH, R. A. MASSY-WESTROPP, M. SLAYTOR and H. SMITH *J. Chem. Soc.* 1958, 365.
22. F. M. HUENNEKENS, H. R. WHITELEY and M. J. OSBORN, *J. Cell. Comp. Physiol.* 1959, **54**, suppl. 1, 109.
23. G. J. ALEXANDER and E. SCHWENK, *J. Amer. Chem. Soc.* 1957, **79**, 4554.
24. A. J. BIRCH, P. FITTON, E. PRIDE, A. J. RYAN, H. SMITH and W. B. WHALLEY, *J. Chem. Soc.* 1958, 4576.
25. E. SCHWENK, G. J. ALEXANDER, A. M. GOLD and D. F. STEVENS, *J. Biol. Chem.* 1958, **233**, 1211.
26. A. J. BIRCH, R. I. FRYER and H. SMITH, *Proc. Chem. Soc.* 1958, 343.
27. A. J. BIRCH, R. I. FRYER and H. SMITH, unpublished work.
28. A. J. BIRCH, J. SCHOFIELD and H. SMITH, *Chem. and Ind.* 1958, 1321.
29. A. J. BIRCH and M. KOCOR, *J. Chem. Soc.* 1960, 866.
30. J. N. COLLIE, *J. Chem. Soc.* 1907, 1806, and earlier papers.
31. cf. R. ROBINSON, "The Structural Relations of Natural Products", Clarendon Press, Oxford, 1955, p. 7.
32. A. J. BIRCH, R. J. ENGLISH, R. A. MASSY-WESTROPP and H. SMITH, *J. Chem. Soc.* 1958, 369.
33. A. J. BIRCH, E. PRIDE and H. SMITH, unpublished work.
34. A. J. BIRCH, A. CASSERA, R. I. FRYER and H. SMITH, unpublished work.
35. A. E. OXFORD and H. RAISTRICK, *Biochem. J.* 1933, **27**, 1473.
36. A. J. BIRCH, A. J. RYAN and H. SMITH, unpublished work.
37. J. F. SNELL, R. L. WAGNER, and F. A. HOCHSTEIN, *Proceedings of the Second United Nations International Conference on the Peaceful Uses of Atomic Energy*, United Nations, Geneva, 1955, **12**, 431.
38. P. A. MILLER, J. R. D. MCCORMICK and A. P. DOERSCHUK, *Science* 1956, **123**, 1030.
39. J. F. SNELL, unpublished work.
40. A. J. BIRCH, J. F. SNELL and P. J. THOMSON, *J. Amer. Chem. Soc.* 1960, 82, 2402.
41. J. R. D. MCCORMICK, N. O. SJOLANDER, P. A. MILLER, U. HIRSCH, N. H. ARNOLD and A. P. DOERSCHUK, *J. Amer. Chem. Soc.* 1958, **80**, 6460.
42. A. P. DOERSCHUK, J. R. D. MCCORMICK, J. J. GOODMAN, S. A. SZUMSKI, J. A. GROWICH, P. A. MILLER, B. A. BITLER, E. R. JENSEN, M. MATRISHIN, M. A. PETTY and A. S. PHELPS, *J. Amer. Chem. Soc.* 1959, **81**, 3069.
43. C. E. HOLMLUND, W. A. ANDRES and A. J. SHAY, *J. Amer. Chem. Soc.* 1959, **81**, 4748, 4750.
44. C. CARDANI, G. CASNATI, F. PIOZZI and A. QUILICO, *Tetrahedron Letters* 1959, **16**, 1.

CHAPTER 2

SOME STRUCTURAL AND BIOGENETIC RELATIONSHIPS OF PLANT PHENOLICS

W. B. WHALLEY

University of Liverpool

ATTEMPTS to deduce structural and biogenetic correlations between natural products from an inspection of their "comparative anatomy" have been made by many chemists. One of the outstanding pioneers in this field is Sir Robert Robinson whose principal contributions have been summarized in his 1953 Weizmann Memorial Lectures.[1] The most recent, comprehensive statement concerning phenolic compounds, including oxygen heterocyclics, was made by Geissman and Hinreiner,[2] in 1952.

Since these authoritative reviews many new natural products have been discovered, the acetate hypothesis of biogenesis has been enunciated and largely substantiated,[3] and biosynthesis has emerged from the realm of pure speculation to be placed, during the last five years, upon a firm foundation. The application of isotopic tracer techniques to the problem of the biosynthesis of fungal metabolites has been particularly successful. Higher plants are less amenable to this procedure.

The purpose of this review is to provide a correlation of the various structural and biogenetic relationships which may now be deduced among plant phenolics.

1. STRUCTURAL AND BIOGENETIC RELATIONSHIPS

The Biosynthesis of Aromatic Rings

It has been firmly established[3] that benzenoid ring systems arise by two main pathways, (a) from acetic acid, and (b) from shikimic acid. Thus ring A of the flavonoids, type (1), is acetate derived and ring B has shikimic acid (2) as its precursor.

This has been demonstrated in the biosynthesis[4] of quercetin (3) from buckwheat (*Fagopyrum tatarcium*), of cyanidin[5] (4) in red cabbage, and of many fungal metabolites.[3]

Variation of the oxygenation* pattern is one of the principal modifications of the aromatic rings thus derived.

* The term "oxygen" in this context means any group which is attached to the aromatic ring by a C—O bond.

20

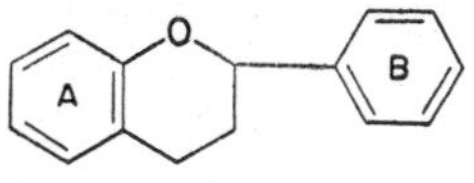

(1)

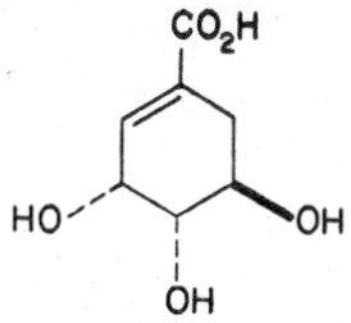

(2)

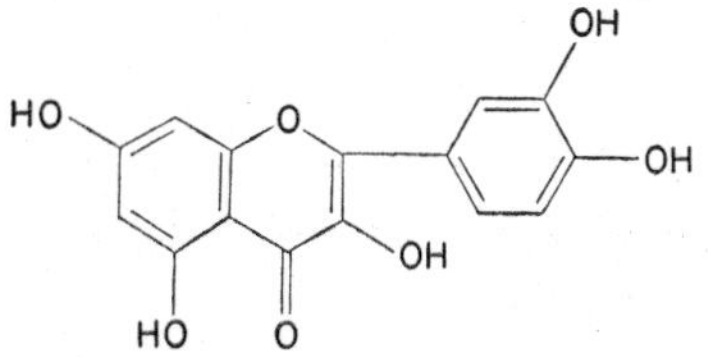

(3)

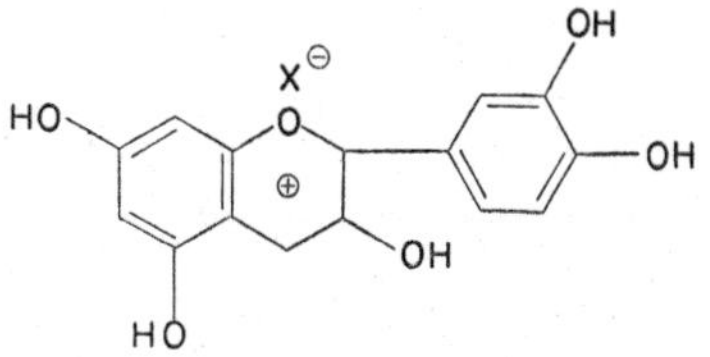

(4)

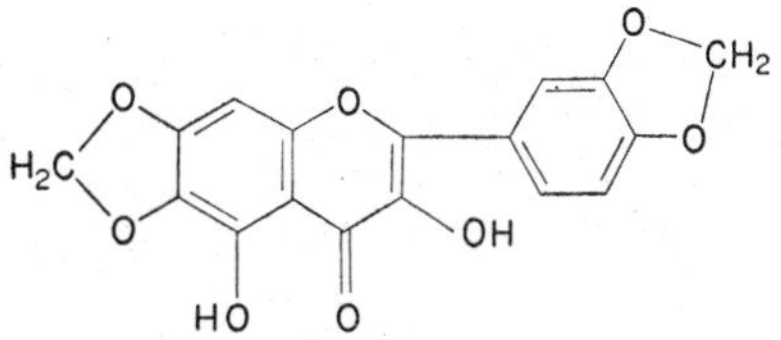

(5)

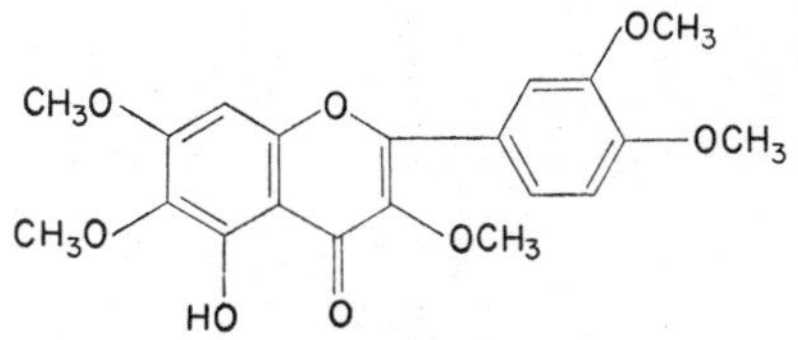

(6)

Introduction of Oxygen

Aromatic rings derived from acetate e.g. rings A of quercetin (3) and cyanidin (4), usually exhibit the expected 1:3:5- or phloroglucinol oxygenation pattern where the oxygen atoms are directly derived from the acetate precursor units.[6] The introduction of additional oxygen which is a characteristic feature of very many natural products, e.g. meliternetin[7] (5) and artemisetin[7] (6), almost certainly occurs at the aromatic ring stage by well-established oxidative processes.

The majority of aromatic rings derived from shikimate have the 4-, 3:4- or 3:4:5-oxygenation pattern. Studies on the biosynthesis of lignin[8,9] have established that mechanisms for the introduction of oxygen in the 3, 4 and 5 positions of C_6–C_3 residues exist in certain plants at least. Thus hard-wood lignin contains 3:4:5-oxygenated derivatives of cinnamic acid for which phenylalanine may function as a precursor. Additional evidence for the direct biological oxygenation of aromatic rings in plants has been obtained by Geissman and Swain[10] who fed 2-^{14}C labelled phenylalanine to *F. esculentum* and *Nicotiana tabacum* and isolated radioactive caffeic acid (3:4-dihydroxy-cinnamic acid).

As an alternative, for example, to de-oxygenation to prephenic acid, followed by re-oxygenation of the resultant shikimate derived aromatic rings, it is probable that in certain cases the hydroxyl groups of shikimic acid are retained in part or *in toto*. Shikimate precursors would then be aromatized by dehydrogenation rather than by dehydration (and dehydrogenation). Dr. Haslam has reported one example of the operation of this pathway (see Chapter 7).

The precise mode of interaction between shikimic and pyruvic acids to furnish C_6–C_3 residues has not been defined but it may be regarded as a nucleophilic displacement of phosphate from 5-phosphoshikimate to give (7) as in (a):

(a)

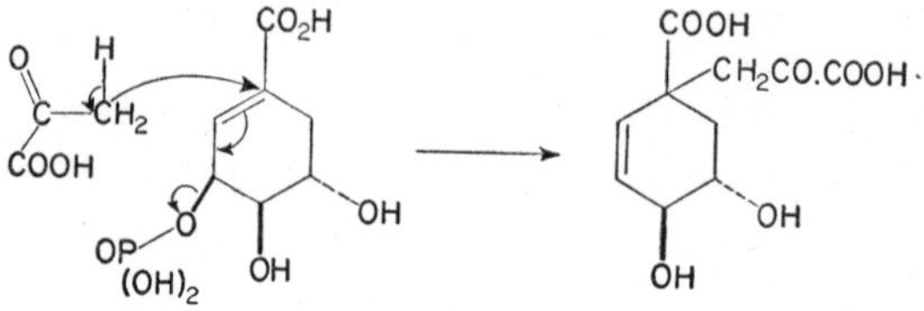

(7)

An alternative route[11] by way of the enol ether of pyruvate with the 5-hydroxyl group of shikimate would furnish the same product (7). In either case only two of the three original hydroxyl groups of the hydroaromatic

(b)

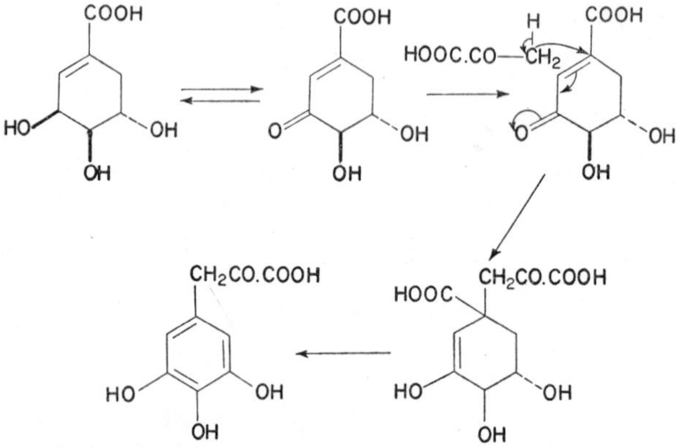

ring are retained, and those 3:4:5-tri-oxygenated substances derived by these routes must have at least *one* hydroxyl group (that at position 5) introduced by direct oxidation. A plausible, unestablished biosynthetic pathway which would retain the three oxygen functions of the shikimate ring is illustrated in (b).

Removal of Oxygen

The existence of numerous substances, e.g. 6-methyl-salicylic acid (8), flavone (9) and pratol (10) which contain acetate and shikimate derived rings with fewer oxygen atoms than expected indicates that de-oxygenation is a common phenomenon in biosynthesis. The derivation of 6-methylsalicylic acid (8) from acetic acid with the consequent removal of the oxygen atom enclosed in parentheses has been demonstrated.[3] The oxygen atoms which have been lost from (9) and (10) during biosynthesis are similarly indicated.

The removal of oxygen from a shikimic acid derived ring proceeds by dehydration (either directly or indirectly) at one of the hydroaromatic stages

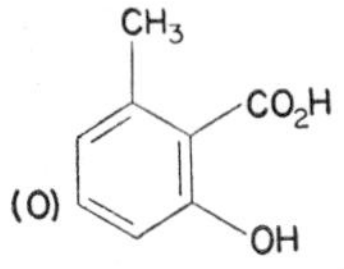

(8) 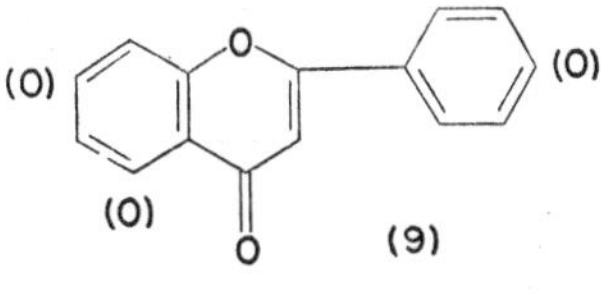   (9)

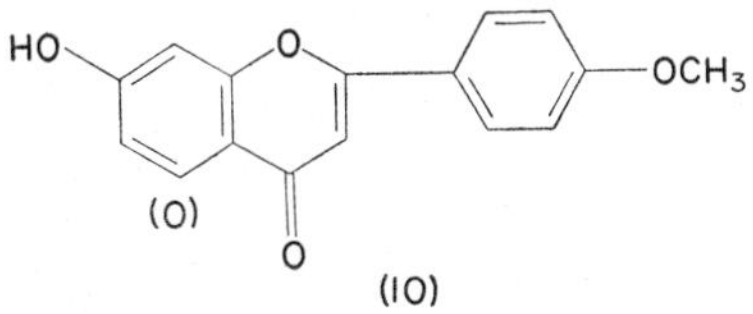

(10)

as in e.g. scheme (a) (p. 22) and in the formation of prephenic acid. Similarly the removal of oxygen from an acetate derived ring to furnish e.g. the resorcinol ring A of pratol (10) must almost certainly occur at a non-aromatic

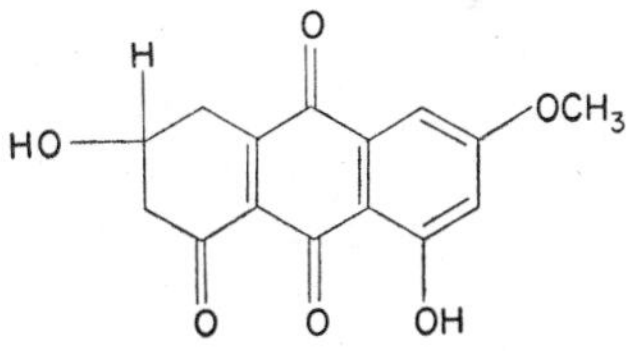

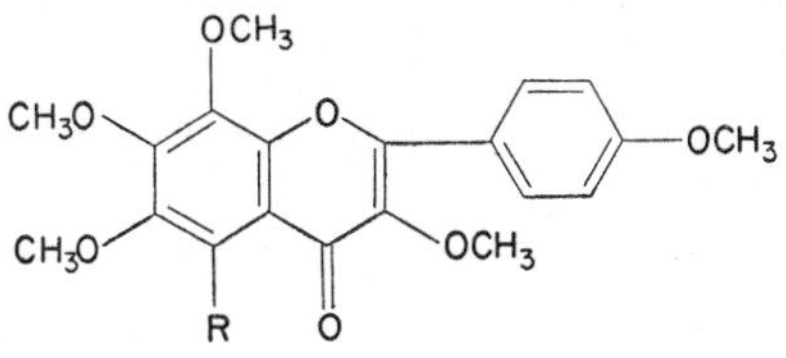

(11)   (12)

intermediate stage (cf. Birch[3]). The structures of certain fungal metabolites e.g. flavoskyrin[12] (11) exemplify the type of non-aromatic precursor which is probably involved.

There are no unequivocally established examples of the biological removal of oxygen from an aromatic ring system. Seshadri[13] maintains that the chemical removal of phenolic hydroxyl groups by the reduction with Raney nickel of the corresponding tosylate constitutes evidence for the possibility of an analogous biological reaction. The co-occurrence of pairs of compounds such as auranetin (12, R = H) and 5-hydroxyauranetin (12, R = OH) has been cited as evidence in support of this thesis. But the 5-hydroxyl group of (12, R = OH) could be readily removed at an earlier non-aromatic stage. For these and other general reasons Seshadri's views are not easily acceptable.

Consequent upon these general remarks it is convenient to consider the inter-relationships of the various types of phenolic and oxygen heterocyclic compounds.

Flavonoids, including Isoflavonoids and Anthocyanidins

Among non-nitrogenous higher plant products these compounds have so far proved the most accessible to biosynthetical investigations. Ring A of the flavonoids and anthocyanidins is derived from acetate and the C_6(ring B)–C_3 system has shikimate as the precursor (cf. p. 24).

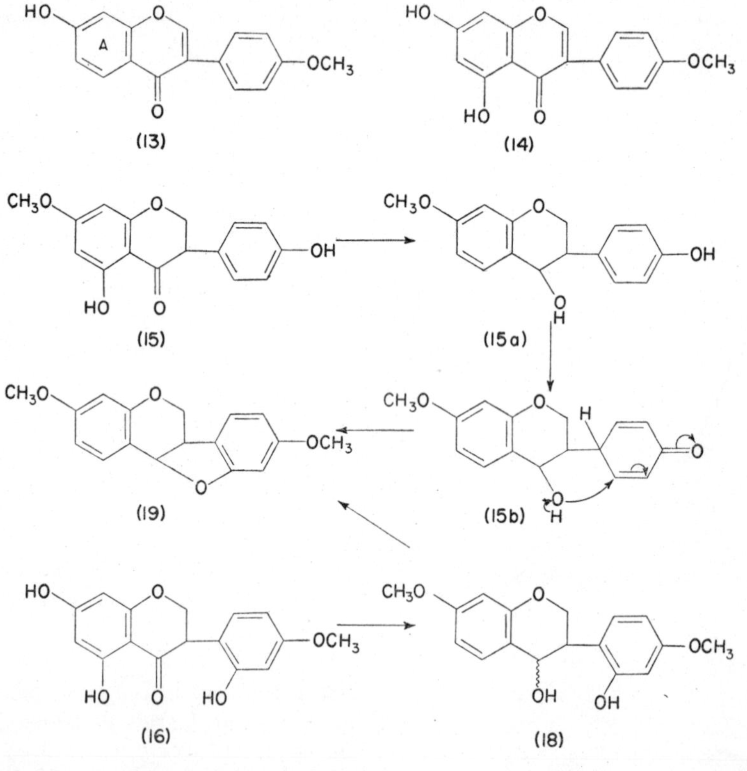

(13)   (14)

(15)   (15a)

(19)   (15b)

(16)   (18)

It has been suggested[1,2,15] that the isoflavones may be produced phytochemically from the corresponding flavonoids (or appropriate C_6–C_3–C_6 intermediate) by a 1:2-phenyl migration. The occurrence of such a migration has been elegantly demonstrated in the biosynthesis of formononetin (13) by Dr. Grisebach (p. 62). Similar studies on biochanin A (14) have shown that an alternative biosynthetic pathway, which does not involve phenyl (or acyl) migration, also operates.[16,17] In each case, however, it seems well established that rings A and B are formed from acetate and shikimate respectively, although the details of isoflavone biosynthesis require further investigation.

Biological reduction of isoflavones could furnish isoflavanones of which padmakastein[18] (15), ferreirin[19] (16) and homoferreirin[19] (17) occur naturally. The tetracyclic congeners homopterocarpin[20] (19) and pterocarpin[20] (20) of the isoflavanones may then be related by either the sequence (15) → (15a) → (15b) → (19) or the alternative (16) → (18) → (19).

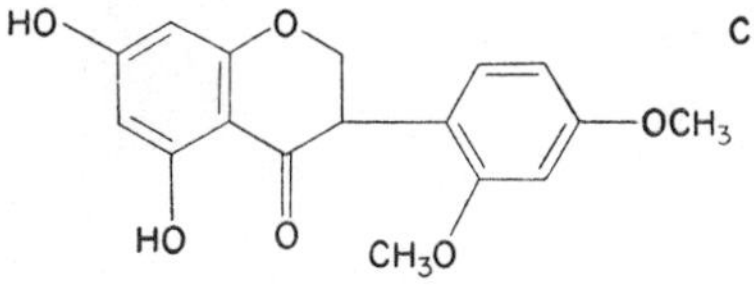

(17) 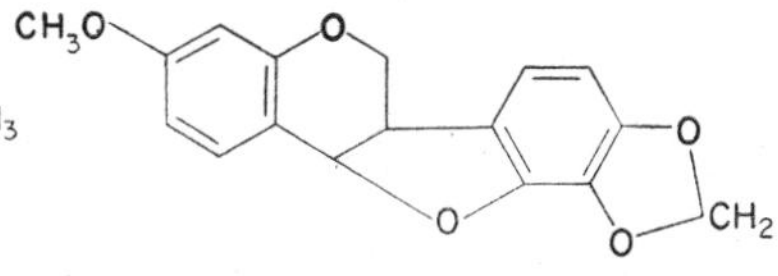   (20)

Numerous representatives of the intermediates to be expected in the biogenesis of flavonoids have been isolated from natural sources. Thus the styryl ketones which are the immediate precursors of flavanones are represented by for example xanthohumol[21] (21), and the flavone, lanceolatin B (23) which occurs together with the protected diketonic compound, pongamol[22] (22)

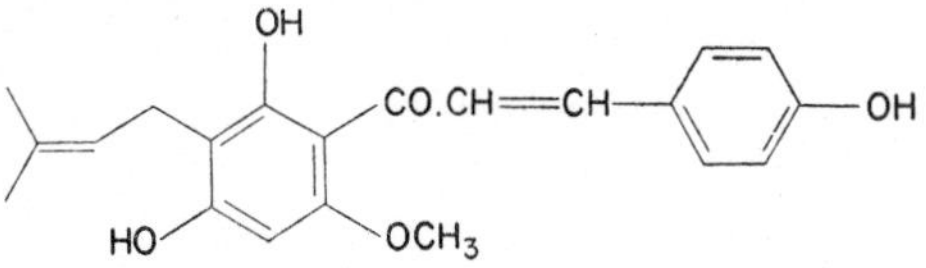

(21) 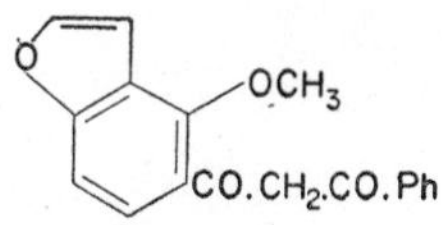   (22)

It is of biological significance that the majority of naturally occurring flavanones (24, R = H) and dihydroflavonols (24, R = OH) have the same absolute configuration at C-2, which is in turn identical with the absolute configuration of (+) catechin (25) and (−) epicatechin (26)[23] at the same centre.

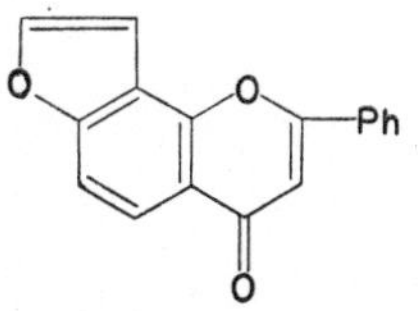

(23) 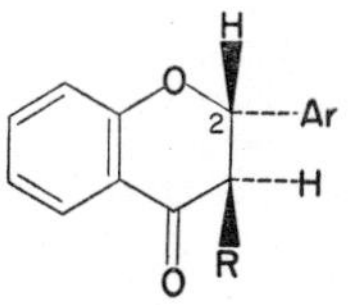   (24)

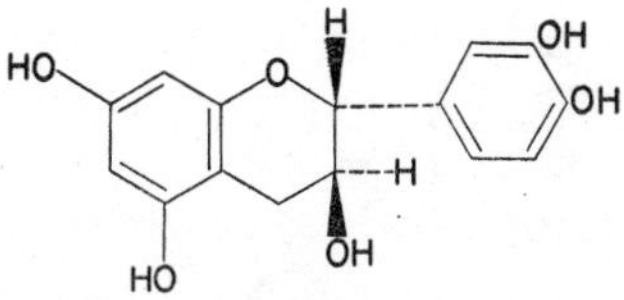

(25) 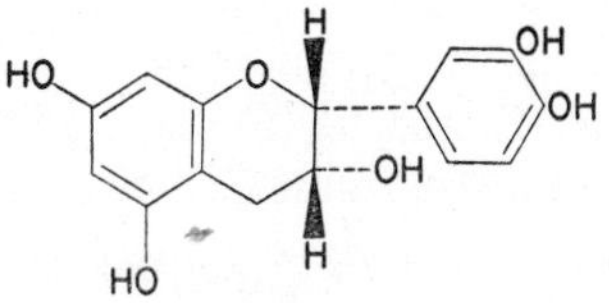   (26)

3

Among the numerous anthocyanidins there are very few which do not have a 3-hydroxyl group and none which is devoid of hydroxyls in both the 3 and the 5 positions. This is in contrast to many flavonoids which are deoxygenated in these positions.

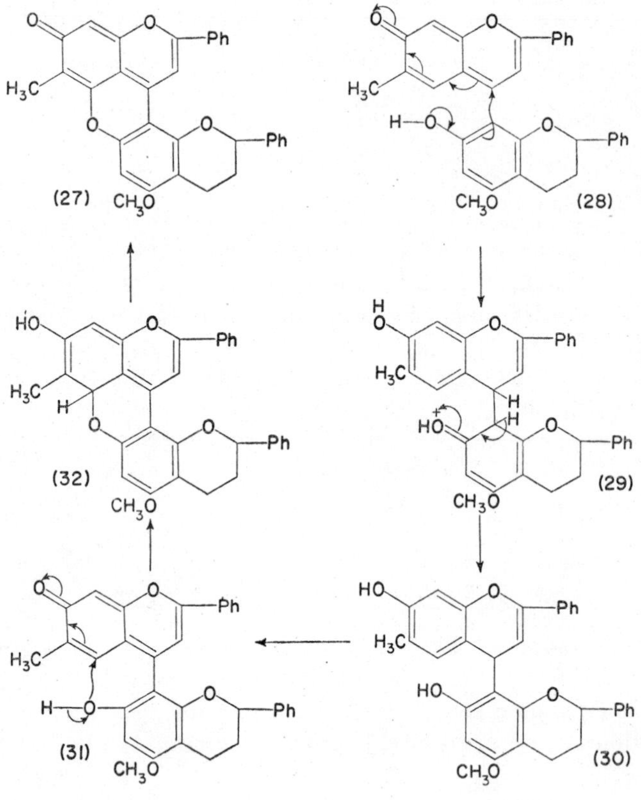

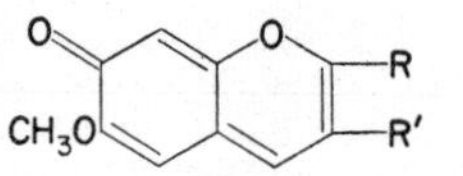

Ring A of the anthocyanidins is of the phloroglucinol type. This marked difference in oxygenation pattern between flavonoids and anthocyanidins may be attributed to (a) the rapid autoxidation of anhydropyranol bases derived from the stable 3:5-di-unsubstituted 7-hydroxybenzpyrylium salts[24] or (b) the reactivity exhibited by the 4-position of 3:5-di-unsubstituted pyrylium salts towards anionoid reagents.[25] Thus if 3:5-di-unsubstituted anthocyanidins were a product of biosynthesis their existence might be expected to be only transitory.

An interesting example of the further transformation of a 3:5-di-unsubstituted authocyanidin is concerned in the probable genesis by way of stages $(28 \rightarrow 32)$ of the complex anhydrobenzopyranol dracorubin[26] (27). This mode of biosynthesis is more acceptable than that proposed by Erdtman.[27]

The pigments santalin and santarubin, partial formulae (33),[28] are the only examples of 5-unsubstituted anhydrobenzpyranol bases which occur naturally. They are stabilized by the 3-aryl-substituent.

Coumarins

The hydroxylation pattern of the majority of coumarins and particularly the ubiquity of the 7-hydroxyl group indicates their derivation from shikimate. Three groups of investigators[29,30,31] have established that the biosynthesis of coumarin (34) proceeds from shikimic acid, and not from acetate.

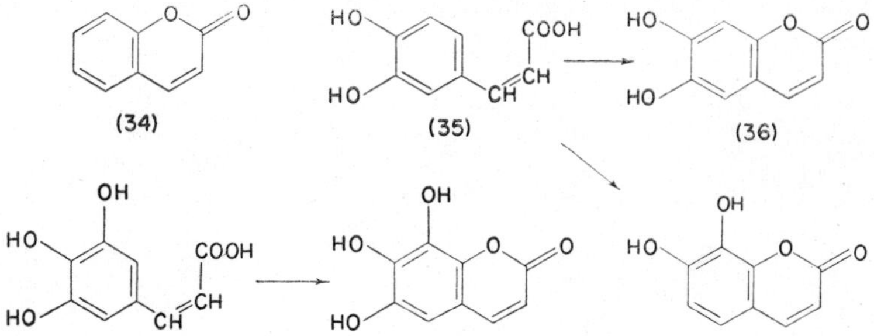

(34)   (35)   (36)

(38)   (39)   (37)

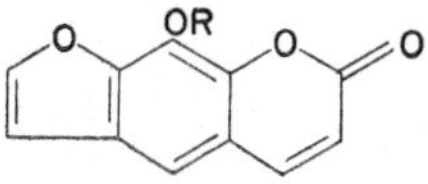

(40) 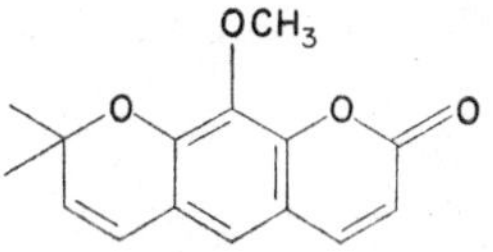   (41)

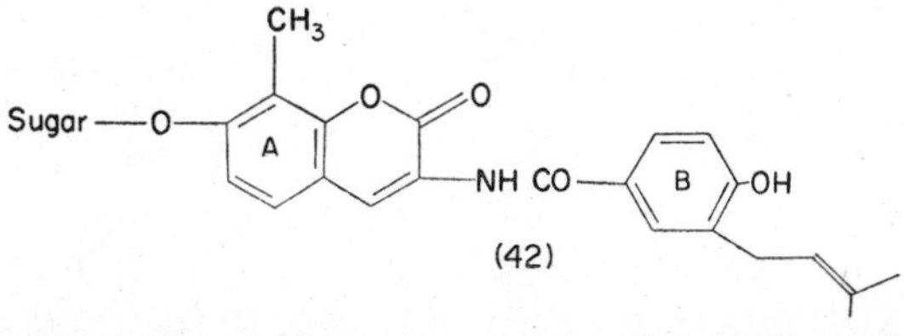

(42)

Although direct oxygenation of 7-hydroxycoumarin could readily furnish the oxygenation patterns (36), (37) and (39), which are characteristic of the majority of coumarins, these patterns may equally be produced by ring closure of the appropriately hydroxylated cinnamic acids. Thus cyclization

of a 3:4-dihydroxycinnamic acid (35) may furnish 6:7-dioxygenated coumarins (36) (e.g. esculin, chicorin, fabiatrin, scopolin and ayapin) or the
alternative 7:8-dioxygenated coumarins (37), such as daphnin, and the
complex coumarins, xanthotoxol (40, R = H), xanthotoxin (40, R = Me)
and luvangetin (41). Similarly 3:4:5-trihydroxycinnamic acid (38) may yield
6:7:8-trioxygenated coumarins (39), e.g. fraxidin and isofraxidin. Strong
circumstantial evidence for the establishment of the oxygenation pattern at
the cinnamic acid, or equivalent precyclized, stage is provided by the fact
that the oxygenation pattern of the biosynthetically equivalent C_6–C_3 residue
of the flavonoids is most probably determined *prior* to its condensation with
the acetate units of ring A.[32]

The fungal metabolite, novobiocin (42) retains the amino group of the
tyrosine precursor of ring A; ring B is also probably derived from shikimate.

By analogy with the mechanism proposed for the conversion of tyrosine
to melanin,[33] Haworth suggested,[34] in 1942, that the cyclization of cinnamic
acids to coumarins proceeds as follows:

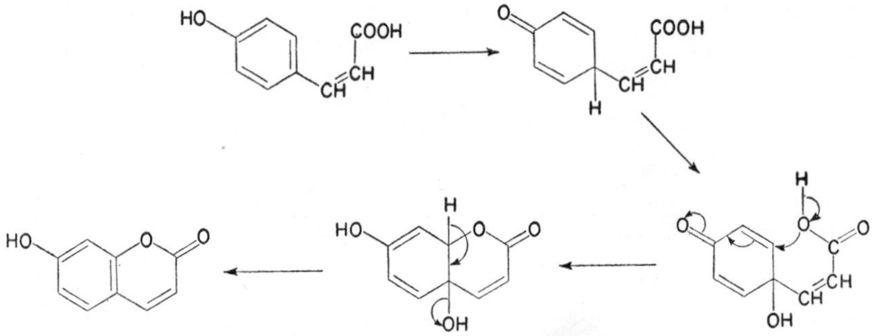

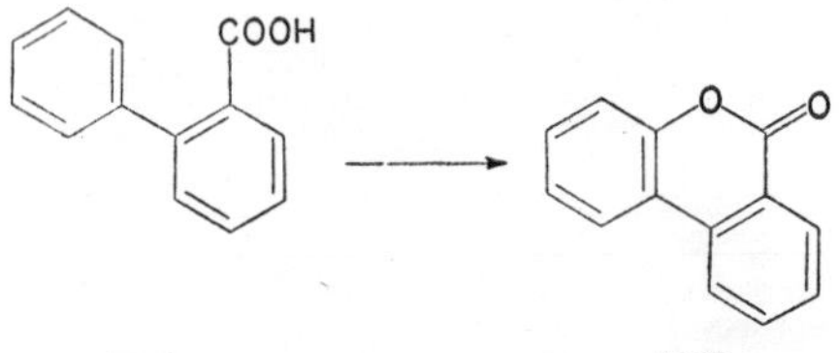

(43)   (44)

Collateral experimental support for the plausibility of an oxidative
cyclization has been provided by the oxidative conversion of diphenyl-2-
carboxylic acid (43) to 3:4-benzocoumarin (44), in high yield.[35]

Although an oxidative, biological transformation of C_6–C_3 residues to
coumarins is most attractive, direct *ortho*-hydroxylation followed by
lactonization cannot be entirely excluded. The formation of *o*-hydroxyphenyl

acetic acid from phenylacetic acid, by *Penicillium chrysogenum*[36] illustrates this biochemical possibility.

Certain flavonoids, isoflavonoids and their congeners, e.g. citronetin[37] (45), homopterocarpin (19), pterocarpin (20), coumestrol[38] (46), wedelolactone[39] (47), the rotenoids, e.g. rotenone (48), pacchyrizin (49) and erosnin (50) have

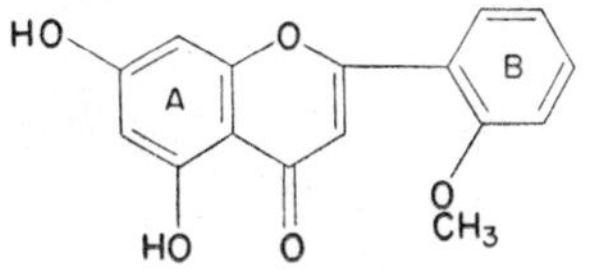

(45)

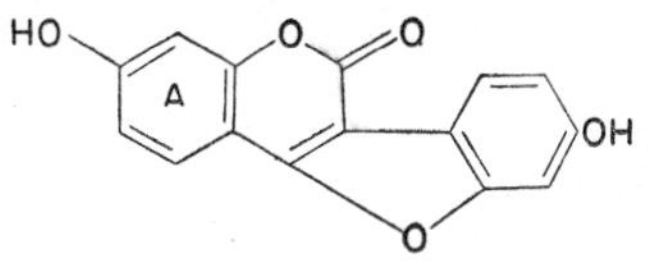

(46)

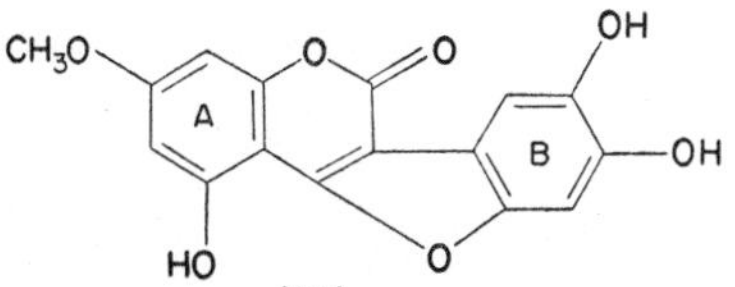

(47)

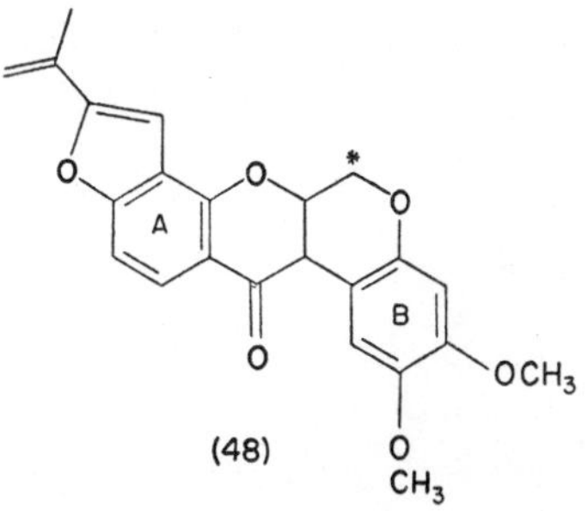

(48)

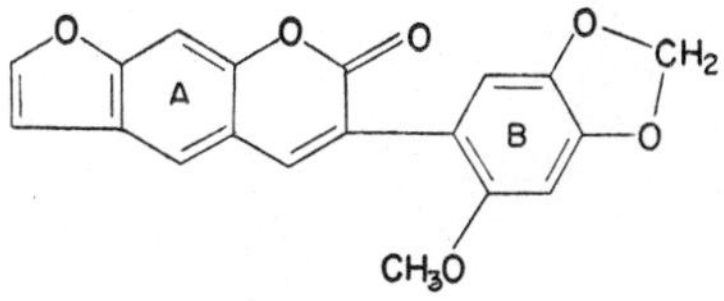

(49)

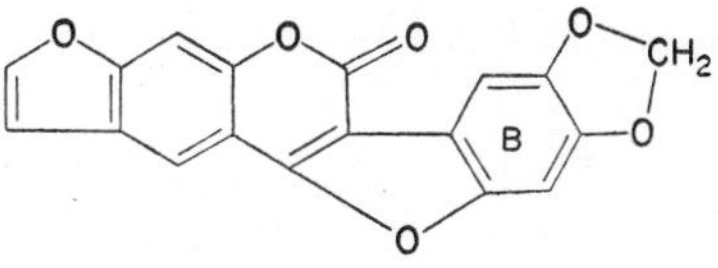

(50)

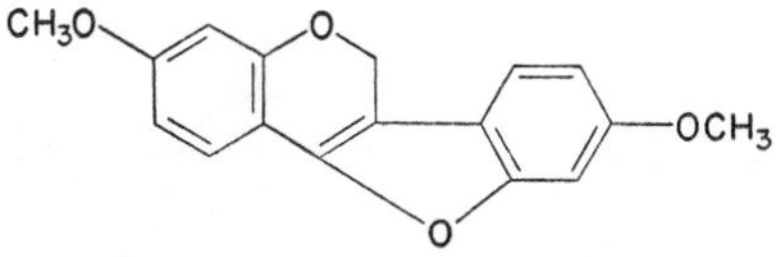

(51)

the uncommon 2'-oxygen group on ring B. The introduction of this 2'-oxygen may be consequent upon the genesis of ring B in these compounds from an *o*-hydroxycinnamic acid, which in turn is derived by ring opening of a coumarin. This would determine at least the 2'-oxygenation of ring B *prior to* ring A formation, in accord with previous concepts (cf. p. 28).

Alternatively the 2'-ether linkage which is characteristic of homoptero-carpin, pterocarpin, coumestrol and wedelolactone could be introduced by the reaction sequence (15) → (15a) → (15b) → (19).

The simple coumarins, limettin (52), 7-methoxy-5-geranyloxycoumarin (53), toddalolactone (54) and certain complex coumarins such as bergaptol (55), isobergapten (56) and xanthoxyletin (57) have a phloroglucinol type oxygenation pattern which is characteristic of acetate derivation. General biogenetical considerations suggest however that these phloroglucinol type

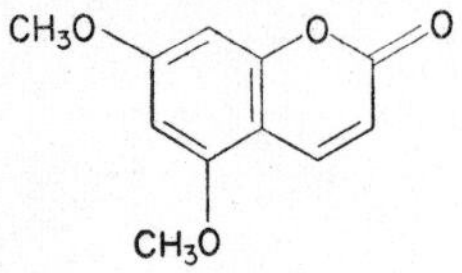

(52)

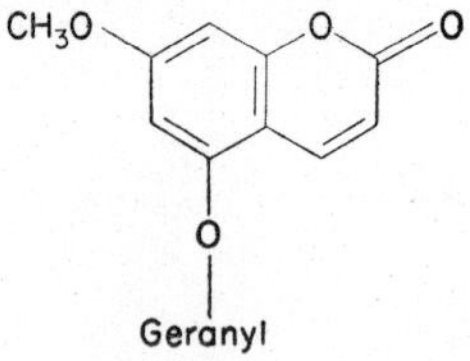

(53)
Geranyl

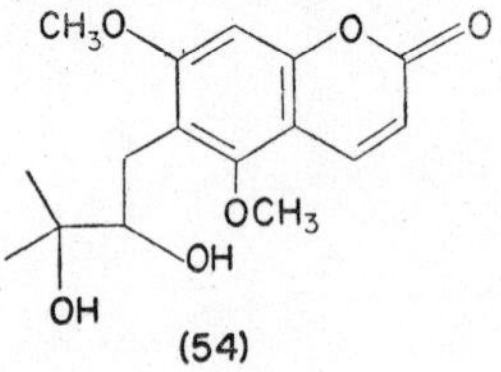

(54)

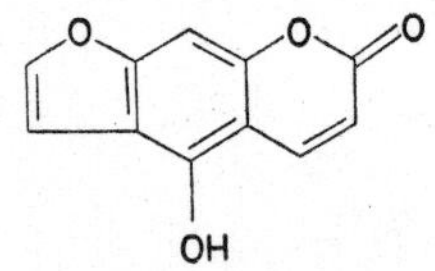

(55)

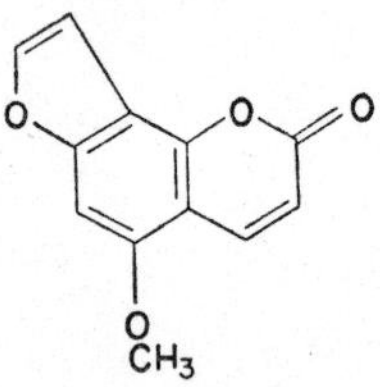

(56)

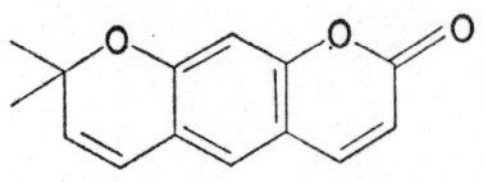

(57)

coumarins are indeed derived from a cinnamic acid precursor by a double oxidative ring closure as follows:

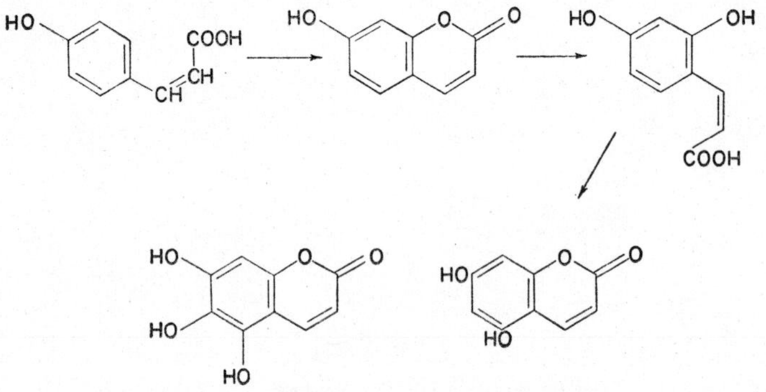

(58)

The fraxinol type coumarins (58) may arise in a similar manner.

3- and 4-Phenylcoumarins

The 3-phenylcoumarins, coumestrol (46), wedelolactone (47), erosnin[40] (50) and pachyrrhizin[41] (49) probably arise by the oxidation of isoflavanones. It may be significant that the laboratory transformation of homopterocarpin

(19) to dehydrohomopterocarpin (51) and then to O-dimethylcoumestrol is readily achieved.[42] Thus ring A of these coumarins will be acetate-derived and ring B will come from shikimate.

The 4-phenylcoumarins, dalbergin[43] (59), the several variants of calo-phyllolide[44] (60) and the substance (62) which occurs in *Mammea americana*

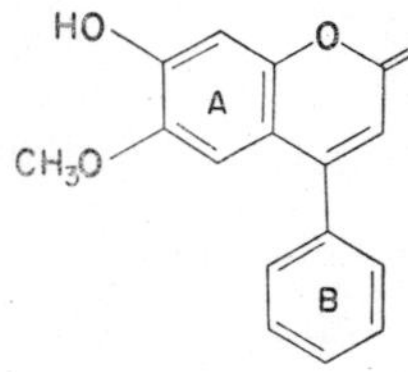

(59)

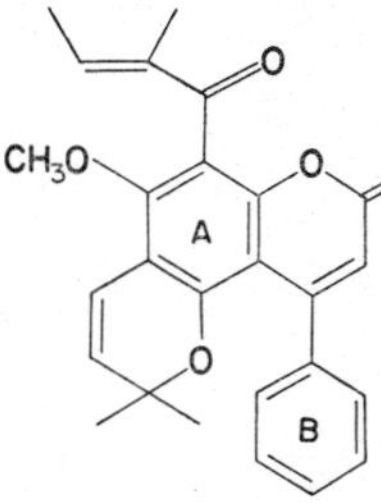

(60)

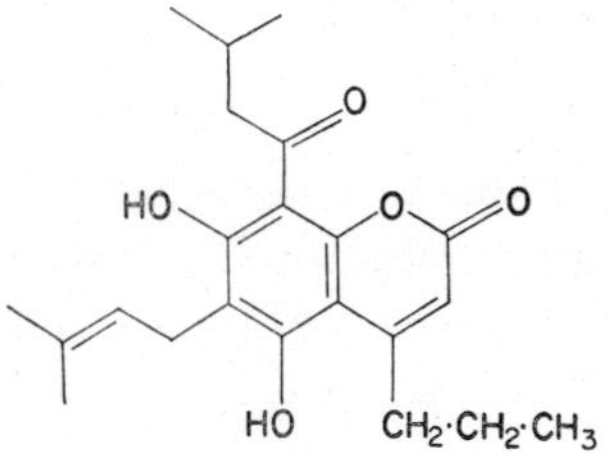

(61)

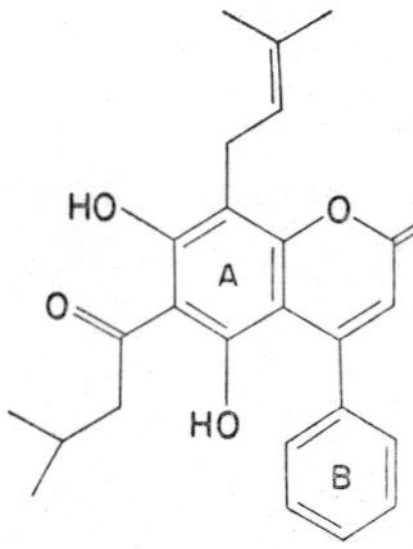

(62)

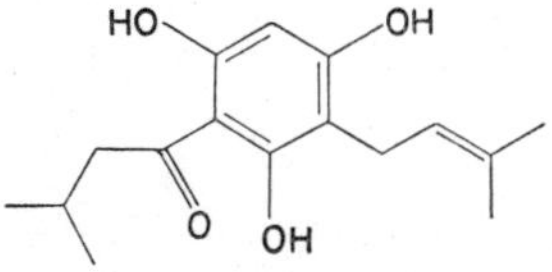

(63)

L.,[45] could be derived from flavonoids by a double 1:2 shift, or more probably by condensation of a phenol and the corresponding β-keto-acid (as in the Pechmann condensation). Either mode of genesis results in ring A being acetate derived and the C_6(ring B)–C_3, residue has shikimate as the precursor. The occurrence of the 4-phenylcoumarin (62) together with the 4-*n*-propylcoumarin, mammein[46] (61), in *Mammea americana L.*, where the coumarin (61) must almost certainly be formed from the phenol (63) and a β-ketohexanoate possibly provides circumstantial evidence for a Pechmann type biosynthesis of 4-phenylcoumarins.

Chromones and Acetophenones

Geissman[2] has suggested that the naturally occurring chromones, eugenin (64), eugenitin (65), isoeugenitol (66) and peucenin (67) together with the furanochromones, visnagin (68) and khellin (69) have a shikimate-derived

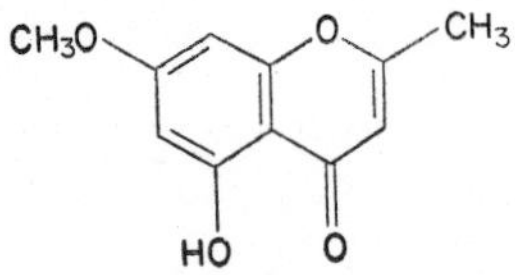

(64) 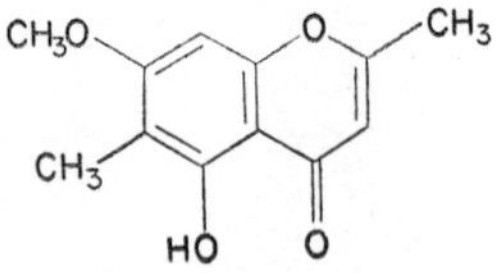   (65) 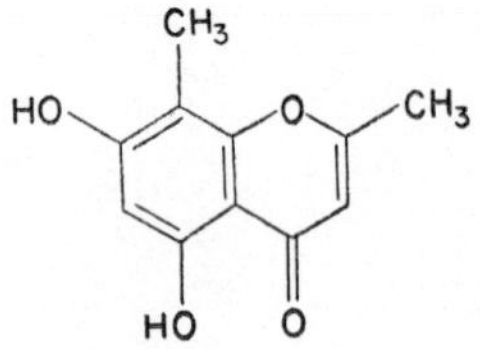   (66)

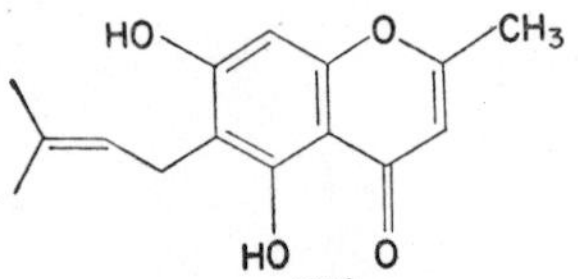

(67) 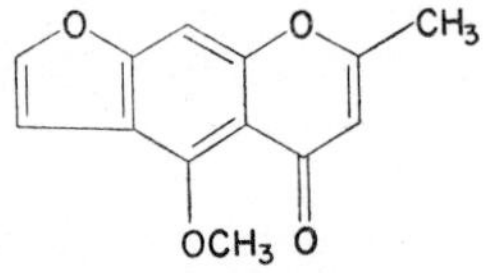   (68) 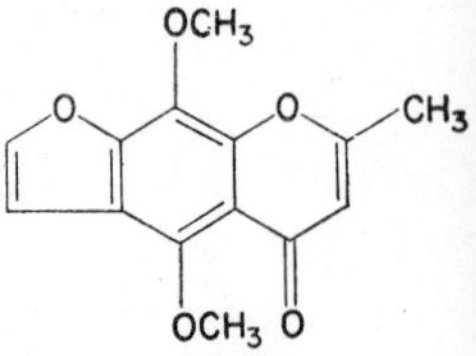   (69)

nucleus. However, these substances correspond in oxygenation pattern to acetate derivation. This also applies to several naturally occurring aceto-phenones such as euparin (72), phloracetophenone and its 4:6-dimethylether

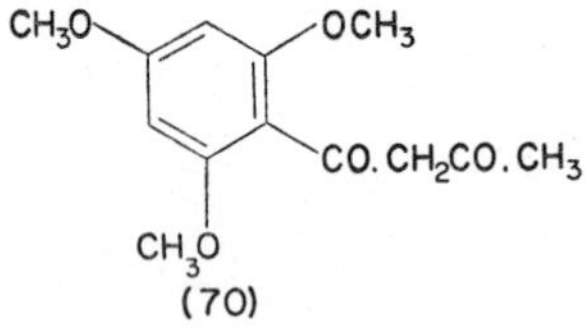

(70) 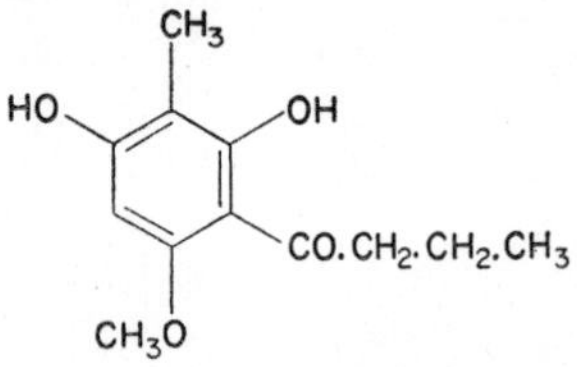   (71)

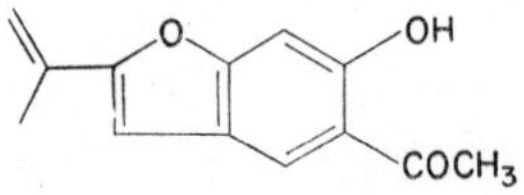

(72) 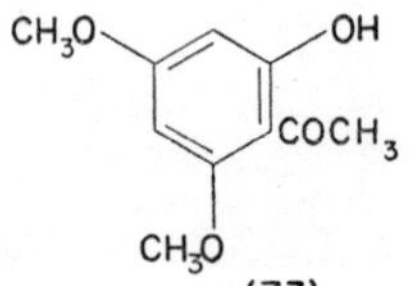   (73)

(73) which may represent intermediates in 2-methylchromone synthesis (or degradation), and the formation of the β-diketone (70). This accompanies the simple chromones in *Eugenia* and is probably their precursor (when unmethylated). Aspidinol (71) is an example of a reduction product of such a diketone. Certain acetophenones, e.g. 4-hydroxy-, and 3-methoxy-4-hydroxy-acetophenone very probably arise from shikimate.

The 2:4:6-trioxygenated acetophenones and chromones occur in the *Rutaceae* and *Umbelliferae*, the sources of the similarly oxygenated

coumarins, and the possibility that they are derived from shikimate by the following sequence, cannot be excluded. Clarification of this point would be of taxonomic significance.

Compounds containing "Extra" Carbon Atoms

Although most natural products are readily accommodated within the framework of current theories of biosynthesis, a few contain an "extra" skeletal carbon atom the genesis of which is not readily apparent.

These substances include brazilin[47] (74, R = H), haematoxylin[47] (74, R = OH), peltogynol[48] (76) distemonanthin[49] (77) and the rotenoids such as rotenone (48) in which the "extra" carbon atom is marked by an asterisk.

Brazilin and haematoxylin may arise from the corresponding flavonoid (or equivalent) by a double 1:2-phenyl migration,[50] or more probably by reduction of the corresponding 4-phenyl coumarin (75) (cf. p. 30). There are numerous well substantiated examples of the biochemical conversion of the carboxyl group to —CH_2OH.[51] It follows that rings A and B in these substances are derived from acetate and shikimate, respectively.

Brazilin, haematoxylin, peltogynol and distemonanthin have the "extra" carbon atom, which might be introduced from a C_1 unit,[3,50] in the 2'-position. This location suggests that it could be derived from the carboxyl group of shikimic acid by the mechanism which Wenkert has invoked in his theory of indole alkaloid biosynthesis,[11] as shown below.

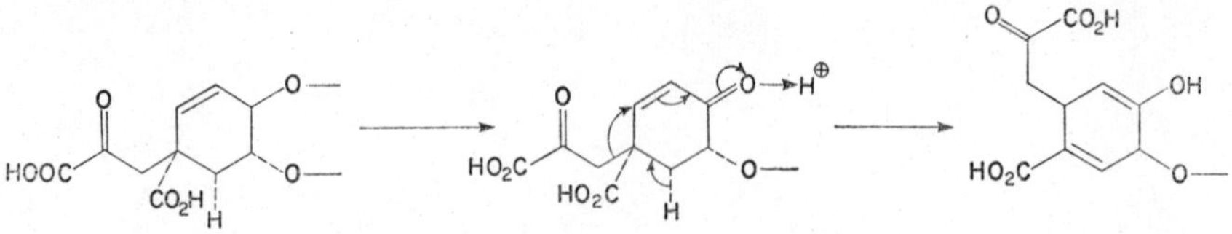

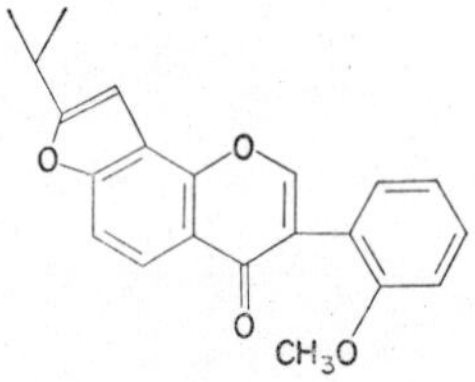

(78) 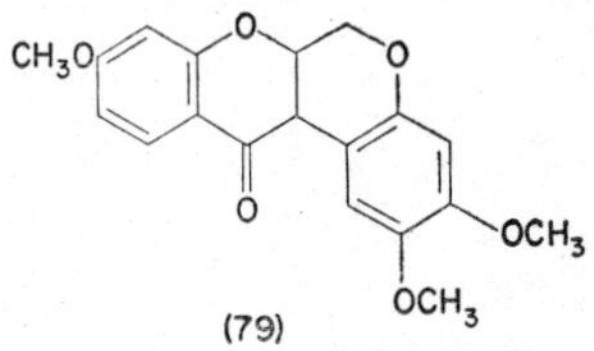   (79)

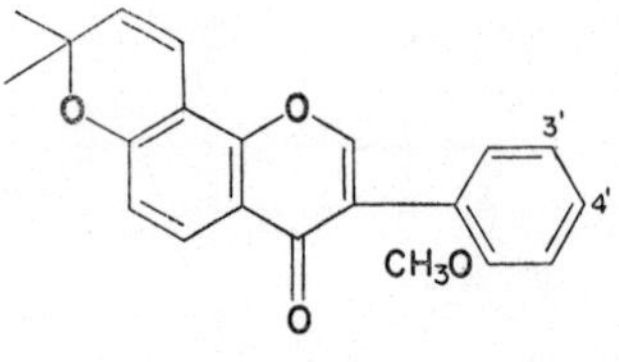

(80) 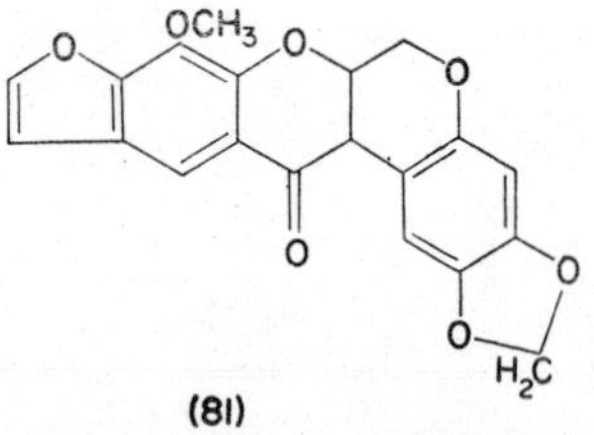   (81)

(82)

(83a)

(83b)

The additional carbon atom in the rotenoids may be variously derived in theory, but the occurrence of the isoflavone (80, 3':4'-dimethoxy) together with the rotenoids in *Derris malaccensis*,[52] of the isoflavone, jamaicin (80, 3':4'-methylenedioxy) and rotenone in *Piscidia erythrina L.*,[53] of rotenone, pachyrrhizone (81), erosnin (50) and pachyrrhizin (49) in *Pachyrrhizus erosus*,[40,41] of rotenone and the isoflavone (78) in *Mundulea suberosa*,[54] and of the rotenoid, munduserone (79), the isoflavone, mundulone (82) and the flavonol, sericetin (83a) or (83b) in *Mundulea sericea*,[55,56] together with the 2':4':5'-trioxygenated ring B in the majority of these compounds, provides compelling circumstantial evidence for a close biogenetical affinity between the rotenoids and the isoflavones (or their C_6–C_3–C_6 precursors) and between the isoflavones and the 3-phenylcoumarins (cf. p. 30). Further, it may be inferred that rotenoids are derived from isoflavones (or their C_6–C_3–C_6 precursors) by insertion of a C_1 unit.

The Introduction of Isopentenyl and Alkyl Substituents

(a) *Branched alkyl residues derived from mevalonate.* Many naturally occurring phenolic and oxygen heterocyclic compounds contain the iso-pentenyl (or isoprenyl) residue (which is frequently modified by oxidation and/or reduction) attached to either carbon or oxygen. Isoprenylation has been considered by Birch,[3] Seshadri[57] and by Ollis and Sutherland (see Chapter 4). Only certain limited aspects of this topic are discussed here.

The obvious affinity of these isoprenoid residues with mevalonic lactone has been confirmed experimentally for auroglaucin (84)[58] and the majority of isoprenoid residues are certainly terpenoid in origin.

The reactive entity in isoprenylation is $\gamma\gamma$-dimethylallyl-pyrophosphate (85) which attaches the C_5 fragment to carbon or oxygen as in (86) and (87) respectively. Hence modification of the isopentenyl fragment occurs *after* its introduction, and *O*- and *C*-isoprenylation take place at the aromatic ring stage that is very late in the biosynthetic sequence. Further, *C*-isoprenylation requires the availability of a highly anionoid position. This requirement rationalizes the high incidence of *C*-isopentenylation in ring A of flavonoids (which usually have the phloroglucinol or resorcinol oxygenation pattern), in contrast to the rarity of *C*-isoprenylation in ring B. Mundulone (82) is the only example of an isoflavonoid *C*-isoprenylated in ring B. In this case ring B

(84)   (85)

(86)

(87)

has the resorcinol oxygenation pattern. In contrast, many of the biologically equivalent, shikimate derived coumarins are *C*-isoprenylated. This may be ascribed to their high degree of oxygenation and to the ubiquity of the resorcinol system provided by cyclization. Since the anionoid reactivity of coumarins is low *C*-isoprenylation probably occurs at the cinnamic or *o*-hydroxycinnamic acid stage. The co-occurrence of mammein (61) and the coumarin (62)[45,46] indicates that isoprenylation of the phloroglucinol ring giving (63) *precedes* coumarin formation since these two coumarins are most probably derived from the same precursor (63) by the addition of the corresponding β-keto-acids in the two alternative orientations (cf. p. 31).

Acid catalysed cyclization of the *o*-hydroxyisopentenyl unit (88) will furnish the 2:2-dimethyl-chroman system (94) as in fuscin,[59] by way of (93). The phytochemical formation of the 2:2-dimethyl-chromene residue may be variously formulated, but the mechanistic ease of oxidation of the allylic methylene group, coupled with the frequent occurrence[2] of the —COCH=C(Me)$_2$ and —COCH$_2$CH(Me)$_2$ residues, makes the route (88) → (89) → (95) → (96) a feasible one.

Epoxides of type (92, R = Me) are well represented among natural products. The normal course of nucleophilic attack by the phenolic hydroxyl group upon the epoxide as in (91, R = H) will furnish an isopropyl coumaran, as in for example marmesin[60] (98). Dehydration of hydroxylisopropylcoumarans (cf. 98) could yield the 2-isopropenyl coumaran group (99) which is characteristic of rotenone (48). Alternatively, the less usual attack by the hydroxyl as in (92) will furnish the 3-hydroxy-2:2-dimethylchroman residue of mundulone (82).

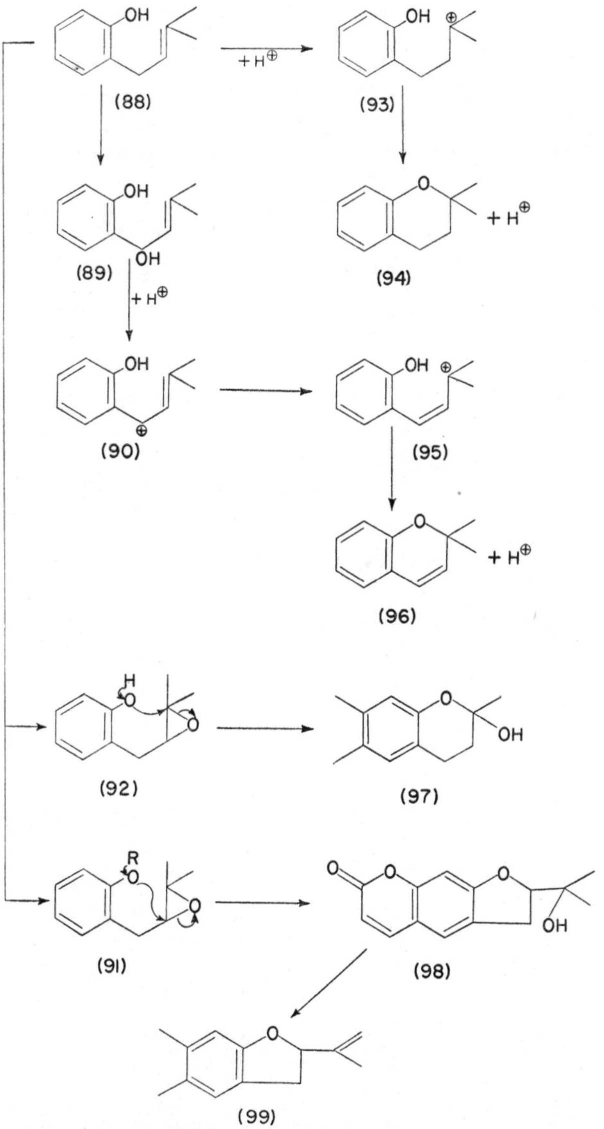

In this connection it is significant that where the C-epoxyisopentenyl group, or the derived glycol, occurs in natural products the *ortho*- oxygen groups

are etherified. The facile transformation[61] of (91, R = H) suggests that
etherification of the *o*-hydroxyl *precedes* epoxidation.

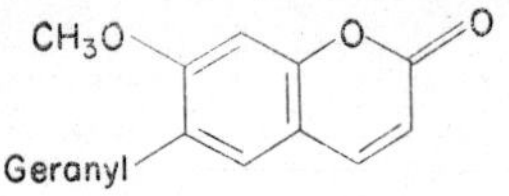

(100) 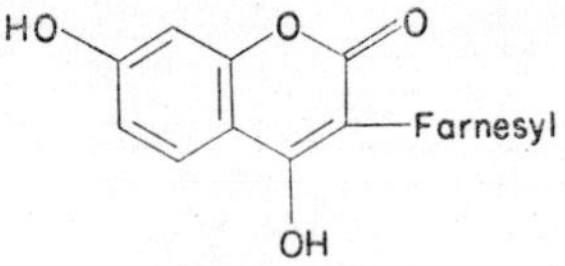   (101)

The attachment to carbon or oxygen of more complex terpenoid residues as
in ostruthin[62] (100), ammoresinol[63] (101), umbelliprenin[64] (102) and chlorophorin[65] (103) will occur in a manner analogous to the isoprenylation process.

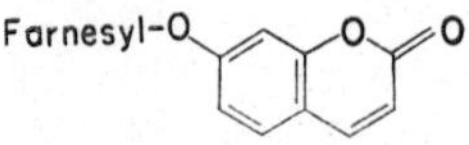

(102) 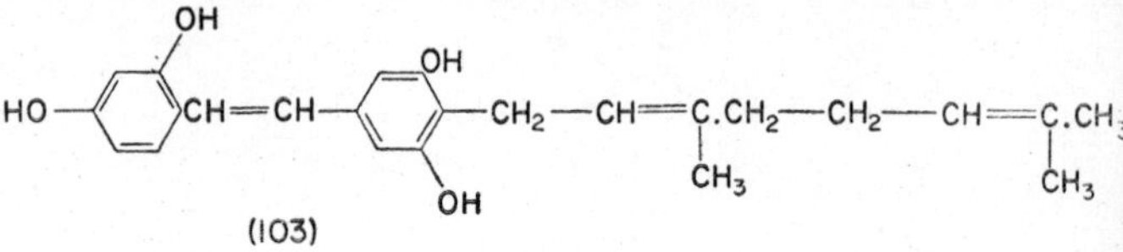   (103)

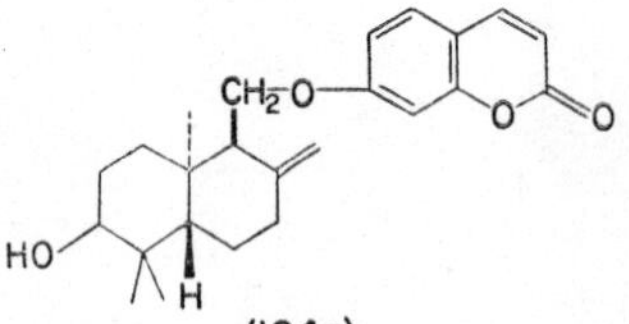

(104a) 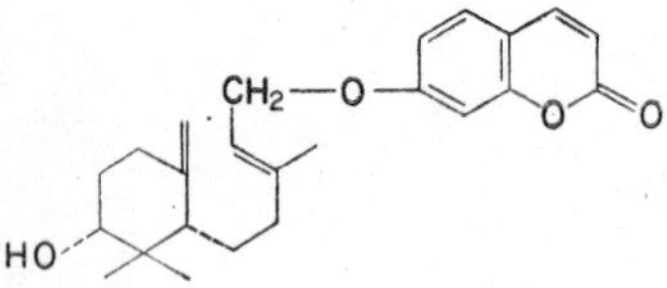   (104b)

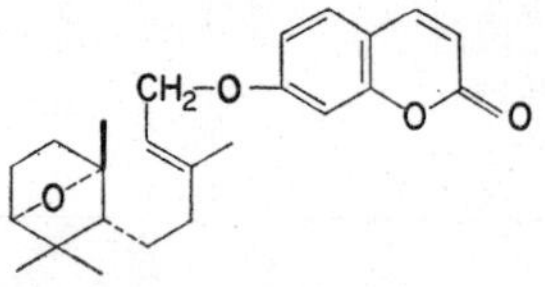

(104c) 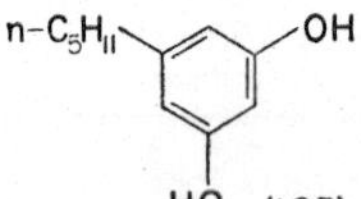   (105)

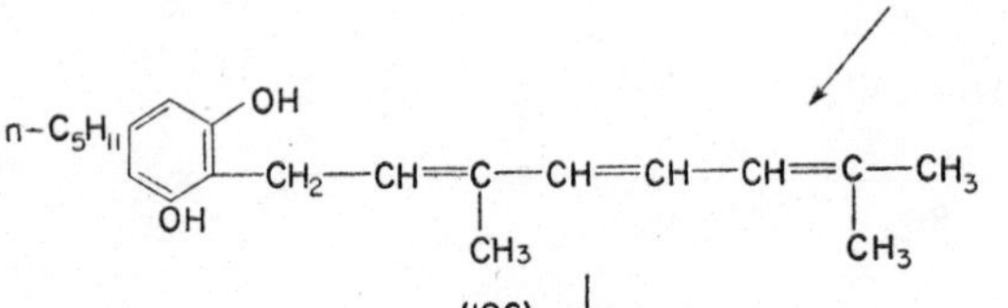

(106)

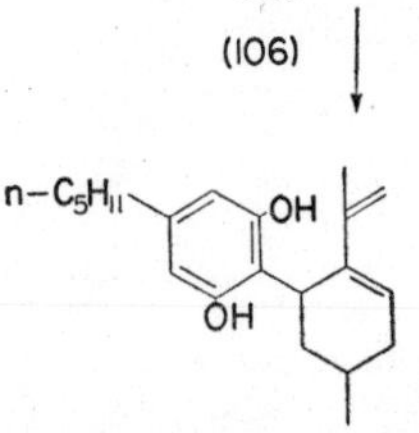

(107)

Secondary transformations of terpenoid residues are apparent. Thus
farnesiferol-a[66] (104a), farnesiferol-b[67] (104b) and farnesiferol-c[67] (104c) may

arise by cyclization of the farnesyl residue of umbelliprenin (102). Cannabidiol[68] (107) is most probably formed by cyclization of the geranyl resorcinol (106) which arises from the condensation of 5-*n*-propyl resorcinol (105) with geranylpyrophosphate. Cannabidiol (107) will yield tetrahydrocannabinol (108) and thence cannabinol (109) by aromatization of ring C.

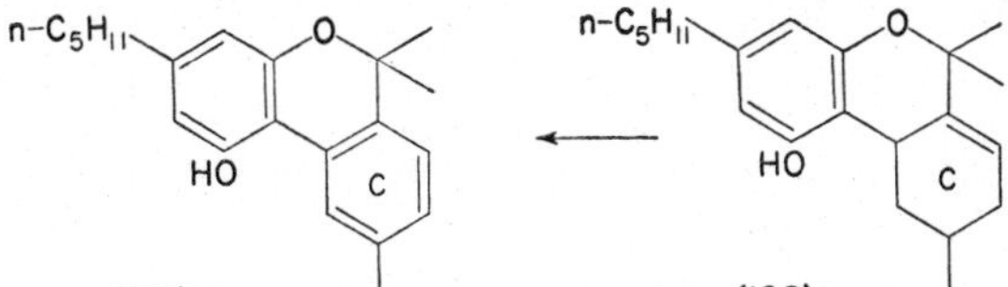

(109)   (108)

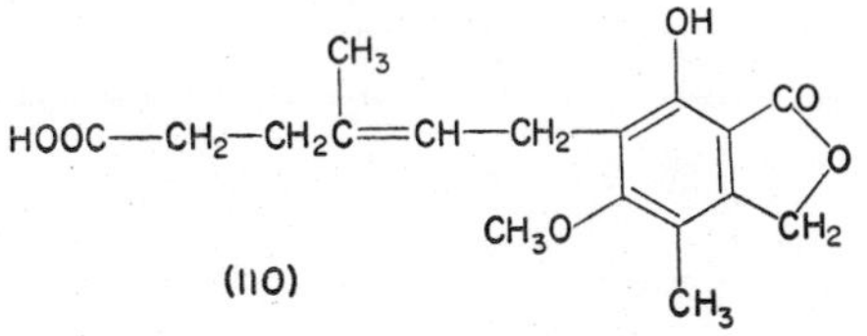

(110)

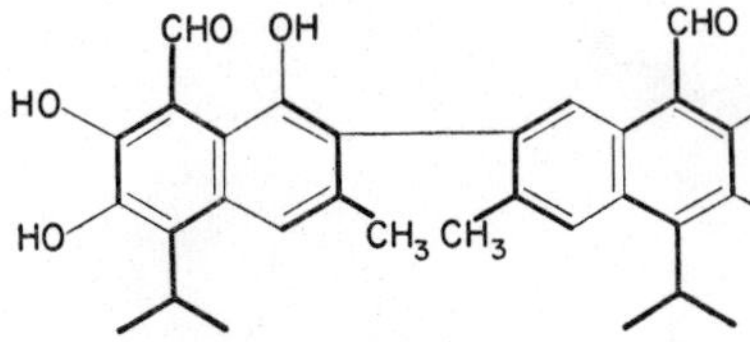

(III)   (II2)

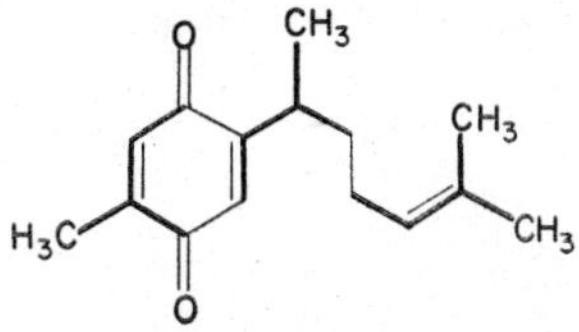

(II3)

On general grounds[69] it could be predicted that the γ-position in the resorcinol (105) and in the stilbene moiety of chlorophorin (103) would be more reactive than the β-positions. Hence the appearance of the terpenoid residues in the γ-positions provides strong circumstantial evidence for their introduction into the preformed phenol at a late stage in biosynthesis.

A similar consideration applies to mycophenolic acid[70] (110) and it would be of interest to ascertain the sequence of introduction of the *C*-methyl and isoprenoid residues.

The derivation of aromatic rings from terpenoid precursors is apparent in

the structures of e.g. gossypol[71] (111), cuminaldehyde (112) and the benzo-
quinone, perezone (pipitzahoic acid)[72] (113), where the isoprene residues are
shown by the thick lines.

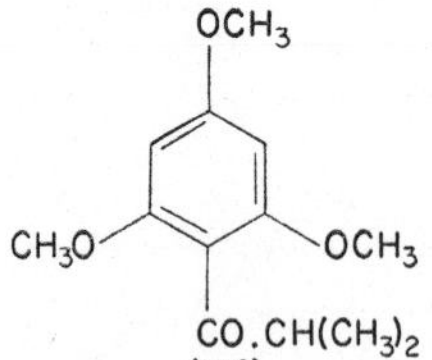

(114) 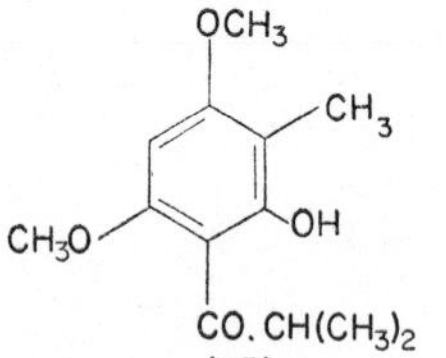   (115) 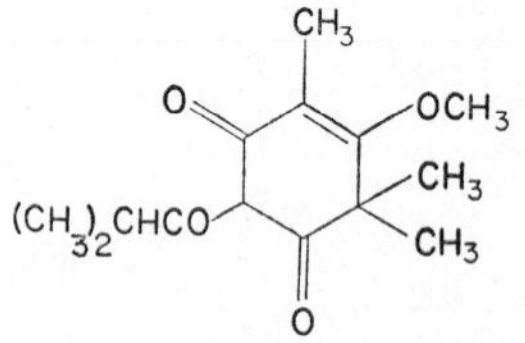   (116)

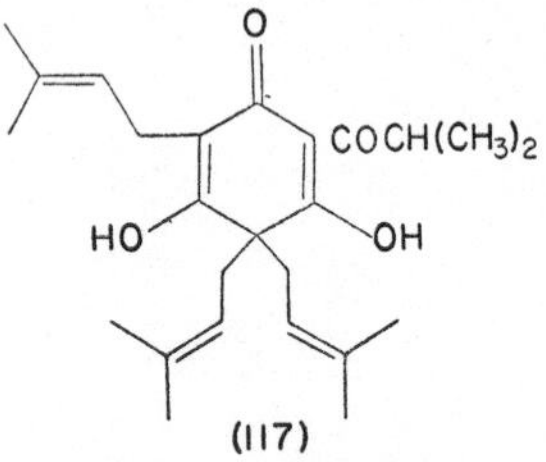

(117) 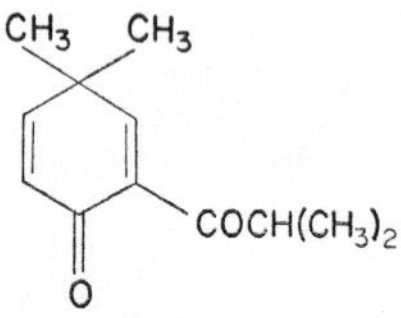   (118)

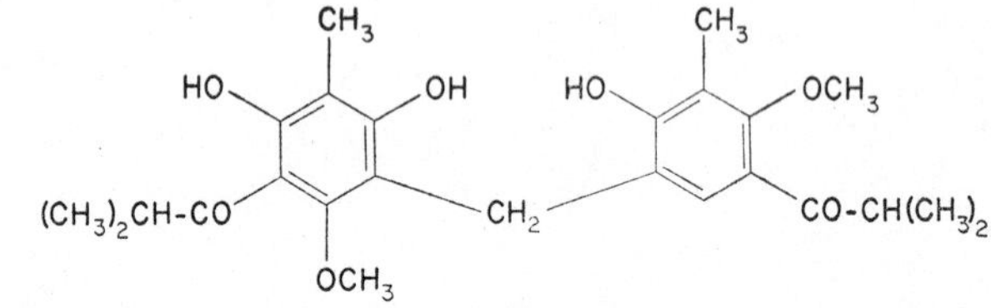

(119) 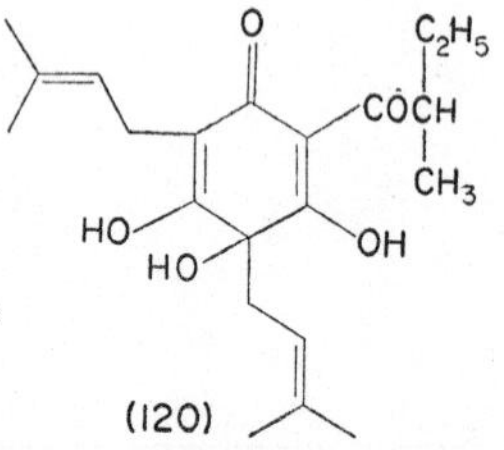   (120)

The group —$COCH(CH_3)_2$, which is characteristic of many natural products, including conglomerone[73] (114), baeckeol[74] (115), tasmanone[75] (116),
colupulone[77] (117), xanthostemon[78] (118), and the various constituents of
kousso[79], for example β-kosin (119), may arise from the isopentenyl residue
as follows:

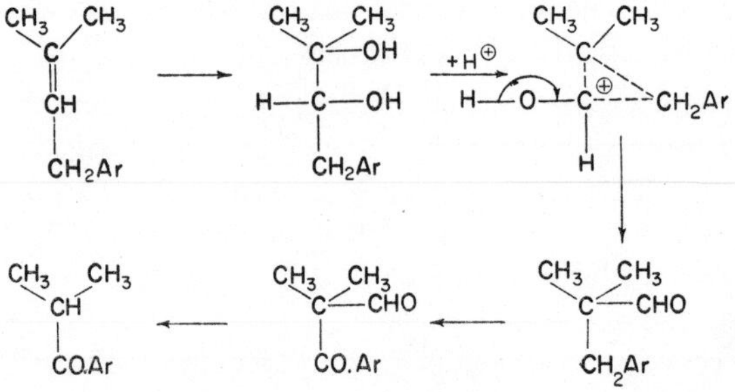

The 2:3-dihydroxyisopentyl group may also furnish the system —CO.C(CH₃)=C.CH₃ of the calophyllolides (60), and the residue —COCH(CH₃)(C₂H₅) of adhumulone[76] (120), by the alternative sequence:

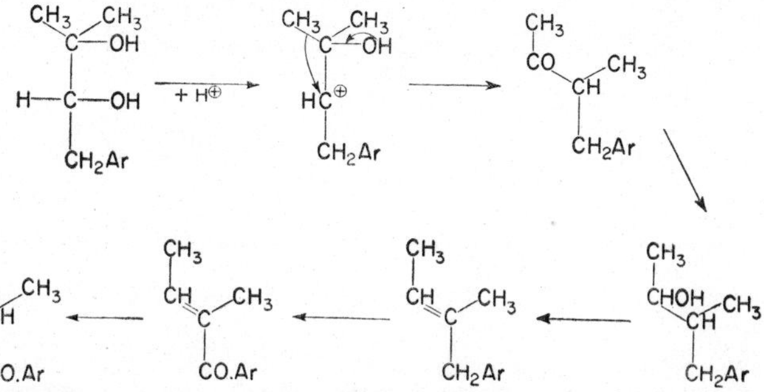

This hypothesis concerning the genesis of the

—COCH(CH₃)₂, —CO.CH(CH₃)=C.CH₃, and —COCHC(CH₃)(C₂H₅)

residues, in phenolic compounds is compatible *inter alia* with (a) the co-occurrence of colupulone (117) and adhumulone (120), (b) the presence of —COCH(CH₃)=CHCH₃ and the isopentenyl group in the same molecules, as in calophyllolide (60), (c) the very frequent occurrence of —CO.CH(CH₃)₂ and isopentenyl residues in the same molecule e.g. colupulone and its congeners and (d) the ubiquity of the oxygen atom at C* in the —C*—CH(CH₃)₂ residue.

(b) *Branched alkyl residues derived from amino acids.* Flavacol[80] (121), and pulcherriminic acid[81] (122) are undoubtedly derived from two molecules

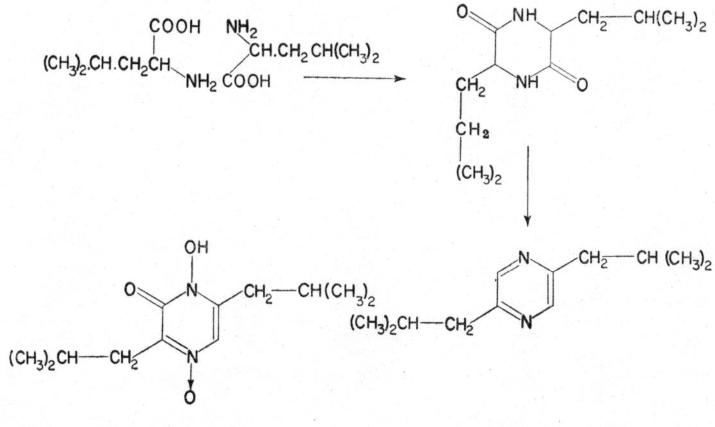

(122)   (121)

4

of leucine. Aspergillic acid[82] (124) and deoxyaspergillic acid[82] (123) similarly arise from one molecule of leucine and one molecule of isoleucine. In accord with these concepts it has been shown that tenuazonic acid[83] (125) is derived from one molecule of isoleucine and two molecules of acetic acid, and

that the $\diagdown$N.CH(CO).C(CH$_3$)$_2$ fragment in penicillin is derived from valine.

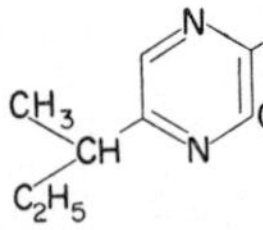

(123) 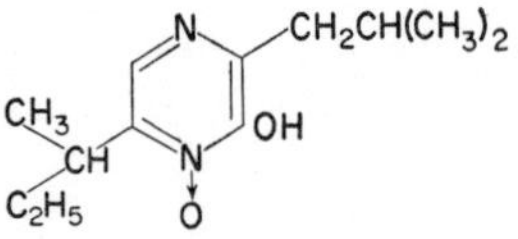   (124) 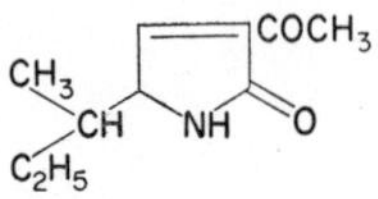   (125)

(c) *C-Glycosides.* The establishment of the structure of vitexin[84] (126), barbaloin[85] (127), homonatoloin[86] (127a), bergenin[87] (128) and carminic acid[88] (130) together with the information contained in Chapter 10 demonstrates the existence of a rapidly expanding group of *C*-glycosides. The sugar residue of these substances is attached to a highly anionoid centre in the aglycone—most probably at an ultimate step in the biosynthesis.

The anion (129) of the phenolic aglycone by interaction with a derivative

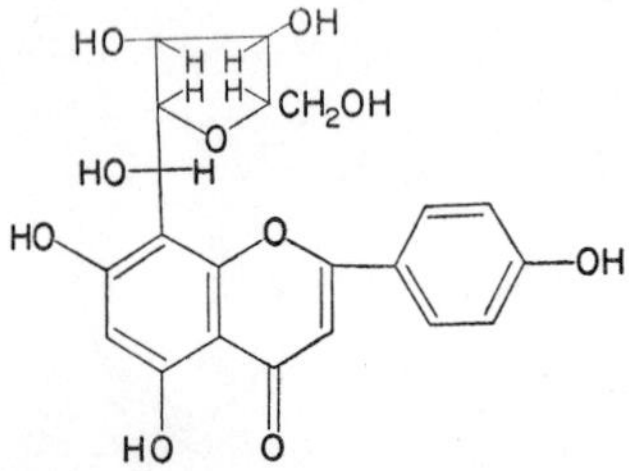

(126) 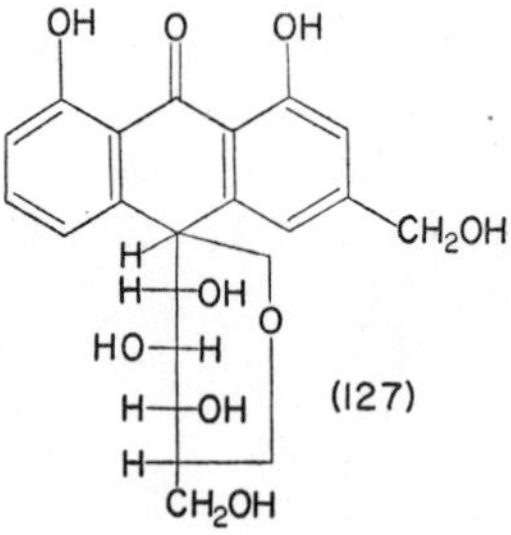   (127)

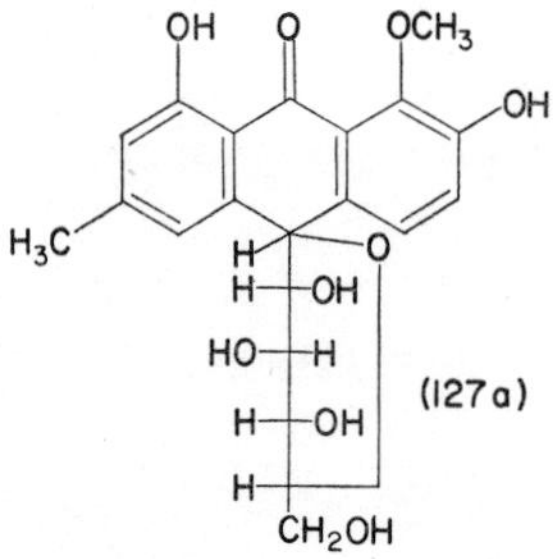

(127a) 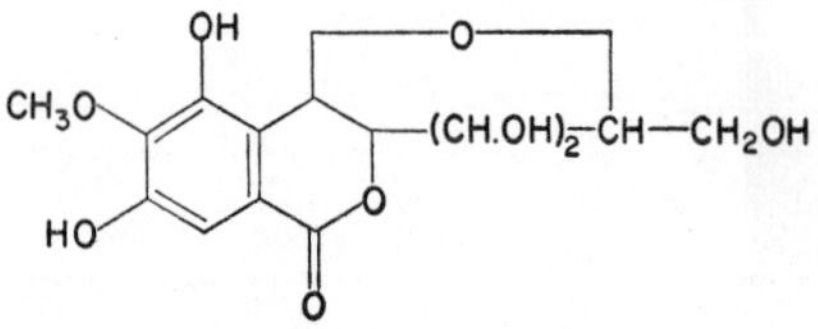   (128)

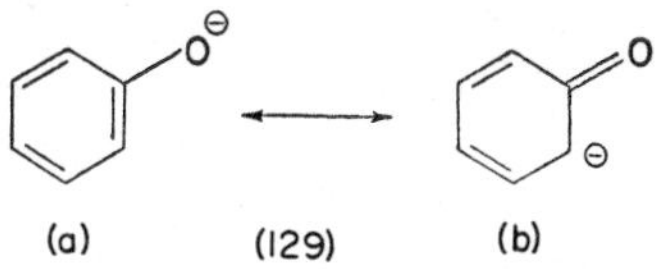

(a)   (129)   (b)

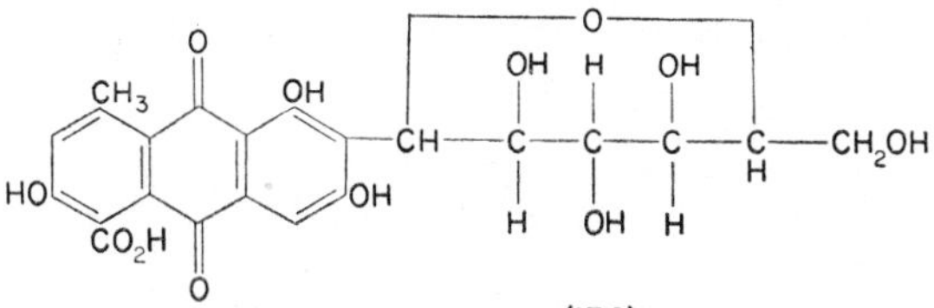

(130)

of a l-phosphorylated sugar will furnish the O- and C-glycoside respectively, in a manner exactly analogous to O- and C-isoprenylation (cf. p. 36).

2. SOME STRUCTURAL CORRELATIONS OF FUNGAL METABOLITES

The biosynthesis of many fungal metabolites from acetic acid is now generally established and it has been suggested that "the initial biogenetic steps proceed to produce a common, large intermediate (or its biological equivalents) and that secondary modifications of this intermediate yield a series of closely inter-related end-products".[89] "Evidence on this point . . . is scanty but on balance favours [this] type of process".[90]

Circumstantial evidence for the validity of this hypothesis in certain areas of biosynthesis is provided by the following analysis of the structures of a number of fungal metabolites, which are derived from the unit (1), related to orsellinic acid. The system (1) is produced by the head-to-tail linkage of four acetate units[3] where R may be hydrogen or an alkyl chain derived from acetate units.

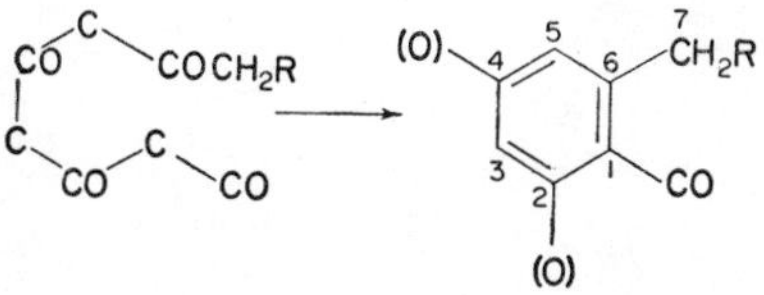

(1) *

Certain preliminary observations concerning the metabolites related to (1) are helpful. Thus the carbon atom attached to C-1 usually retains an oxygen group. The 2:4-di-oxygenated (resorcinol) pattern is frequently exhibited, but there are examples, such as 6-methylsalicylic acid, where the 4-oxygenated function is absent. Peripheral modification of the unit (1) may arise by the usual processes of oxidation and C- and O-substitution.

* The formula numbering in the second and third Parts is independent of the numbering of the first Part.

Metabolites Related Directly to Orsellinic Acid

The fungus, *Penicillium brevicompactum* furnishes[91] the metabolites (2), (3), (4) and (5) which are almost certainly derived sequentially from (2) which in turn is formed from five acetate units. *P. brevicompactum* also produces mycophenolic acid (6) which exhibits further peripheral modifications of the orsellinic acid nucleus.

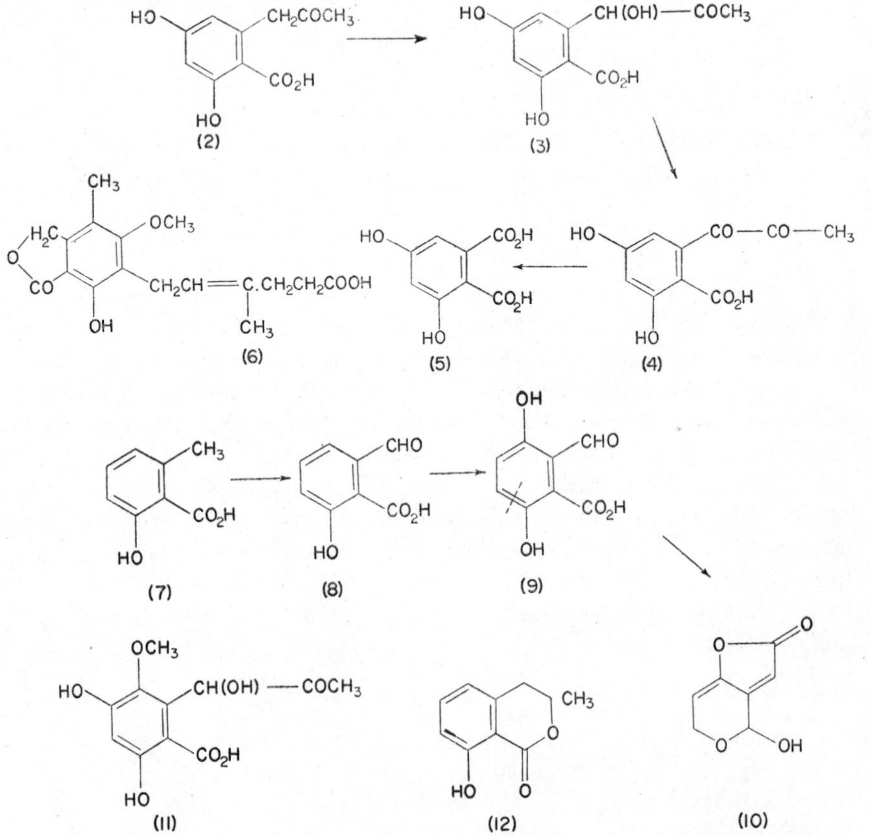

Removal[3] of the 4-oxygen function from unit (1) furnishes 6-methylsalicylic acid (7), an acetate derived metabolite of *P. griseofulvum* and *P. patulum*.[91] These organisms also convert 6-methylsalicylic acid into gentisyl alcohol and gentisic acid by way of (8) and (9).[92] Analogous *para*-oxidation of (3) gives ustic acid (11), a metabolite of *A. ustus*. Ring fission of (9) yields the metabolite patulin (10).[92]

A. melleus and *A. ochraceus* furnish mellein[3] (12) which is derived from (1, R = COCH₃) by 4-deoxygenation as in the formation of 6-methylsalicylic acid.

The quinone aurantiogliocladin (13, $R = CH_3$) and the related compound, gliorosein (14) or (15), metabolites of *Gliocladium roseum*, probably arise from the unit (1) by C-1 decarboxylation, followed by alkylation.[93]

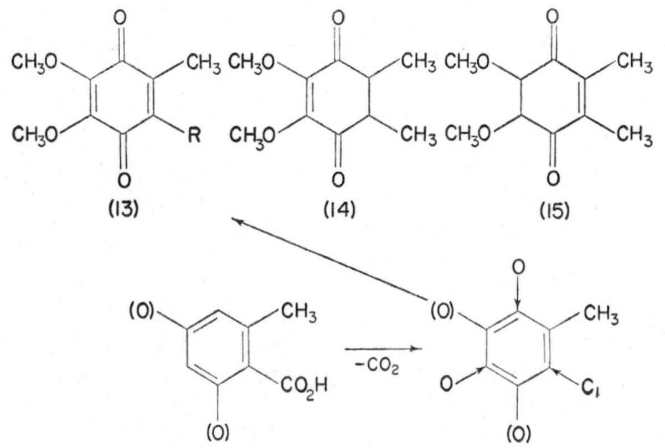

(13)   (14)   (15)

-CO_2

(0)   (0)

The genesis of the structurally related ubiquinones,

$$[13, R = (-CH_2.CH{=}CMe-CH_2)n]$$

is probably analogous.[93]

Other groups of fungal metabolites which have obvious affinities with orsellinic acid are the lichen acids for example olivetoric acid (16) and depsidones such as physodic acid (17).[3] Interesting variations on the orsellinic acid theme are siphulin[94] (18), a lichen acid, and alternariol[95] (19), from *Alternaria tenuis*.

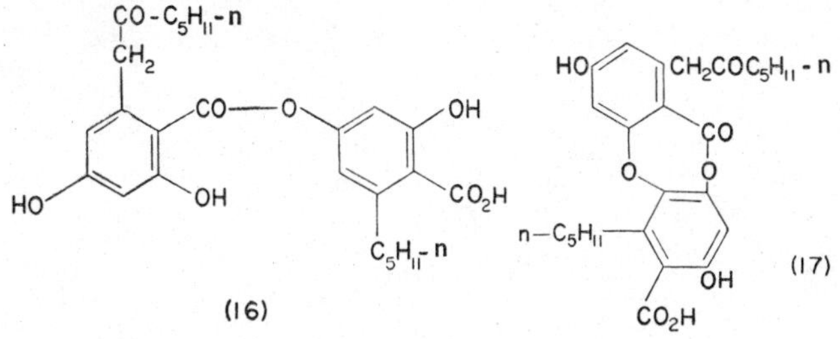

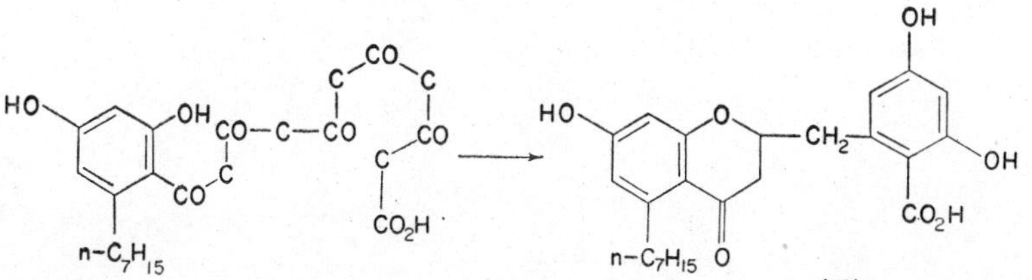

(16)   (17)

(18)

Substitution of R in (1) by a chain of three acetate units furnishes pali-tantin[96] (20), a metabolite of *P. palitans* and *P. frequentans*, and frequentin (21), a metabolite of *P. frequentans*. These metabolites exemplify non-aromatic stages in the biosynthesis of the aromatic residue (1).

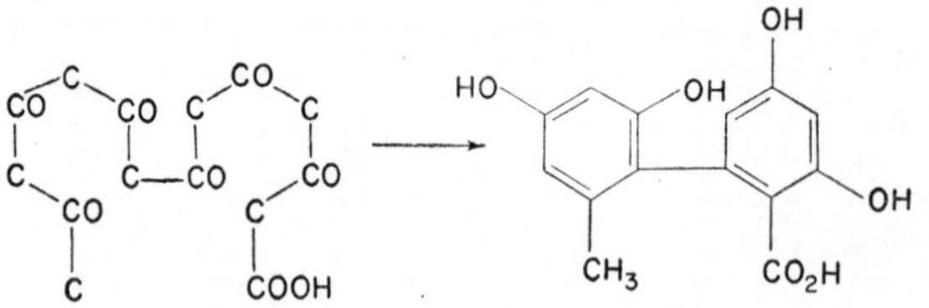

(19)

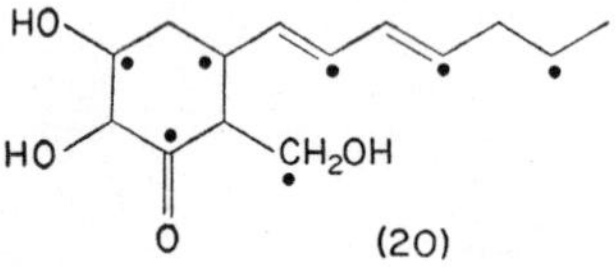

(20)

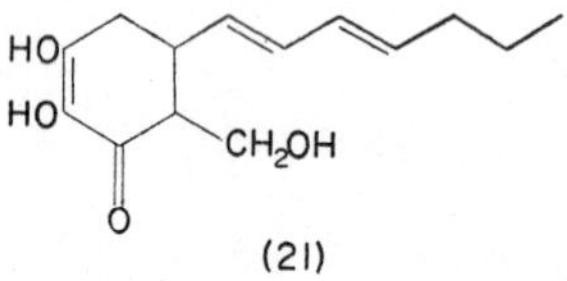

(21)

Auroglaucin[58] (21a) and flavoglaucin (21b) are derived by more extensive peripheral modification of the palitantin type precursor, as shown below

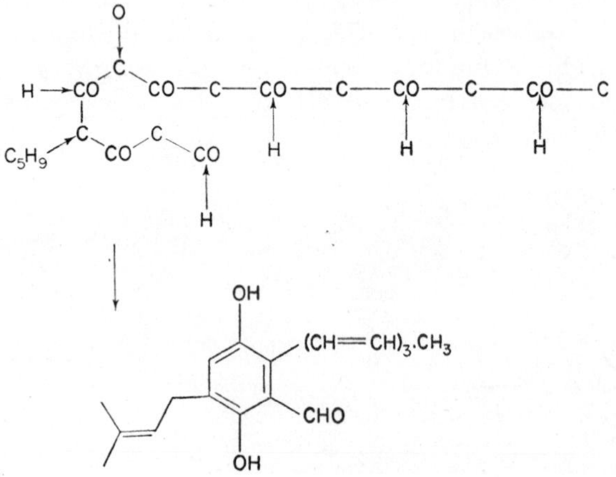

(21a)

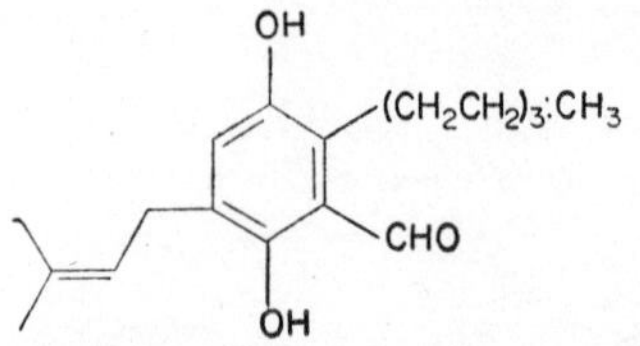

(21b)

Metabolites Related Indirectly to Orsellinic Acid

Development of (1) (see p. 43) yields the system (22) which may be cyclised as in (a) to yield a six-membered oxygen heterocyclic type (23) or as in (b) giving a naphthalene derivative (23a).

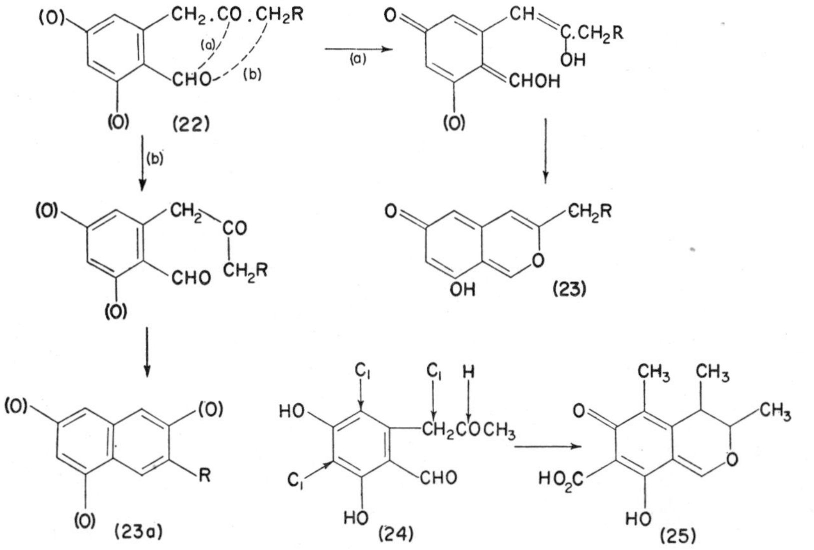

Citrinin[97] (25), a metabolite of many fungi including *P. citrinum* and *A. terreus*, is biosynthesized from five acetate and three C_1 units,[51] by way (presumably) of the orsellinic system (24). Citrinin is thus a dihydro derivative of the pyronoquinone (23).

Substitution of R in (1) with a linear chain of four acetate units followed by cyclization as in (22a) furnishes the quinone (26) which is converted by peripheral modification[51] into sclerotiorin[98] (27), a characteristic metabolite of *P. sclerotiorum* and *P. multicolor*. Introduction of three C_1 units into (26), oxidation, and acylation with $CH_3COCH_2COSCoA$ gives (28) which on aldolization forms rotiorin[99] (29) a co-pigment of sclerotiorin.

Similarly the correspondingly derived quinone (30) will produce rubropunctatin[100] (30, R = n-C_5H_{11}), and monascorubrin[101] (31, R = n-C_7H_{15}), metabolites of *Monascus rubropunctatus* Sato and *M. purpureus* Wentii, respectively. These organisms also furnish monascin[102] (32), a nonaromatic molecule analogous to palitantin (20) and frequentin (21). Palitantin and frequentin probably represent stages of biosyntheses *preceding* aromatisation whilst monascin is more likely a reduction product of the aromatic precursor, rubropunctatin (31, R = n-C_7H_{15}).

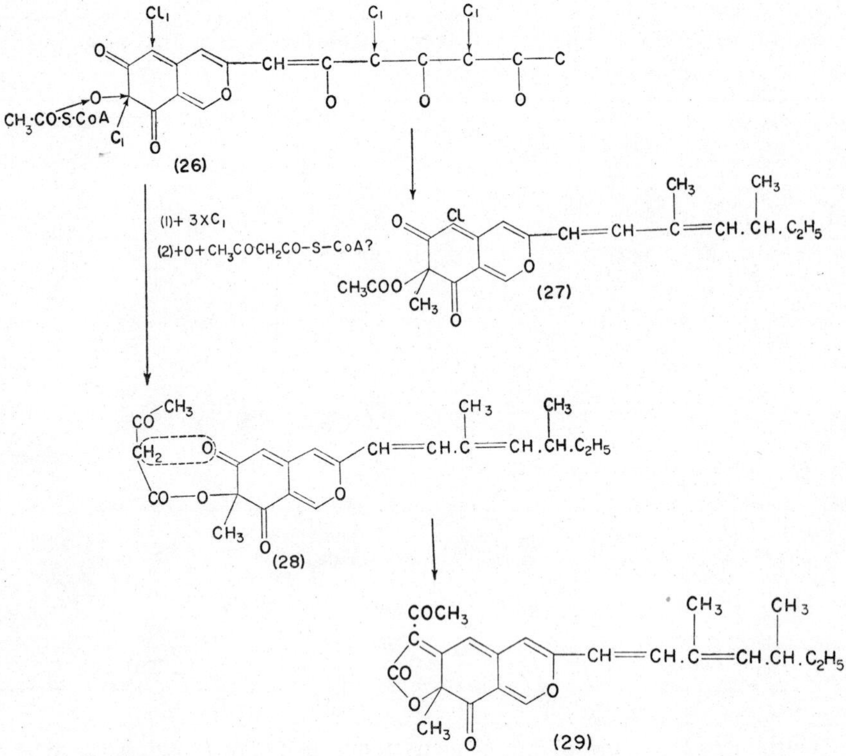

(26) (27) (28) (29)

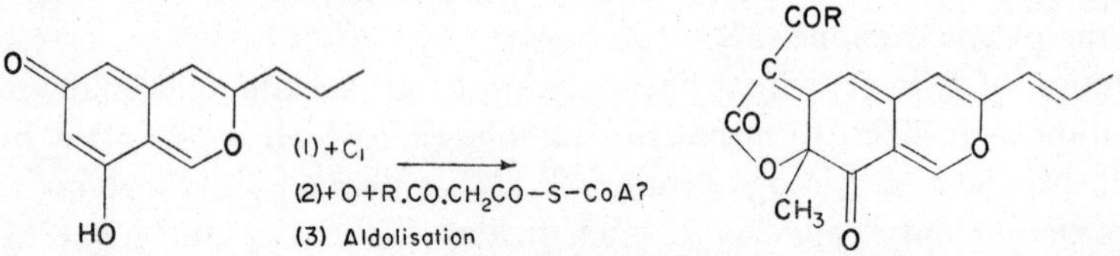

(30) (31)

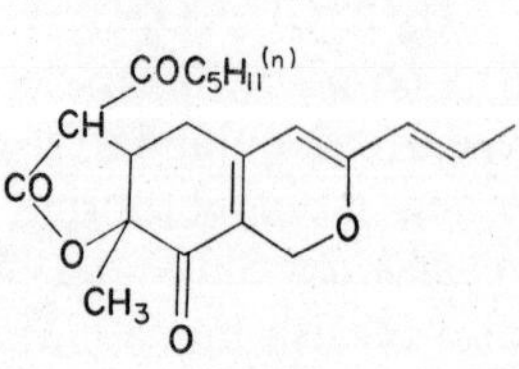

(32)

Cyclization of (22) by route (b) gives derivatives of naphthalene. Thus flaviolin[3] (33) from *A. citricus*, may readily be derived as follows:

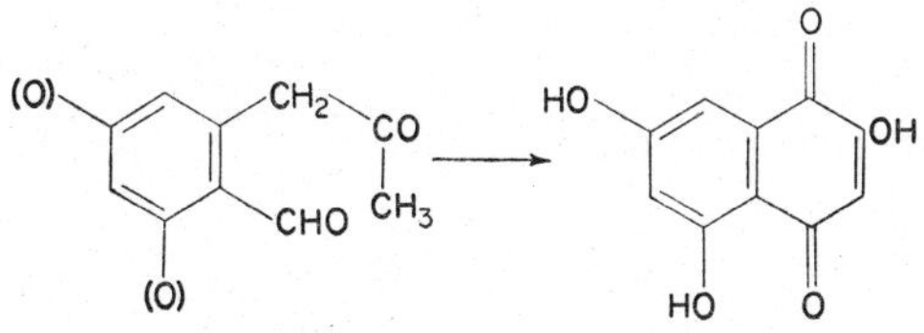

(33)

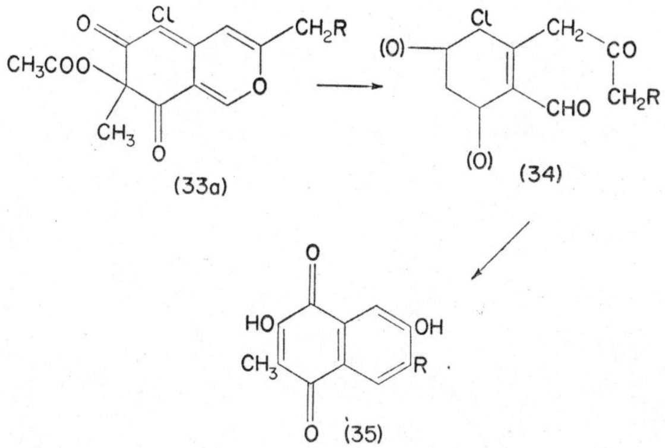

(33a)   (34)

(35)

A laboratory analogy is provided by the facile conversion[103] of various hydrosclerotiorin derivatives, type (33a), into naphthaquinones, type (35), by way, *inter alia*, of the intermediate (34).

Citromycetin[104] (36) is a metabolite of various penicillia including *P. frequentans*.[90] Experiments with *P. frequentans* using $CH_3.^{14}COOH$ and $H.^{14}COOH$ have shown that the carbon skeleton is entirely derived from acetic acid and that there are seven *equally* labelled carbon atoms[51] as in (36). This labelling pattern may be rationalized by the elimination as indicated of the two carbon atoms from a precursor of type (37), but this is not a particularly acceptable interpretation of the results.

However, the production of frequentin (21), palitantin (20) and citromycetin by *P. frequentans* and the definition of the labelling pattern of palitantin using $CH_3.^{14}COOH$ as in[105] (20) suggest that citromycetin is derived by way of (38) → (39) → (40) → (36). The oxygenation of (38) to (39) involves the same (enzymatically equivalent?) position as that concerned in the conversion of 6-methylsalicylic acid (7) to (9), of (3) to ustic acid (11) and of (49) to the javanicin-fusarubin group of metabolites (*q.v.* p. 51). Further the intermediate (40) is equivalent to (41) which may be the progenitor of fulvic acid[106] (42), a metabolite of *P. griseofulvum*.

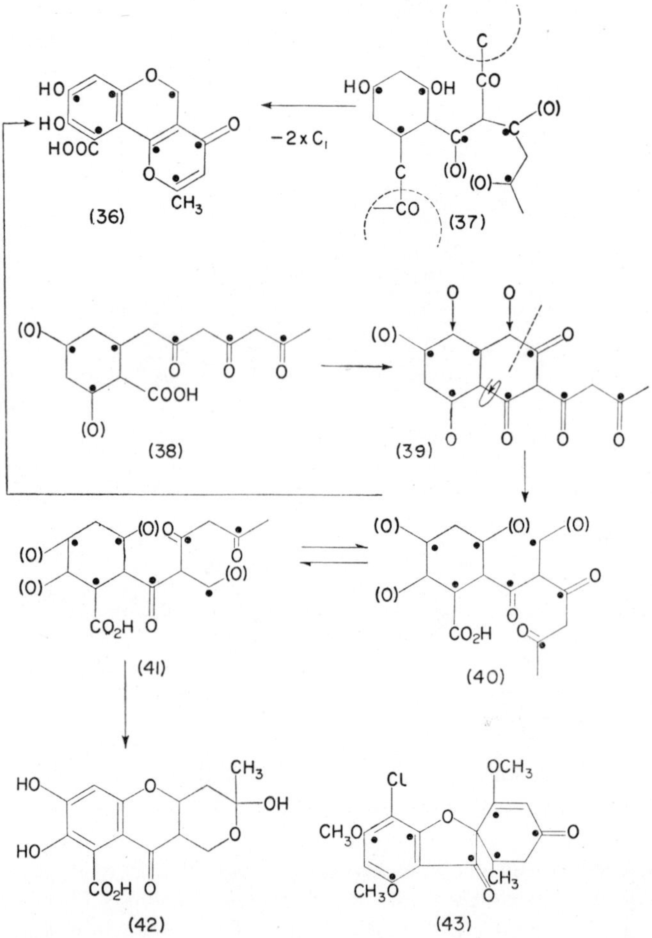

The oxidative fission of (39) → (40) has been established in the conversion of (9) into patulin (10) (p. 44) and is an extension of the well recognized "Woodward" oxidation.

The process just outlined for the rationalization of the biosynthesis of citromycetin may operate in other cases too, where alternative explanations are equally applicable, and have hitherto been assumed.

For example, *P. griseofulvum* produces 6-methylsalicylic acid, fulvic acid (42) and griseofulvin, which has the labelling pattern[3] (43) using $CH_3.^{14}COOH$ as precursor.

The derivation of griseofulvin from an acetate chain folded as in (44) readily accommodates this pattern. But the structural and biogenetical affinity of citromycetin and fulvic acid together with the production of fulvic acid and

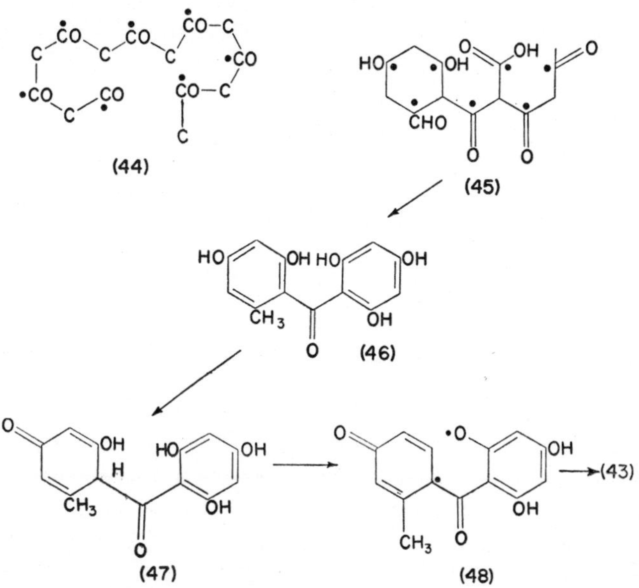

(44)

(45)

(46)

(47)   (48)   →(43)

griseofulvin by the same fungus suggests that griseofulvin may be derived by the less direct route $(38) \rightarrow (39) \rightarrow (45) \rightarrow (46) \rightarrow (47) \rightarrow (48) \rightarrow (43)$ or its appropriate sequential variations.

Extension of unit (1) at C-1 and C-6 furnishes an intermediate of type (49) which is the probable precursor[89] of oxyjavanicin (50), javanicin[107] (51) and

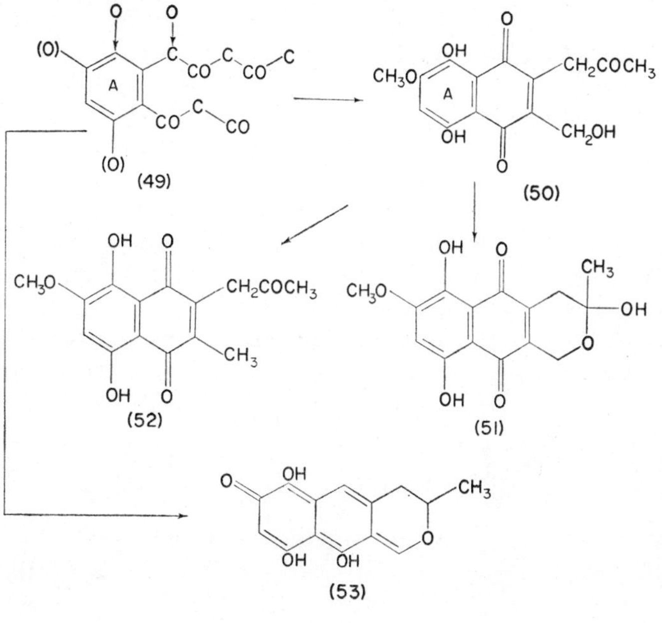

(49)

(50)

(52)

(51)

(53)

fusarubin[108] (52). The additional oxygen atom of ring A is introduced into a position corresponding to that involved in the conversion of (3) into ustic acid (11).

The position of the methoxyl group in (50), (51) and (52), which has not been chemically defined, thus becomes indicated. Purpurogenone[109] (53) may arise from the same precursor (49). The determinative factor in the diversion of the reaction sequence from the purpurogenone type to the javanicin-fusarubin type is the introduction of the methoxyl which must occur relatively early in the biosynthetic sequence.[89]

The foregoing survey indicates a close structural and biogenetic affinity between the fungal metabolites discussed. This affinity substantiates the concept that they are derived by secondary modifications of relatively few, similarly constituted, primary progenitors.

It is becoming evident that a limited number of ubiquitous biosynthetic reactions operate in fungi, and that an increasing degree of correspondence is apparent between the metabolites of fungi and higher plants. Thus, there is overwhelming circumstantial evidence that O- and C-isopentenyl groups (and multiples thereof) are introduced into metabolites of both higher plants and fungi by the same mechanism and at a similar stage in biosynthesis.

The chemical correlation of fungal metabolites may find application in the taxonomy of fungi. In particular, taxonomic sub-division, based upon the chemical relationships of metabolites, might enable further sub-divisions of extensive genera such as *Aspergillus* and *Penicillium*. Chemical taxonomy may also enable the assignment to specific genera of those organisms which are difficult to classify morphologically and may indicate hitherto unsuspected relationships between genera.

3. THE STEREOCHEMISTRY OF NATURAL PRODUCTS

In conclusion a few comments concerning the biochemical significance of the stereochemistry of natural products are appropriate.

With the determination of numerous absolute configurations it has been established that the majority of optically active natural products have a 'normal' absolute configuration, characteristic of each class. There are however, significant exceptions which include:

(a) The A/B ring junction of the polycyclic terpenes and steroids has the normal absolute configuration (54), but a minority of terpenoid compounds,

(54)   (55)

e.g. cafestol,[110] eperuic acid,[111] iresin,[112] farnesiferol-A[66] (104), (—)-juneol[113] and certain diterpenoid alkaloids have the enantiomeric configuration (55).

(b) Although the majority of the numerous flavanones (56) and 3-hydroxy flavanones (57) together with (+)-catechin (58) have the same absolute configuration at C-2,[23] the flavanone, fustin, has the enantiomeric configuration (59). The two flavan-3:4-diols, (—)-*leuco*-fisetinidiol (60) and gleditsin (60) are enantiomorphic and thus one of them has the absolute configuration of fustin at C-2.

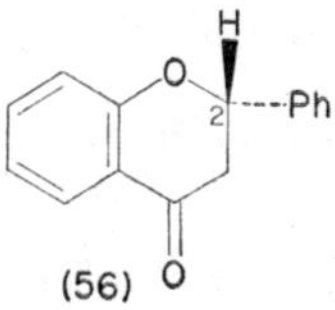

(56) 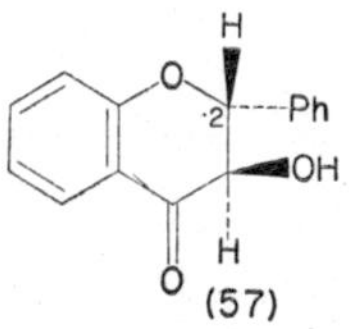   (57)

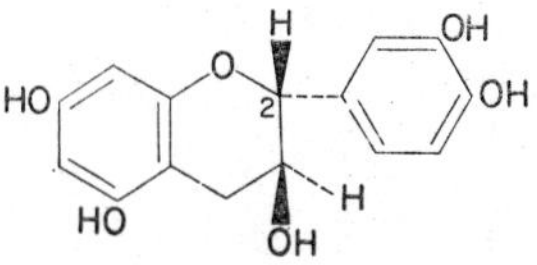

(58) 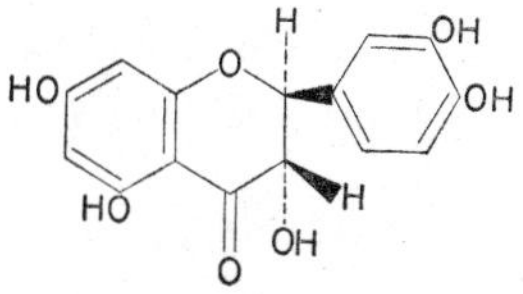   (59)

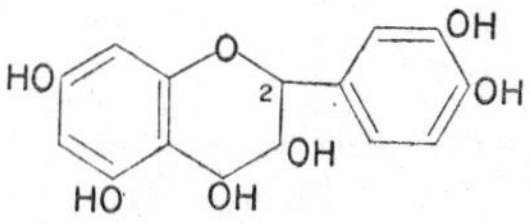

(60) 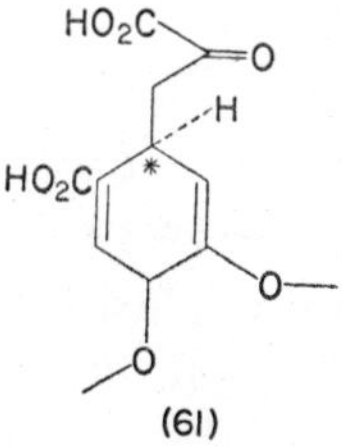   (61)

(c) The majority of naturally occurring sugars have the D-configuration, but certain members, for example vitamin C and L-streptamine belong to the L-series.

(d) The various morphine alkaloids have the same absolute configuration with the exception of sinomenine[114] which is enantiomeric.

(e) Most naturally occurring α-amino-acids belong to the L-series, but those derived from polypeptide antibiotics frequently belong to the D-series.

Although D-amino-acids may be directly synthesized in this configuration they may arise indirectly. For example, racemization of an L-acid followed by preferential metabolism of the L-acid from the racemate would furnish the D-amino-acid.

Similarly there is some evidence that L-sugars may arise by C-5 epimerization,[115] of the corresponding D-sugar. But the configurationally "abnormal" flavanoids, terpenes and sinomenine cannot be produced by secondary transformations of the "normal" series and must arise as enantiomers of the "normal" series *ab initio*.

Djerassi[110] has associated "abnormal" absolute configuration in sesqui- and di-terpenes with the presence of the 3-hydroxyl group. But this view is untenable: recent structural determinations have shown the existence of "abnormal" diterpenes, e.g. eperuic acid,[111] which are devoid of the 3-hydroxyl and of "normal" diterpenes, e.g. cassaic acid[116,117] which possess this group. The problem is of wider and more fundamental significance than hitherto suggested and peripheral groups probably have little if any influence upon the establishment of the skeletal configuration.

The determinative factor is undoubtedly an enantiomeric relationship between the enzyme surfaces involved, and this relationship has probably been determined by evolution and is thus a problem of biology rather than of chemistry.

No "abnormal" steroids have yet been characterized, but their ultimate discovery may be confidently predicted.

The various indole alkaloids which have been correlated have the same absolute configuration at C-15.[11] This is in agreement with their genesis from the same asymmetric, shikimate derived precursor type (61), in which the asymmetry of the asterisked centre is maintained throughout the biosynthetical sequence. Indole alkaloids enantiomeric at C-15 will most probably be discovered and on the basis of the Wenkert hypothesis[11] the enantiomer of (61) will be their precursor.

CONCLUSION

Inspection of the whole field of natural products shows that the majority of those which have an acetate derived "primary skeleton"* contain fourteen to eighteen carbon atoms in this skeleton. The total molecular size may frequently exceed C_{18}, but this is almost always achieved by the operation of secondary processes. Thus, for example, the bi-anthronyls are derived by the oxidative coupling of two anthrones, and sclerotiorin, $C_{21}H_{23}O_5Cl$, stems from a C_{16} primary skeleton by insertion of three C_1 units and an acetyl residue.

It is particularly significant that isotopic experiments have demonstrated the uniformity of the specific activity in primary skeletons of those carbon atoms which are derived from acetate.

These comments apply especially to fungal metabolites and indicate that the initial biosynthetic reaction in the production of complex products is the assembly of the requisite number of acetate units on the surface of the appropriate enzyme. These units are then linked by a concerted process to

*The primary skeleton is derived from the complete molecule by abstraction of those groups which have been independently biosynthesized and introduced by secondary processes. Thus the primary skeleton of citrinin is (23, R = H) and of sclerotiorin and rotiorin is (26).

yield a polyketomethylene chain which is the precursor of the primary skeleton. Certain initial secondary modifications of this carbon chain will occur on this enzyme surface, but many of the transformations which lead to the completed metabolite may occur after desorption from this assembling enzyme. Hence the absence of intermediates between acetic acid and some primitive transformation products of the polyketomethylene chain equivalent to the primary skeleton may be inferred. Various intermediate, discrete species corresponding to the chemical transformations required to convert the primitive chain into the completed metabolite should be isolable.

The general absence from acetate derived molecules of primary skeletons containing more than eighteeen to twenty carbon atoms suggests that the active portion of the assembling enzyme can accommodate a maximum of nine to ten molecules of acetic acid (as acetyl CoA ?) simultaneously. The maximum active area of the enzymes concerned in the assembling of small units other than acetate appears to be similar. Thus, although derived from acetate and/or propionate, the macrolides have a lactone moiety which contains a maximum of eighteen carbon atoms (magnamycin). Likewise, the primary skeleton of the tetracyclines, although biosynthesized[118] from seven acetate units and one molecule of glutamic acid, has eighteen carbon atoms.

A similar maximum area for the assembling enzyme may operate in higher plants where C_{15} products are ubiquitous and characteristic. Their formation[3] requires the linkage of three acetate units to a C_6–C_3 precursor. This process almost certainly demands the simultaneous adsorption of three acetate units and a considerable proportion of the shikimate fragment. The resultant total occupied area of the enzyme will thus be approximately equivalent to six to eight acetate residues.

It may thus be inferred that the assembling enzymes concerned in these diverse syntheses which utilize acetate and kindred small molecules have a maximum active area equivalent to the simultaneous accommodation of eighteen carbon atoms, in their various biologically activated forms.

This suggests[119] the existence of a very definite upper limit to the molecular size of natural products (and hence to the various types available) with the exception of those derived by secondary processes such as oxidative coupling or polymerization reactions.

Acknowledgement

The author wishes to acknowledge the helpful and valuable contributions of Mr. D. F. Jones, B.Sc., to the section concerning the Structural Correlations of Fungal Metabolites.

REFERENCES

1. R. ROBINSON, *The Structural Relations of Natural Products*, Clarendon Press, Oxford (1955).
2. T. A. GEISSMAN and E. HINREINER, *Bot. Rev.* 1952, **18**, 77.

3. A. J. BIRCH, *Biosynthetic Relations of Some Natural Phenolic and Enolic Compounds*, Fortschritte der Chemie Organischer Naturstoffe, 1957, **14**, 186.
4. E. W. UNDERHILL, J. E. WATKIN and A. C. NEISH, *Canad. J. Biochem. Physiol.* 1957, **35**, 219, 229.
5. H. GRISEBACH, *Z. Naturforsch.* 1957, **12b**, 227.
6. See e.g. S. GATENBECK, *Acta Chem. Scand.* 1960, **14**, 296.
7. L. H. BRIGGS and R. H. LOCKER, *J. Chem. Soc.* 1951, 3131.
8. S. A. BROWN and A. C. NEISH, *Nature. London* 1955, **175**, 688.
9. S. A. BROWN and A. C. NEISH, *Canad. J. Biochem. Physiol.* 1955, **33**, 948.
10. T. A. GEISSMAN and T. SWAIN, *Chem. and Ind.* 1957, 984.
11. E. WENKERT and N. V. BRINGI, *J. Amer. Chem. Soc.* 1959, **81**, 1474.
12. S. SHIBATA, T. MURAKAMI, I. KITAGAWA and M. TAKIDO, *Proc. Japan Acad.* 1956, **32**, 356.
13. T. R. SESHADRI, *Tetrahedron* 1959, **6**, 169.
14. P. S. SARIN and T. R. SESHADRI, *Tetrahedron* 1960, **8**, 64.
15. W. B. WHALLEY at a Meeting of the Plant Phenolics Group: Cambridge, September 1958.
16. T. A. GEISSMAN, J. W. MASON and J. R. ROWE, *Chem. and Ind.* 1959, 1577.
17. T. A. GEISSMAN and J. W. MASON, *Chem. and Ind.* 1960, 291.
18. S. RAMANUJAM and T. R. SESHADRI, *Proc. Nat. Acad. Sci. India* 1958, A **47**, 175.
19. F. E. KING, M. F. GRUNDON and K. G. NEILL, *J. Chem. Soc.* 1952, 4580.
20. A. McGOOKIN, A. ROBERTSON and W. B. WHALLEY, *J. Chem. Soc.* 1940, 787.
21. H. HUBNER and W. RIEDL, *Chem. Ber.* 1960, **93**, 312.
22. S. RANGASWAMI and B. V. R. SASTRY, *Current Sci.* 1955, **24**, 13.
23. W. B. WHALLEY in *The Chemistry of Flavonoid Compounds*. Editor T. A. GEISSMAN. Pergamon Press, in the press.
24. W. B. WHALLEY, unpublished observations.
25. M. BLACKBURN, G. B. SANKEY, A. ROBERTSON and W. B. WHALLEY, *J. Chem. Soc.* 1957, 1573.
26. A. ROBERTSON, W. B. WHALLEY and J. YATES, *J. Chem. Soc.* 1951, 2013.
27. H. ERDTMAN and C. A. WACHTMEISTER, *A. Stoll Festschrift* 1957, p. 153. Birkhäuser.
28. A. ROBERTSON and W. B. WHALLEY, *J. Chem. Soc.* 1954, 2794.
29. W. W. REID, *Chem. and Ind.* 1958, 1439.
30. S. A. BROWN, G. H. N. TOWERS and D. WRIGHT, *Canad. J. Biochem. Physiol.* 1960, **38**, 143.
31. F. WEYGAND and H. WENDT, *Z. Naturforsch.* 1959, **14b**, 42.
32. See e.g. L. BOGORAD, *Ann. Rev. Plant Physiol.* 1958, **9**, 429 *et seq.*
33. H. S. RAPER, *Biochem. J.* 1927, **21**, 89.
34. R. D. HAWORTH, *J. Chem. Soc.* 1942, 448.
35. G. W. KENNER, M. A. MURRAY and C. M. B. TAYLOR, *Tetrahedron* 1957, **1**, 259.
36. M. ISANO, *J. Agric. Chem. Soc. Japan* 1953, **27**, 255, 1954, **28**, 196.
37. R. YAMAMOTO and Y. OSHIMA, *J. Agric. Chem. Soc. Japan* 1931, **7**, 312.
38. O. H. EMERSON and E. M. BICKOFF, *J. Am. Chem. Soc.* 1958, **80**, 4381.
39. T. R. GOVINDACHARI, K. NAGARAJAN and B. R. PAI, *J. Chem. Soc.* 1956, 629.
40. J. EISENBEISS and H. SCHMID, *Helv. Chim. Acta* 1959, **42**, 61.
41. E. SIMONITSCH, H. FREI and H. SCHMID, *Monatsh.* 1957, **88**, 541.
42. B. O. HANDFORD and W. B. WHALLEY, unpublished observations.
43. V. K. AHLUWALIA and T. R. SESHADRI, *J. Chem. Soc.* 1957, 970.
44. J. POLONSKY, *C.R. Acad. Sci., Paris* 1956, **242**, 2961.
45. R. A. FINNEGAN and C. DJERASSI, *Tetrahedron Letters* 1959, **13**, 11.
46. C. DJERASSI, E. J. EISENBRAUN, R. A. FINNEGAN and B. GILBERT, *Tetrahedron Letters* 1959, **1**, 10.
47. *Heterocyclic Compounds*, Editor R. C. ELDERFIELD, 1951, Vol. II, p. 363. John Wiley, New York.
48. W. R. CHAN, W. G. C. FORSYTH and C. H. HASSALL, *J. Chem. Soc.* 1958, 3174.
49. F. E. KING, T. J. KING and P. J. STOKES, *J. Chem. Soc.* 1954, 4594.
50. W. B. WHALLEY, *Chem. and Ind.* 1956, 1049.

51. See e.g. A. J. BIRCH, P. FITTON, E. PRIDE, A. J. RYAN, H. SMITH and W. B. WHALLEY, *J. Chem. Soc.* 1958, 4576.
52. S. H. HARPER, *J. Chem. Soc.* 1940, 1178.
53. O. A. STAMM, H. SCHMID and J. BÜCHI, *Helv. Chim. Acta* 1958, **41**, 2006.
54. N. L. DUTTA, *J. Indian Chem. Soc.* 1959, **36**, 165.
55. N. FINCH and W. D. OLLIS, *Proc. Chem. Soc.* 1960, 176.
56. B. F. BURROWS, N. FINCH, W. D. OLLIS and I. O. SUTHERLAND, *Proc. Chem. Soc.* 1959, 150.
57. R. ANEJA, S. K. MUKERJEE and T. R. SESHADRI, *Tetrahedron* 1958, **4**, 256.
58. A. J. BIRCH, J. SCHOFIELD and H. SMITH, *Chem. and Ind.* 1958, 1321.
59. D. H. R. BARTON and J. B. HENDRICKSON, *J. Chem. Soc.* 1956, 1028.
60. A. CHATTERJEE and S. S. MITRA, *J. Amer. Chem. Soc* 1949, **71**, 606.
61. F. E. KING, J. R. HOUSLEY and T. J. KING, *J. Chem. Soc.* 1954, 1392.
62. E. SPÄTH and K. KLAGER, *Ber.* 1934, **67**, 859.
63. E. SPÄTH and F. KESZTLER, *Ber.* 1937, **70**, 1255, 1679.
64. E. SPÄTH and F. VIERHAPPER, *Ber.* 1938, **71**, 1667.
65. F. E. KING and M. F. GRUNDON, *J. Chem. Soc.* 1950, 3547.
66. L. CAGLIOTI, H. NAEF, D. ARIGONI and O. JEGER, *Helv. Chim. Acta* 1958, **41**, 2278.
67. L. CAGLIOTI, H. NAEF, D. ARIGONI and O. JEGER, *Helv. Chim. Acta* 1959, **42**, 2557.
68. R. ADAMS, R. B. BAKER and B. R. WEARN, *J. Amer. Chem. Soc.* 1940, **62**, 2204.
69. Compare J. P. BROWN, N. J. CARTWRIGHT, A. ROBERTSON and W. B. WHALLEY, *J. Chem. Soc.* 1949, 867.
70. J. H. BIRKINSHAW, A. BRACKEN, E. N. MORGAN and H. RAISTRICK, *Biochem. J.* 1948, **43**, 216.
71. R. ADAMS *et al.*, *J. Amer. Chem. Soc.* 1941, **63**, 528, 535, 2439.
72. M. ASANO and Z. HASE, *J. Pharm. Soc. Japan* 1940, **60**, 650.
73. F. N. LAHEY and T. G. H. JONES, *Univ. Queensland Papers, Dept. Chem.* 1939, **1**, No. 12, p. 4.
74. B. A. HEMS and A. R. TODD, *J. Chem. Soc.* 1940, 1208.
75. A. J. BIRCH and P. ELLIOT, *Australian J. Chem.* 1956, **9**, 95.
76. G. A. HOWARD and A. R. TATCHELL, *Chem. and Ind.* 1954, 992.
77. G. A. HOWARD, J. R. A. POLLOCK and A. R. TATCHELL, *J. Chem. Soc.* 1955, 174.
78. A. J. BIRCH and P. ELLIOT, *Australian J. Chem.* 1956, **9**, 238.
79. A. J. BIRCH and A. R. TODD, *J. Chem. Soc.* 1952, 3102.
80. G. DUNN, G. T. NEWBOLD and F. S. SPRING, *J. Chem. Soc.* 1949, 2586.
81. A. H. COOK and C. A. SLATER, *J. Chem. Soc.* 1956, 4133.
82. G. T. NEWBOLD, W. SHARP and F. S. SPRING, *J. Chem. Soc.* 1951, 2679.
83. C. E. STICKINGS and R. J. TOWNSEND, *Biochem. J.* 1960, **74**, 36 P.
84. W. H. EVANS, A. MCGOOKIN, L. JURD, A. ROBERTSON and W. R. N. WILLIAMSON, *J. Chem. Soc.* 1957, 3510.
85. J. E. HAY and L. J. HAYNES, *J. Chem. Soc.* 1956, 3141.
86. L. J. HAYNES and J. I. HENDERSON, *Chem. and Ind.* 1960, 50.
87. J. E. HAY and L. J. HAYNES, *J. Chem. Soc.* 1958, 2231.
88. M. A. ALI and L. J. HAYNES, *J. Chem. Soc.* 1959, 1033.
89. W. B. WHALLEY, *Chem. and Ind.* 1958, 131.
90. A. J. BIRCH and H. SMITH, *Chem. Soc. Special Publ.* 1958, No. **12**, 1
91. H. RAISTRICK, *Proc. Roy. Soc.* 1949–50, **136**, 481.
92. J. D. BU'LOCK and A. J. RYAN, *Proc. Chem. Soc.* 1958, 222.
93. A. J. BIRCH, R. I. FRYER and H. SMITH, *Proc. Chem. Soc.* 1958, 343.
94. T. BRUNN, *Tetrahedron Letters* 1960, No. **4**, p. 1.
95. R. THOMAS, *Proc. Chem. Soc.* 1959, 88.
96. K. BOWDEN, B. LYTHGOE and D. J. S. MARSDEN, *J. Chem. Soc.* 1959, 1662.
97. N. J. CARTWRIGHT, A. ROBERTSON and W. B. WHALLEY, *J. Chem. Soc.* 1949, 1563.
98. F. M. DEAN, J. STAUNTON and W. B. WHALLEY, *J. Chem. Soc.* 1959, 3004.
99. G. B. JACKMAN, A. ROBERTSON, R. B. TRAVERS and W. B. WHALLEY, *J. Chem. Soc.* 1958, 1825.
100. E. J. HAWS, J. S. E. HOLKER, A. KELLY, A. D. G. POWELL and A. ROBERTSON, *J. Chem. Soc.* 1959, 3598.

101. B. C. FIELDING, E. J. HAWS, J. S. E. HOLKER, A. D. G. POWELL, A. ROBERTSON, D. N. STANWAY and W. B. WHALLEY, *Tetrahedron Letters* 1960, **5**, 24.
102. J. S. E. HOLKER and W. B. WHALLEY, unpublished observations.
103. N. B. GRAHAM, H. PAGE, A. ROBERTSON, R. B. TRAVERS, K. TURNER and W. B. WHALLEY, *J. Chem. Soc.* 1957, 4924.
104. A. ROBERTSON, W. B. WHALLEY and J. YATES, *J. Chem. Soc.* 1951, 2013.
105. A. J. BIRCH and M. KOCOR, *J. Chem. Soc.* 1960, 866.
106. F. M. DEAN, R. A. EADE, R. MOUBASHER and A. ROBERTSON, *Nature, London* 1957, **179**, 366: *J. Chem. Soc.* 1957, 3497.
107. H. R. V. ARNSTEIN and A. H. COOK, *J. Chem. Soc.* 1947, 1021.
108. H. W. RUELIUS and A. GAUHE, *Annalen* 1950, **569**, 38.
109. J. C. ROBERTS and C. W. H. WARREN, *J. Chem. Soc.* 1955, 2992.
110. C. DJERASSI, M. CAIS and L. A. MITSCHER, *J. Amer. Chem. Soc.* 1959, **81**, 2386.
111. F. E. KING and G. JONES, *J. Chem. Soc.* 1955, 658.
112. C. DJERASSI and S. BURSTEIN, *J. Amer. Chem. Soc.* 1958, **80**, 2593.
113. S. C. BATTACHARYYA, A. S. RAO and A. M. SHALIGRAM, *Chem. and Ind.* 1960, 469.
114. *The Chemistry of the Morphine Alkaloids*, K. W. BENTLEY, Oxford Press, 1954, p. 333.
115. F. A. LOEWUS, B. J. FINKLE and R. JANG, *Biochem. Biophys. Acta* 1958, **30**, 629.
116. W. J. GENSLER and G. M. SHERMAN, *Chem. and Ind.* 1959, 223.
117. F. E. KING, T. J. KING and J. M. UPRICHARD, *J. Chem. Soc.* 1958, 3428.
118. J. F. SNELL, A. J. BIRCH, and P. L. THOMSON, *J. Amer. Chem. Soc.* 1960, **82**, 2402.
119. cf. R. B. WOODWARD, *Angew. Chem.* 1957, **69**, 50.

CHAPTER 3

THE BIOSYNTHESIS OF ISOFLAVONES

H. GRISEBACH

The University, Freiburg, Germany

THE isoflavones are derivatives of 3-phenylbenz-γ-pyrone and in contrast to most flavones and to the anthocyanins which are derivatives of 2-phenylbenz-γ-pyrone, the isoflavones are colourless or light yellow compounds. The number of isoflavones found to date in Nature is relatively small compared

with the widespread occurrence of the flavonoids. Recently, however, the iso-flavones have aroused considerable interest because some of them possess oestrogenic activity.[1] In Australia during World War II, infertility in sheep grazed on pastures of subterranean clover (*Trifolium subterraneum L.*) was observed, and in 1951, Bradbury and White[2] demonstrated that this infertility was due to the presence in the clover of genistein (5,7,4′-trihydroxyisoflavone), which has oestrogenic activity. The so-called "spring flush" in dairy cows, associated with an increased milk yield and the improved quality of the milk which occurs in the spring, is probably due to the presence of isoflavones or other oestrogenic substances in the grass.[1]

The biogenesis of isoflavones is also of particular interest. Although their skeletal structure differs from that of the flavonoid derivatives only in the position of the aryl group on the heterocyclic ring, it is necessary, on the basis of present knowledge regarding the formation of flavonoids in the plant, to assume that a special mechanism is involved in the biogenesis of isoflavones. In order to understand this problem, it is first necessary to consider briefly the previous results of investigations on the biogenesis of flavonoids.

BIOGENESIS OF FLAVONOIDS

The results of experiments with ^{14}C-labelled precursors in the study of the biosynthesis of cyanidin (Grisebach[3]) and of quercetin (e.g. Neish[4], Geissman[5]) are of particular importance. It is now known that ring A of cyanidin and quercetin is formed by a head-to-tail condensation of three acetyl units, while ring B and carbon atoms 2, 3 and 4 originate from an intact phenyl-propane unit (see Fig. 1). With great probability, this biosynthetic pattern is applicable to the formation of all flavanoid derivatives.

Nothing certain is yet known about the intermediate steps in these bio-syntheses. According to experiments by Ehrensvärd[6] on polycyclic quinones, most of the oxygen in the phenolic hydroxyl groups comes from the carboxyl group of acetate and by analogy the oxygens of the hydroxyl groups in positions 5 and 7 of the flavonoids as well as the oxygen atom of the hetero-cyclic ring can be assumed to originate from the carboxyl group of acetate.

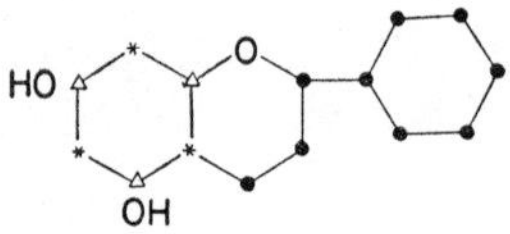

FIG. 1. Biosynthetic origin of the carbon atoms of the flavonoid skeleton.
Δ carboxyl group of acetic acid
* methyl group of acetic acid
• carbon atoms of a phenylpropane unit (e.g. cinnamic acid)

Hydroxyl groups in positions 6 and 8 on ring A, which occur relatively less frequently, are most likely to have been introduced by secondary oxidative processes in the plant. For thermodynamic reasons, it is more probable that the condensation of three acetyl units to form ring A does not proceed directly *via* acetyl-CoA but is more likely to involve malonyl-CoA (cf. ref. 7.)

According to the theory of Ehrensvärd[8], the acetyl- or malonyl-CoA units are joined together on the surface of an enzyme and are released only after cyclization of the β-polyketoacid chain has occurred. If this view is correct, then it will not be possible to isolate intermediates preceding the formation of ring A.

A large number of related compounds can serve as the phenylpropane precursors for ring B and the carbon atoms 2, 3 and 4 of the flavanoids. Thus phenylalanine, cinnamic acid, phenylpyruvic acid and phenyllactic acid are good precursors of quercetin. On the other hand tyrosine, *p*-hydroxyphenylpyruvic acid and *p*-hydroxyphenyllactic acid are incorporated to a much smaller degree, even though quercetin has a 4'-hydroxyl group.[4,9] In contrast, *p*-coumaric acid is a good precursor[4] of quercetin so it is likely that the hydroxylation of ring B takes place at the cinnamic acid stage. Kinetic experiments[10] also support the conclusion that cinnamic acid or *p*-coumaric acid are closer in structure to the biological phenylpropane precursor than are some of the other C_9-compounds which have been examined.

If cinnamic acid is assumed to be the intermediate then condensation with three acetyl units could produce a chalcone.

Various authors have postulated chalcones as intermediates in flavone biosynthesis (e.g. ref. 11) and to investigate this possibility we have synthesized the ^{14}C-labelled chalcones (1) and (2).

The incorporation of these chalcones (1) and (2) into quercetin in buckwheat or into cyanidin in red cabbage[12] has not yet been achieved but whether these negative results are due to an inability of the relatively large molecules to reach the site of synthesis in the cell, or whether the chalcones are not actually intermediates in the biosynthesis, is not yet known.*

(1)

(2)

(R = H or glucosidyl)

There are also many unsolved problems concerning the biogenetic relationships between flavan derivatives which differ in the state of oxidation of their heterocyclic ring, as exemplified by the flavones, anthocyanidins, and catechins. Kinetic experiments by Grisebach and Bopp[13] have demonstrated a parallel formation of flavone and anthocyanin in buckwheat so it seems that branching occurs in the biosynthetic pathway before the oxidation state of the heterocyclic rings is finally determined.

THEORETICAL CONSIDERATION OF ISOFLAVONE BIOGENESIS

The structure of the isoflavones immediately shows that ring B and carbon atoms 2, 3 and 4 cannot originate from an intact 1-phenylpropane precursor, since branching occurs at C_3. Theoretically there are two possibilities for the formation of the isoflavone skeleton as indicated in Fig. 2.

1. Ring B and carbon atoms 2, 3 and 4 could originate from a phenylpropane precursor. This is possible only if a rearrangement occurs during the course of the biogenesis and this could occur either at the level of a 1,3-diarylpropane intermediate or at the level of the 1-phenylpropane precursor.

2. Ring B and carbon atoms 3 and 4 could originate from a C_6–C_2 precursor formed from a phenylpropane unit or by another pathway. The carbon

---

* *Note added in proof:* Later experiments have shown that the chalcone glucoside (1; R = glucosidyl) is incorporated into cyanidin in red cabbage with the label located in the expected position. The incorporation of the chalcone (1; R = H) into quercetin is still under investigation (H. Grisebach, unpublished results).

atom in position 2 would then have to be provided by a separate single carbon source.

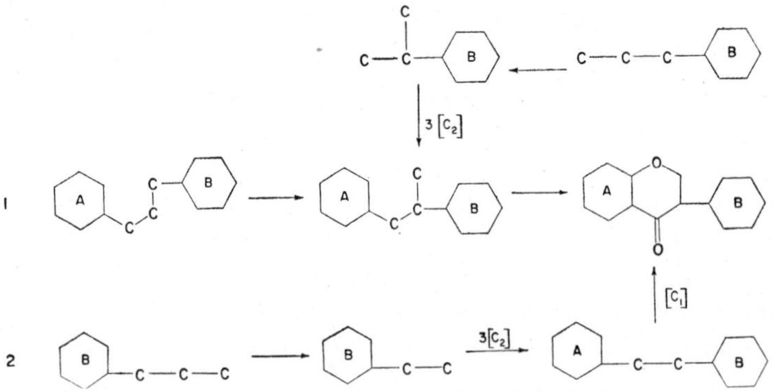

FIG. 2. Possible biosynthetic routes for the formation of the isoflavone carbon skeleton.

EXPERIMENTAL STUDIES ON THE BIOSYNTHESIS
OF FORMONONETIN

About two years ago, we began an investigation of the biogenesis of isoflavones with the aid of ^{14}C-labelled precursors[14] and until now we have been mainly concerned with the biogenesis of formononetin (7-hydroxy-4'-methoxyisoflavone) in red clover (*Trifolium pratense*).

Preliminary experiments on the isoflavone content of the clover indicated that the amount of isoflavone varied greatly according to the conditions of growth and the age of the clover. Before each experiment the isoflavone content of several clover leaves was determined semi-quantitatively. For the introduction of radioactive compounds the clover leaves were cut at the

TABLE 1. ACTIVITIES OF ISOFLAVONE MEASURED AS AN
"INFINITELY THICK" LAYER ON SILICIC ACID

Compound added*	Activity of isoflavone
Phenylalanine-1-[14]C	532 i.p.m.
Acetate-1-[14]C	137 i.p.m.
Formate-[14]C	33 i.p.m.

* An equal amount of activity was added in each case.
i.p.m. = Impulses per minute.

lower end of their stems and put into an aqueous solution of the compound to be studied. The duration of the experiments was 48 hr. After extraction of the dried plants with ether, the isoflavone was purified by paper chromatography and by chromatostrip,[14a] diluted with 300 mg of synthetic isoflavone, and recrystallized to constant specific activity. In preliminary experiments the incorporation of DL-phenylalanine-1-^{14}C, acetate-1-^{14}C and formate-^{14}C was investigated. The results are given in Table 1.

These experiments, carried out under the same conditions, showed a good incorporation of phenylalanine and acetate, whereas formate, which in many cases functions naturally as a one-carbon building unit, was incorporated

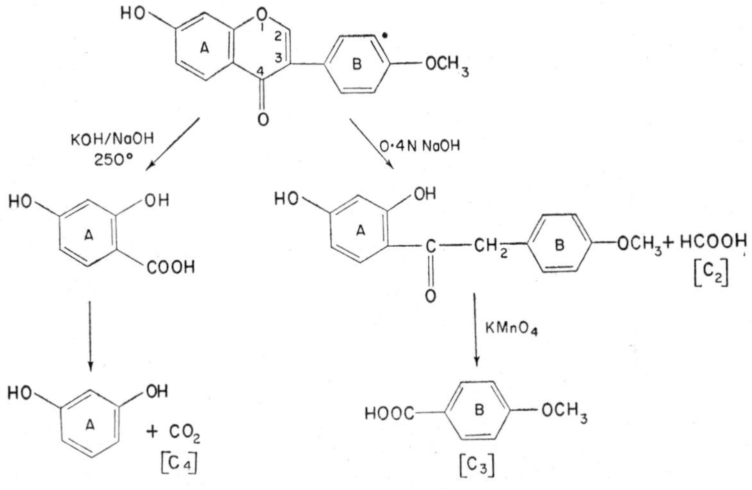

Fig. 3. Degradation of formononetin.

only to a very small extent. Thus the results are in agreement with pathway 1 (Fig. 2). They are not in accord with pathway 2, since this route requires that the carboxyl atom of phenylalanine should not be incorporated.

In further experiments the isoflavone obtained after feeding phenylalanine-1-^{14}C was degraded according to the scheme shown in Fig. 3 in order to

TABLE 2. ACTIVITY OF THE DEGRADATION PRODUCTS (SEE FIG. 3) OF THE FORMONONETIN DERIVED FROM PHENYLALANINE-1-^{14}C

Compound	i.p.m./mmol	Percent activity of the isoflavone
Formononetin	17,135	100
β-Resorcylic acid	15,659	91·4
CO_2 from β-resorcylic acid	15,995	93·3
Resorcinol	0	0
Formic acid	0	0

locate the labelled carbon atoms. After purification with either a Celite/ Norite column, or by sublimation, the degradation products were oxidized with potassium perchlorate to carbon dioxide and the activity of the latter was measured in a gas proportional counter.[15] The results of these measurements are shown in Table 2 (counting error ±2%).

As the degradation shows, 92–93% of the activity is localized in C_4 (carbonyl group) of the isoflavone. Thus phenylalanine is incorporated into the isoflavone in a specific way, and a rearrangement must take place in the

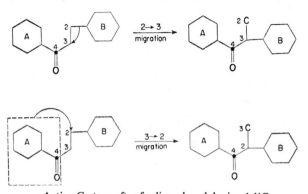

• Active C-atom after feeding phenylalanine-1-^{14}C

FIG. 4.   Rearrangement of a 1,3-diarylpropane intermediate.

course of the biogenesis. At first sight it would appear that an aryl migration (2 → 3 migration) has taken place, but on further consideration it becomes evident that the isotope distribution could also be explained by a migration

TABLE 3.   ACTIVITY OF THE DEGRADATION PRODUCTS FROM THE ISOFLAVONE

Compound	i.p.m./mmol	Activity of the compound expressed as percentage activity of the isoflavone
Isoflavone derived from		
phenylalanine-2-^{14}C	13,185	100
Deoxybenzoin ($C_3 + C_4$)	12,040	91·3
Formic acid (C_2)	—	(8·7)
p-Methoxybenzoic acid (C_3)	10,280	82
β-Resorcylic acid (C_4)	1392	10· 5
Isoflavone derived from		
phenylalanine-3-^{14}C	149,853	100
Deoxybenzoin ($C_3 + C_4$)	1310	0·85
Formic acid (C_2)	143,124	95·6*
p-Methoxybenzoic acid (C_3)	0	0
β-Resorcylic acid (C_4)	468	0·3

* Since the alkali which was used to titrate the formic acid was not free of carbonate, this value may be too low due to dilution by inactive carbon dioxide.

of a C_6–C_1 unit (3 → 2 migration). The two possible migrations are indicated in Fig. 4.

As will be explained in more detail later, the migration of an aroyl group (C_6–C_1) has been observed in the rearrangement of chalcone epoxides so further experiments were necessary to determine which type of rearrangement is involved in this case. Further experiments were therefore carried out with phenylalanine-2-^{14}C and -3-^{14}C, as these precursors would lead to different locations of activity depending upon whether a 2 → 3 or a 3 → 2 migration had occurred. The activities of the degradation products (see Fig. 3) of the isoflavones isolated in the experiments with phenylalanine-2-^{14}C and -3-^{14}C as precursors are shown in Table 3.

The distribution of activity obtained with the three differently labelled phenylalanines is illustrated in Fig. 5.

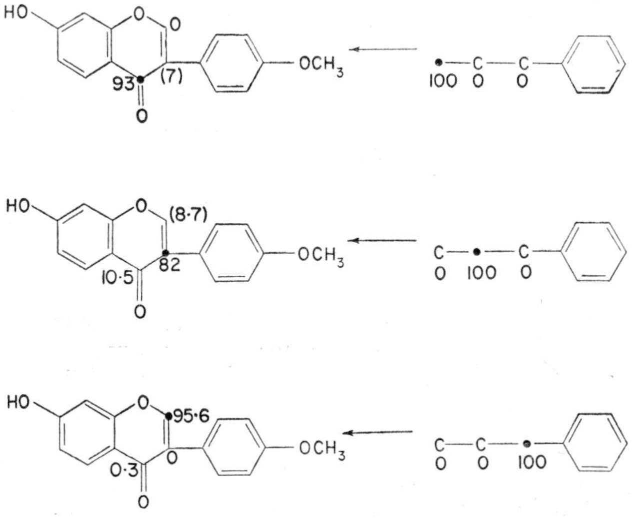

FIG. 5. Distribution of activity in the isoflavone after the feeding of phenylalanine-1-^{14}C, -2-^{14}C and -3-^{14}C.

The figures given in Fig. 5 represent percentage activities and the figures in parentheses were obtained by difference. These results show unequivocally that a phenyl migration has taken place during the course of the biogenesis and that the C-atoms 2, 3 and 4 of the isoflavone originate from the three carbon-side chain of phenylalanine. Thus the biogenesis of formononetin in red clover follows pathway 1 (Fig. 2).

EXPERIMENTAL INVESTIGATIONS ON THE BIOGENESIS OF BIOCHANIN-A

About the same time as we were investigating the biogenesis of formo-nonetin, Geissman et al.[16] were studying the biogenesis of biochanin-A (5,7-dihydroxy-4'-methoxyisoflavone) in Cicer arietinum L. (chana germ). Surprisingly, these workers have obtained results which are quite different from ours. After feeding phenylalanine-2-^{14}C and -3-^{14}C, the radioactive biochanin-A was isolated and was degraded by the method shown in Fig. 6, giving the results illustrated diagrammatically in Fig. 7. They show clearly that in this case no aryl migration has taken place but that the carbon atoms 3 and 4 of the isoflavone are derived respectively from the C_3 and the C_2 of the phenylalanine side chain. As yet no experimental evidence has been presented on the biosynthetic origin of the C_2 in the biochanin-A molecule.

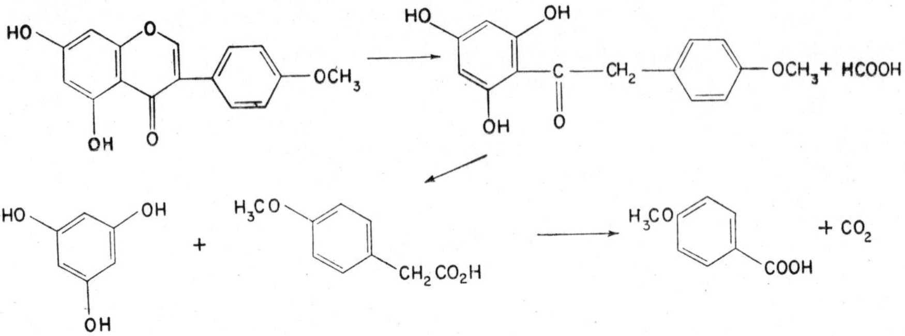

FIG. 6. Degradation of biochanin A.[16]

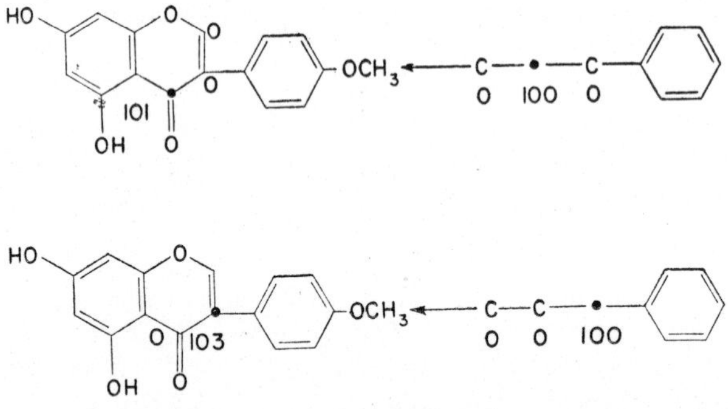

FIG. 7. Distribution of activity in biochanin A after the feeding of phenylalanine-2-^{14}C and -3-[14]C. The figures represent percentage activity.[16]

Thus it seems that both biogenetic pathways to isoflavones discussed above (see Fig. 2) actually occur in plants. This result is quite remarkable because biochanin-A only differs from formononetin in having one more hydroxyl group, and *Cicer arietinum* and *Trifolium pratense* both belong to the same family, the Papilionaceae. At the moment we are investigating the biogenesis of isoflavones in other plants in order to determine which mechanism operates more frequently.*

    * *Added in proof*: Experiments by Grisebach and Brandner with chana germ (*Z. Natu-forschg.* 1961, **16b**, 2, and investigations by Geissman and Mortimer (personal communication) using higher activities than in their earlier experiments, have proved that the biosynthesis of biochanin-A also involves an aryl migration.

THEORIES ON THE MECHANISM OF THE ARYL MIGRATION

A rearrangement involving an aryl group migration, like the one which occurs in the biogenesis of formononetin, has not been established in Nature previously. The results so far obtained do not permit conclusions regarding the nature of the intermediate in which the aryl migration takes place.

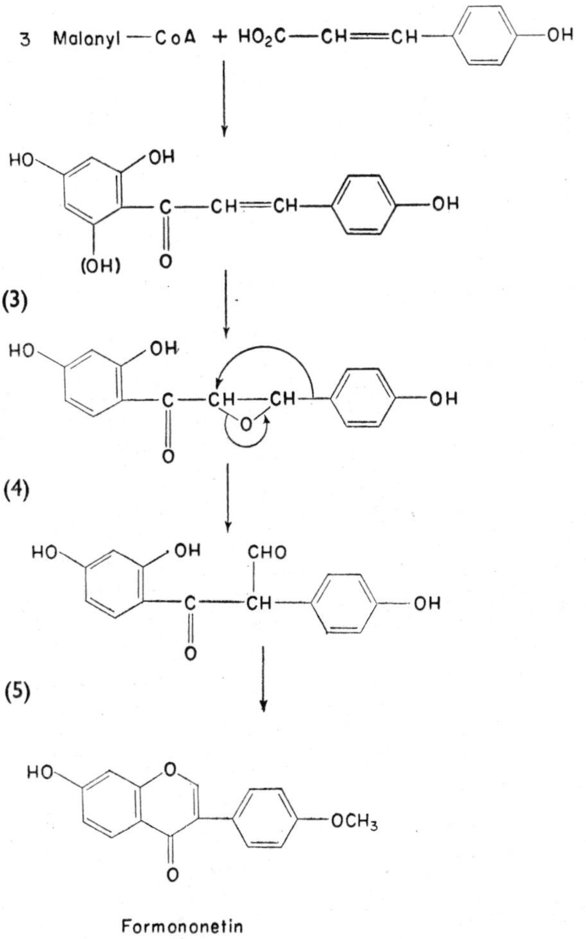

FIG. 8. Hypothetical biogenetic pathway to formononetin.

However, by analogy with known chemical reactions it is possible to formulate, intermediates as working hypotheses for the design of further experiments. In principle p-coumaric acid (or cinnamic acid) could condense with three acetyl- or malonyl-CoA units to form a chalcone (3) whose epoxide (4) could undergo aryl migration giving a formyldeoxybenzoin (5). Methylation of the 4'-hydroxyl group could finally lead to formononetin.*

Concerning this suggestion, the epoxidation of a double bond *in vivo* has recently been demonstrated in the biogenesis of hyoscine.[16a] The rearrangement of chalcone epoxides has been studied in detail by House[17] and with the aid of ^{14}C-labelled benzalacetophenone oxide (6) he was able to show during the rearrangement of this compound to formyldeoxybenzoin under the influence of boron trifluoride that it is the benzoyl residue and not the phenyl group which migrates. This observation can be rationalized by

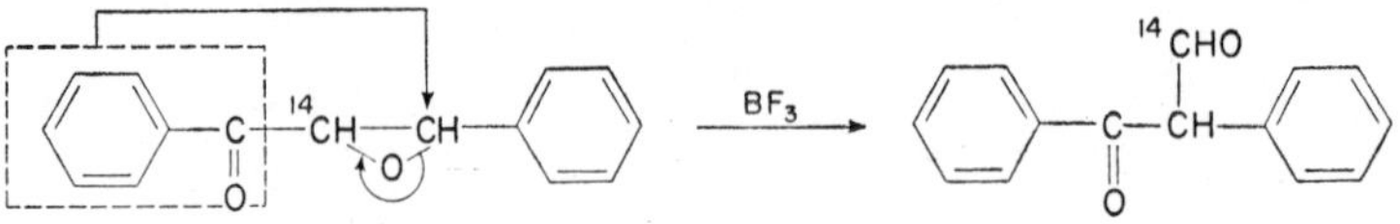

(6)

making a comparison of the stabilities of the two possible intermediate carbonium ions (7) and (8) where because of the proximity of the positive charge to the carbonyl group in (7), it follows that the carbonium ion (8) will be favoured.

(7)   (8)

However, House has shown with other examples that the course of the rearrangement is also influenced by the steric configuration of the epoxide

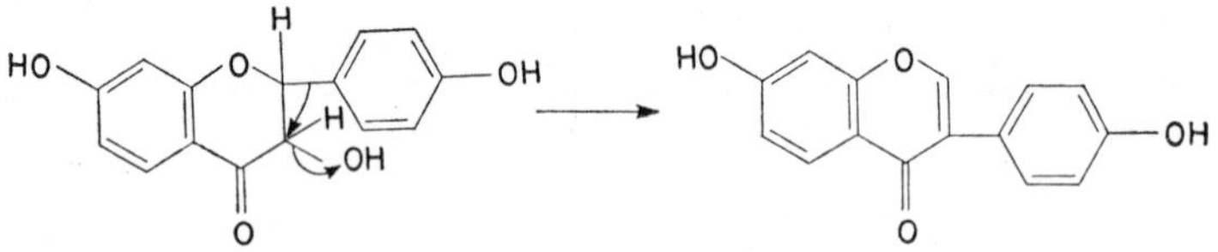

(9)

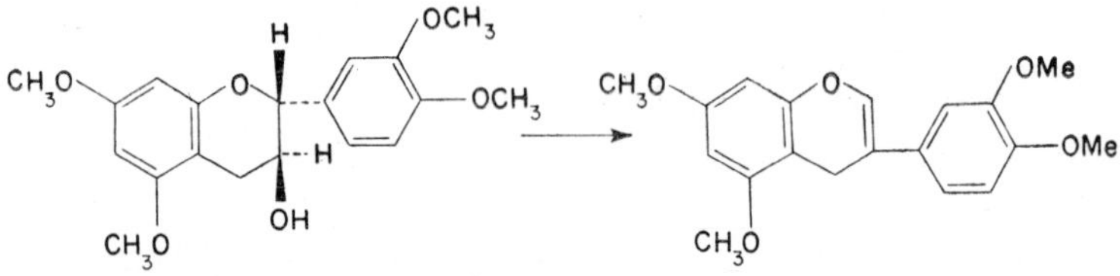

(10)

* *Note added in proof*: In red clover and chana germ the chalcone glucoside (2; R = glucosidyl) is incorporated into formononetin with the label in the expected position (H. Grisebach and L. Patschke, *Chem. Ber.*, 1960, 93, 2326).

and that aryl group migration rather than aroyl group migration occurs in some cases. It is therefore possible that an aryl group migration of the type envisaged in Fig. 8 could take place in the plant. An alternative possibility would be that the aryl migration does not take place until heterocyclic ring closure has occurred as in, for example, the rearrangement of the dihydro flavonol (9). An analogous reaction to this is the rearrangement of tetra-*O*-methylcatechin (10) to the isoflavene (11) which was discovered by Freudenberg et al.[18].

MODEL REACTIONS FOR THE BIOGENESIS OF ISOFLAVONES

During their synthetic studies, Baker and Robinson[19] in 1932 tried to obtain isoflavones by the rearrangement of chalcone epoxides. However, under the conditions they used the ethylene oxide ring always opened without a rearrangement. Later, Algar and McKenna[20] succeeded in promoting the rearrangement of suitable substituted chalcone epoxides.

For example, under the influence of aqueous sulphuric acid the epoxide (12) rearranged to form the formyldeoxybenzoin (13) in about 35% yield. Treatment of (13) with aluminium bromide in benzene produced 7-hydroxy-isoflavone in 4% yield.

By substituting boron trifluoride for sulphuric acid we have been able to obtain rearrangement of the epoxide (12) and other methoxy-substituted epoxides to the corresponding formyldeoxybenzoins in yields ranging from 60–70%.[21] Theoretically, rearrangement of chalcone epoxides with a free hydroxyl group in the position *ortho* to the carbonyl group should produce isoflavones in high yield but so far our attempts to prepare *o*-hydroxychalcone epoxides have not been successful (cf. ref. 22).

BIOGENETIC RELATIONSHIPS OF ISOFLAVONES
TO OTHER NATURAL PRODUCTS

On the basis of structural similarities it can be assumed that the isoflavones are biogenetically related to a large number of other natural products. Thus the formyldeoxybenzoin (5) could also be an intermediate in the formation of coumestrol (see Fig. 9) which has recently been isolated from clover by Bickoff et al.[23].

Reduction of the aldehyde group of the formyldeoxybenzoin (5) could produce angolensin, which occurs together with isoflavones in the heartwood of *Pterocarpus angolensis*.[24] Although to our knowledge the reduction of a formyl group or a primary alcoholic group to a methyl group has not yet been

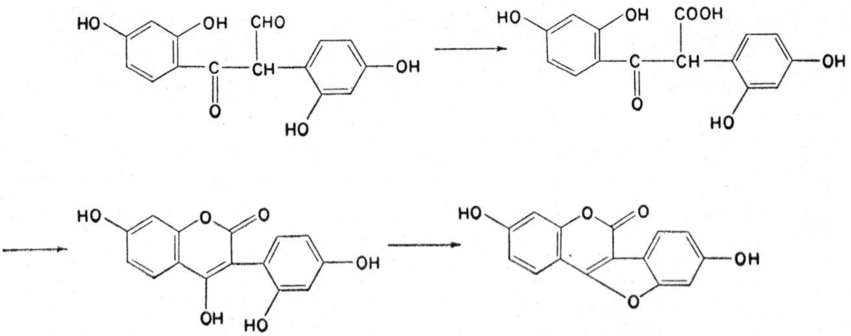

FIG. 9. Hypothetical biogenetic scheme for coumestrol.

demonstrated in nature, this reaction is certainly feasible. Alternatively, angolensin could be a reduction product of an isoflavone.

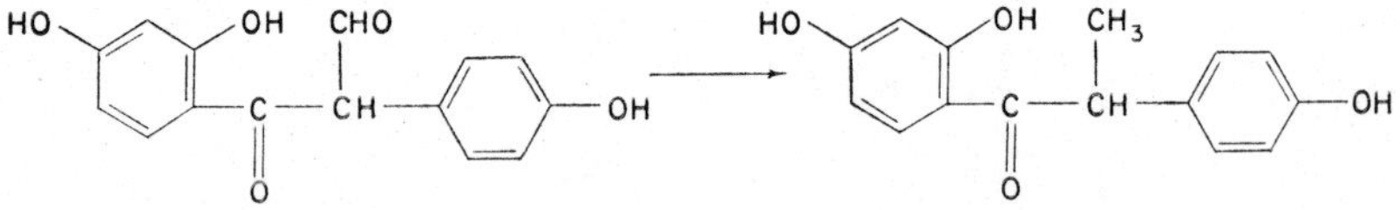

Angolensin

The rotenoids are very likely to be related biogenetically to the isoflavones and as suggested by Ollis[25] the scheme illustrated in Fig. 10 indicates a possible route for the formation of the carbon skeleton of the rotenoids.

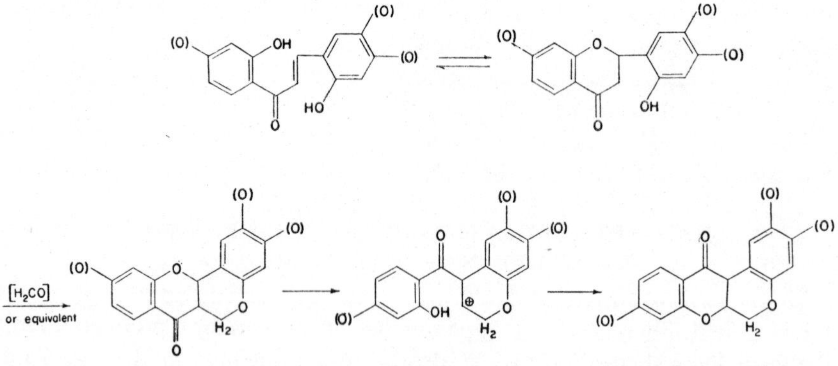

FIG. 10. Hypothetical biogenetic scheme for the rotenoids.[25]

Various mechanisms for the transformation of the tetracyclic intermediate (14) may be envisaged.

There are some natural products where the possibility of two successive aryl migrations during the course of their biogenesis may be recognized.

An example of this is dalbergin, recently isolated from the heartwood of *Dalbergia sissoo*,[26] the biogenesis of which could be formulated as shown in Fig. 11, starting with a chalcone epoxide. The formation of the pigments of

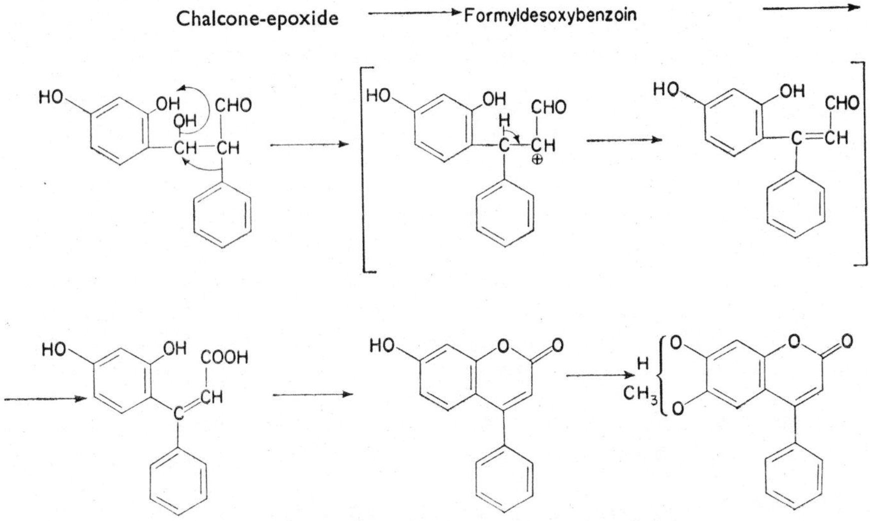

FIG. 11. Hypothetical biogenetic pathway to dalbergin.

red-wood and log-wood or their respective leuco compounds brazilin and haematoxylin can also be explained by assuming two successive aryl migrations[25] (see Fig. 12).

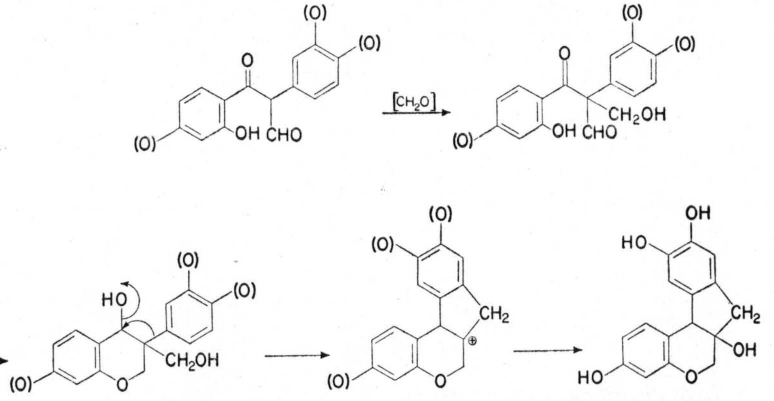

FIG. 12. Hypothetical biogenetic scheme for the pigments of the brazilin type.[25]

In his "Häufigkeitsregel", Paech[27] has pointed out that the more numerous the steps which are required for the synthesis of a plant product, the smaller is the probability that this synthetic chain has been developed in a large number of plant types which are phylogenetically not closely related. The isoflavones and the compounds which would seem to be biogenetically related to them, like the rotenoids, the pigments of red-wood and log-wood and coumestrol, have so far been found primarily in Leguminosae. It is therefore possible that the enzyme systems which are probably required for the aryl migration occur only in the Leguminosae family.

However, further experiments with other plants will establish whether the pathway involving an aryl migration or whether the biosynthetic route discovered by Geissman for biochanin-A is more wide-spread in nature. It will also be important to find out more about the nature of the inter-mediates and to investigate experimentally the hypothetical biogenetic relationship between the isoflavones and the other natural products mentioned above. The work done so far on the biogenesis of isoflavones has led to the discovery of new biogenetic mechanisms. It is to be expected that further research on this interesting class of compounds will make additional contri-butions to our knowledge of the metabolic processes which occur in plants.

This work was supported by the Deutsche Forschungsgemeinschaft. I should like to thank Norbert Doerr for his skilful technical assistance.

REFERENCES

1. The Pharmacology of Plant Phenolics (Editor J. W. FAIRBAIRN), Academic Press Ltd., London 1959, p. 51.
2. R. B. BRADBURY and D. E. WHITE, J. Chem. Soc. 1951, 3447.
3. H. GRISEBACH, Z. Naturforschg. 1956, 11b, 370; Ibid. 1957, 12b, 597; Ibid. 1958, 13b, 335; Proceedings IVth International Congress of Biochemistry, Vienna 1958, Pergamon Press, London 1959, Vol. II, p. 56–69.
4. E. W. UNDERHILL, J. E. WATKIN and A. C. NEISH, Canad. J. Biochem. Physiol. 1957, 35, 219; J. E. WATKIN, E. W. UNDERHILL and A. C. NEISH, Ibid. 1957, 35, 229.
5. T. A. GEISSMAN and T. SWAIN, Chem. and Ind. 1957, 984.
6. G. EHRENSVÄRD, S. GATENBECK and K. MOSBACH, Abstracts XVIIth International Congress of Pure and Applied Chemistry, Munich 1959, Vol. II, p. 11.
7. S. J. WAKIL and J. GANGERLY, J. Amer. Chem. Soc. 1959, 81, 2597.
8. G. EHRENSVÄRD, lecture at the XVIIth International Congress of Pure and Applied Chemistry, Munich 1959.
9. J. F. WATKIN and A. C. NEISH, Proceedings of the International Botanical Congress, Montreal 1959, Vol. II, p. 425.
10. D. R. McCALLA and A. C. NEISH, Canad. J. Biochem. Physiol. 1959, 37, 537.
11. M. SHIMOKORIYAMA, J. Amer. Chem. Soc. 1957, 79, 4199.
12. H. GRISEBACH and L. PATSCHKE, unpublished results.
13. H. GRISEBACH and M. BOPP, Z. Naturforschg. 1959, 14b, 485.
14. H. GRISEBACH, Z. Naturforschg. 1959, 14b, 802; H. GRISEBACH and N. DOERR, Ibid. 1960, 15b, 284.
14a. E. STAHL, Chemiker Ztg. 1958, 82, 323.
15. H. SIMON, H. DANIEL and J. F. KLEBE, Angew. Chem. 1959, 71, 303.
16. T. A. GEISSMAN, J. W. MASON and J. R. ROWE, Chem. and Ind. 1959, 1577; T. A. GEISSMAN and J. W. MASON, Ibid. 1960, 291.
16a. G. FODOR, A. ROMEIKE, G. JANZSÓ and I. KOCZAR, Tetrahedron Letters 1959, 7, 19.
17. H. O. HOUSE, J. Amer. Chem. Soc. 1954, 76, 1235; H. O. HOUSE and D. J. REIF, Ibid. 1955, 77, 6525; H. O. HOUSE, Ibid. 1956, 78, 2298; H. O. HOUSE, D. J. REIF and R. L. WASSON, Ibid. 1957, 79, 2490.

18. K. FREUDENBERG, G. CARRARA and E. COHN, *Liebigs Ann. Chem.* 1926, **446**, 87.
19. W. BAKER and R. ROBINSON, *J. Chem. Soc.* 1932, 1789.
20. J. ALGAR and J. MCKENNA, *Proc. Royal Irish Acad.* 1944, Vol. XLIX, Section B, **15**, 225.
21. H. GRISEBACH and N. DOERR, unpublished results.
22. T. A. GEISSMAN and D. K. FUKUSHIMA, *J. Amer. Chem. Soc.* 1948, **70**, 1686.
23. E. M. BICKOFF, R. L. LYMAN, A. L. LIVINGSTON and A. N. BOOTH, *J. Amer. Chem. Soc.* 1958, **80**, 3969.
24. F. E. KING, T. J. KING and A. J. WARWICK, *J. Chem. Soc.* 1952, 1920.
25. W. D. OLLIS, private communication. H. GRISEBACH and W. D. OLLIS, *Experientia*, 1961, **11**, 4.
26. V. K. AHLUWALIA and T. R. SESHADRI, *J. Chem. Soc.* 1957, 970.
27. K. PAECH, *Biochemie und Physiologie der Sekundären Pflanzenstoffe*, Springer Verlag, Berlin 1950, p. 29.

CHAPTER 4

ISOPRENOID UNITS IN NATURAL PHENOLIC COMPOUNDS

W. D. OLLIS and I. O. SUTHERLAND

The University, Bristol

THIS chapter reviews the occurrence, structure, and synthesis of those phenolic natural products which contain isoprenoid residues. The variety of structural type exhibited in these isoprenoid units is quite remarkable and demonstrates the versatility of biosynthetic processes. However, it also emphasizes the essential economy of biosynthetic processes, for this variety of structure arises from one precursor, isopentenyl pyrophosphate, the substance which is also involved in the biosynthesis of steroids and terpenoids.

The different types of natural product which contain these isoprenoid units in their structure are indicated in the first part of this chapter and reference may be made to the interesting review of this topic by Seshadri.[30] The next section provides examples of various structure determinations; these have been selected in order to illustrate the wide variety of methods, both physical and chemical, which have been used. Studies directed towards the synthesis of these types of natural products are not extensive and the final section describes the approaches which have so far been investigated.

STRUCTURAL RELATIONSHIPS

The structures of many natural aromatic and heterocyclic compounds contain C_5 units which are apparently derived from the same C_5 precursor as the isoprene units of terpenes and steroids. The wide distribution of these compounds, which occur not only in the higher plants but also as mould metabolites, has been commented on by several authors.[1,26,30] Such compounds include derivatives of benzene, naphthalene, quinoline, acridone and indole, but many are derivatives of α- or γ-benzpyrone including coumarins, xanthones, rotenoids, isoflavones, flavanols, flavonols, flavans and chromenes. Examples illustrating this range of structural types are given in formulae 1–20.

The combined results of a number of research groups[21,22] have shown that the biosynthesis of terpenes and steroids may be represented by the scheme shown opposite.[22]

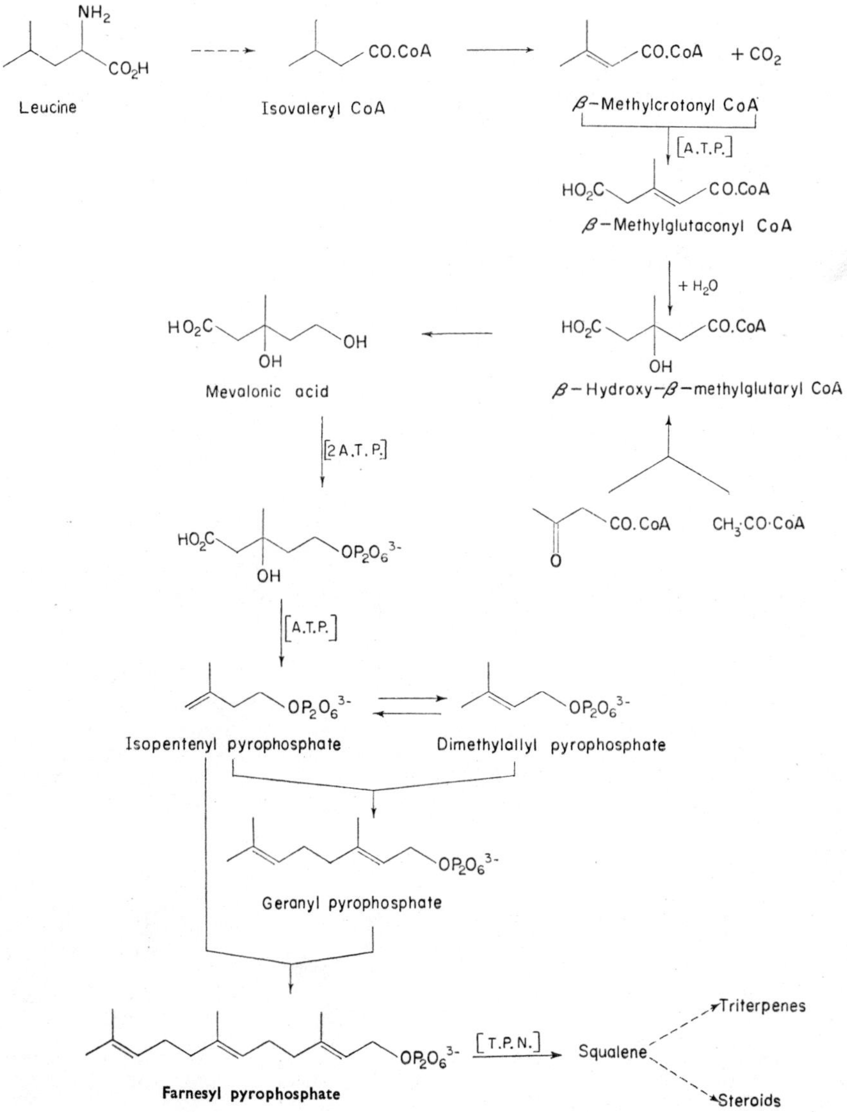
NH2
CO2H
Leucine
CO.CoA
Isovaleryl CoA
CO.CoA + CO2
β-Methylcrotonyl CoA
[A.T.P.]
HO2C
CO.CoA
β-Methylglutaconyl CoA
+ H2O
HO2C
CO.CoA
OH
β-Hydroxy-β-methylglutaryl CoA
HO2C
OH
OH
Mevalonic acid
[2 A.T.P.]
CO.CoA
O
CH3·CO·CoA
HO2C
OP2O6 3-
OH
[A.T.P.]
OP2O6 3-
Isopentenyl pyrophosphate
OP2O6 3-
Dimethylallyl pyrophosphate
OP2O6 3-
Geranyl pyrophosphate
OP2O6 3-
Farnesyl pyrophosphate
[T.P.N.]
Squalene
Triterpenes
Steroids

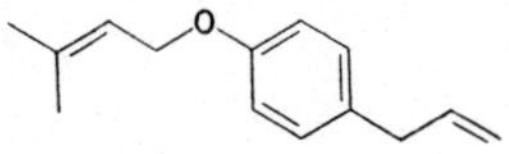

(1) Foeniculin[2]

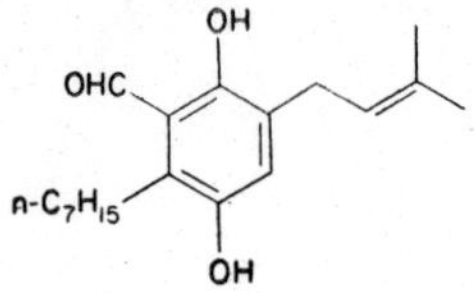

(2) Flavoglaucin[3]

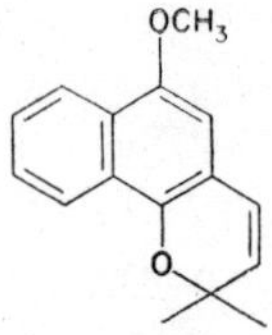

(3) Lapachenole[4]

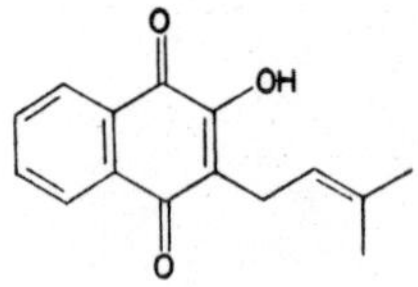

(4) Lapachol[5]

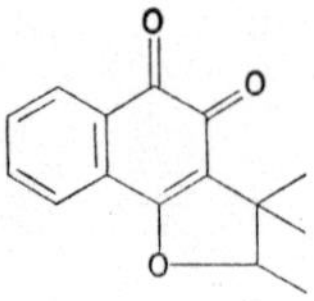

(5) Dunnione[6]

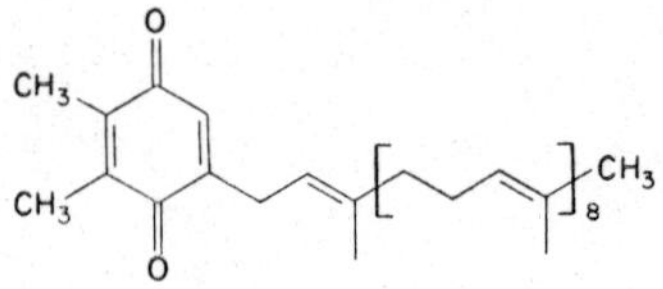

(6) Kofler's quinone[7]

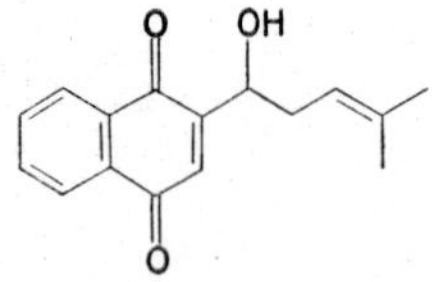

(7) Alkannin[8]

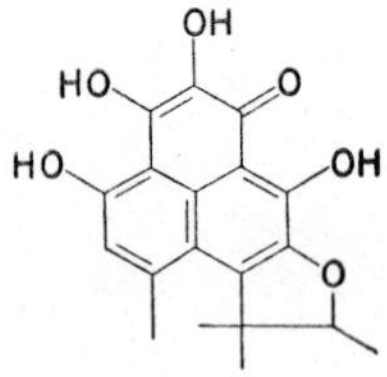

(8) Atrovenetin[9] *

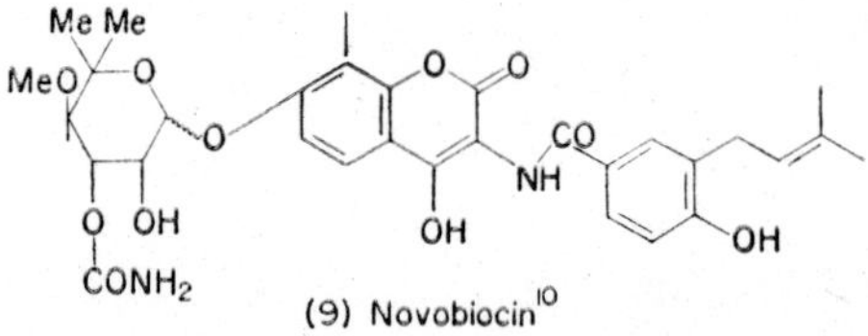

(9) Novobiocin[10]

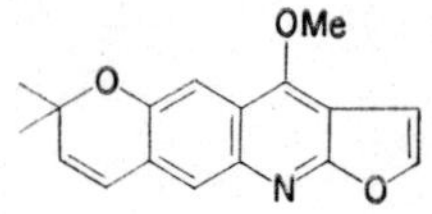

(10) Medicosmine[11]

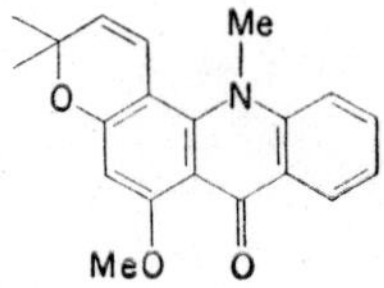

(11) Acronycine[12]

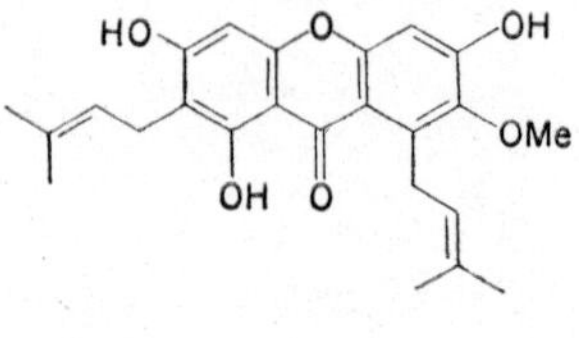

(12) Mangostin[13]

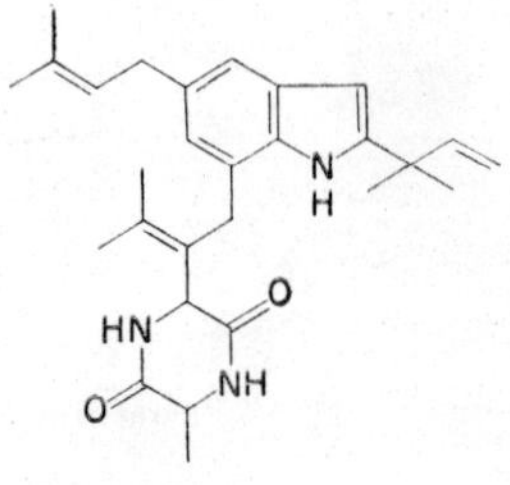

(13) Echinulin[14]

* This structure may require modification (see p. 104).

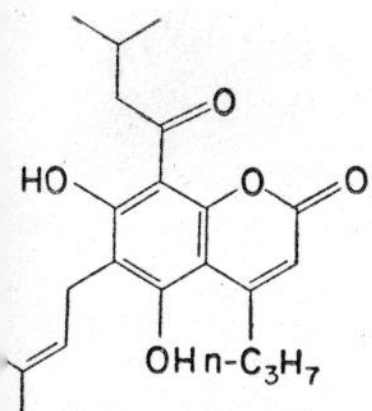

(14) Mammein[15]

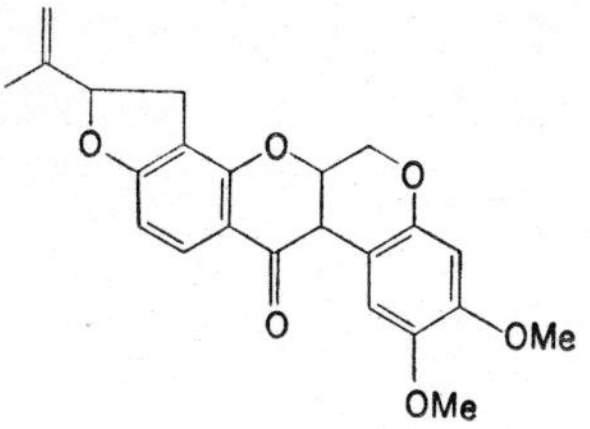

(15) Rotenone[16]

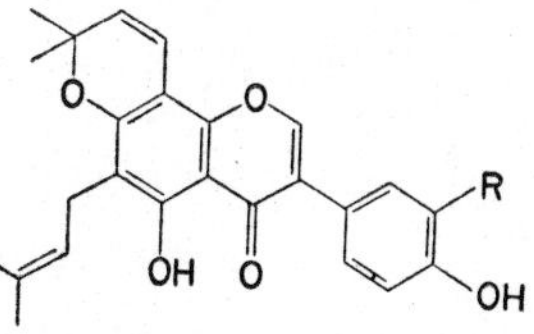

(16) Pomiferin, R = OH[17]

(17) Osajin, R = H[17]

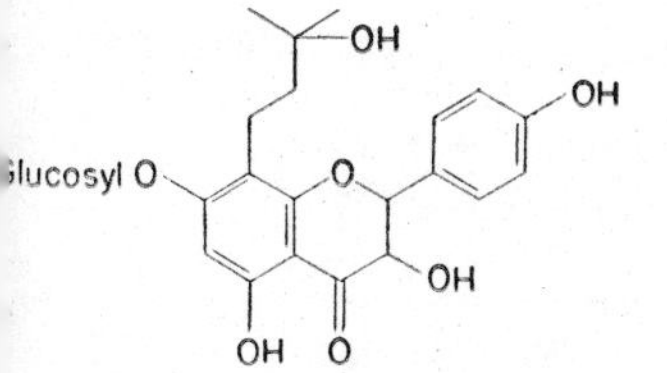

(18) Phellamurin[18]

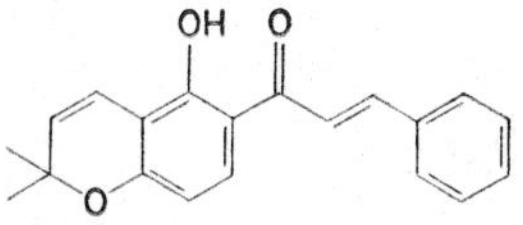

(19) Lonchocarpin[19]

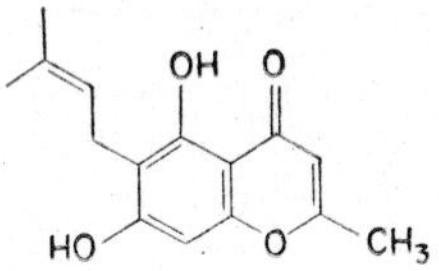

(20) Peucenin[20]

It has been demonstrated by Birch and his co-workers[23] that when 2-^{14}C-mevalonic acid lactone (21) is added to the culture medium it is incorporated into the mould metabolite auroglaucin (22). Ozonolysis of the radioactive auroglaucin yielded acetone, which contained all the incorporated activity. It

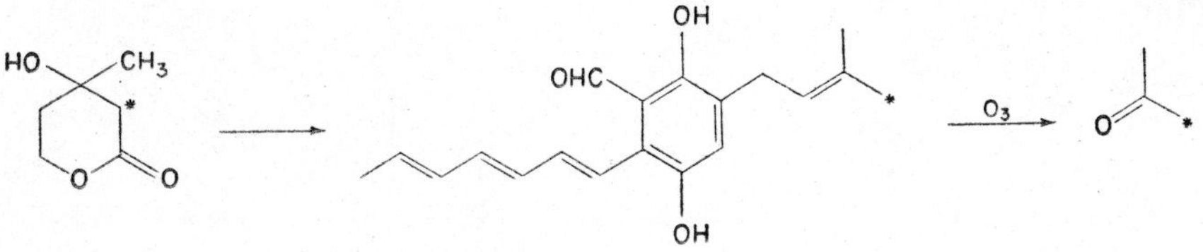

(21)

(22) Auroglaucin

was suggested by Birch[24] that the biosynthetic introduction of isopentenyl and related groups into naturally occurring aromatic compounds involves a C-isopentenylation reaction, and Todd[25] has pointed out that $\gamma\gamma$-dimethylallyl pyrophosphate could be effective as an alkylating agent. A similar suggestion that $\gamma\gamma$-dimethylallyl alcohol or its equivalent might be the C_5 alkylating agent was made[9] to account for the unusual isoprenoid residue in atrovenetin (8). The isolation of $\gamma\gamma$-dimethylallyl pyrophosphate from baker's yeast has been described by Lynen,[22] and it was suggested that this compound would react with isopentenyl pyrophosphate to yield geranyl pyrophosphate (23). The product of the reaction would be an allylic pyrophosphate and additional C_5 units could be added by further reaction with isopentenyl pyrophosphate leading to polyisoprenoid compounds including the steroids and terpenoids.

It has also been suggested that ubiquinone$_{50}$ (24) might be formed by C-alkylation of a suitable phenolic intermediate, the alkylating agent being an allyl pyrophosphate built up by successive reactions similar to those leading

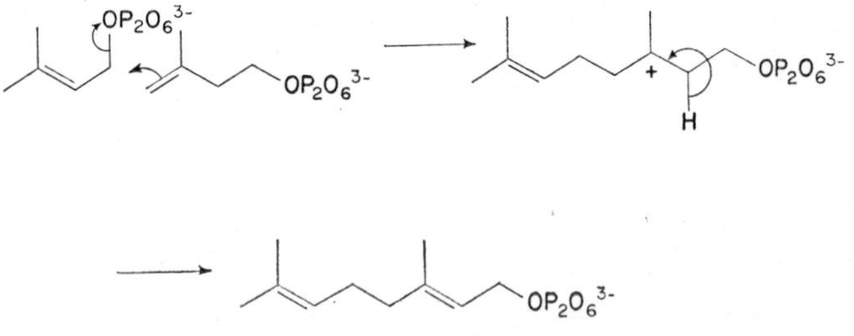

(23) Geranyl pyrophosphate

to geranyl pyrophosphate (23); oxidation of the alkylated phenol to the quinone occurs as the last stage of the biosynthesis. It has been shown that labelled mevalonic acid is incorporated into the ubiquinone of rat liver.[27]

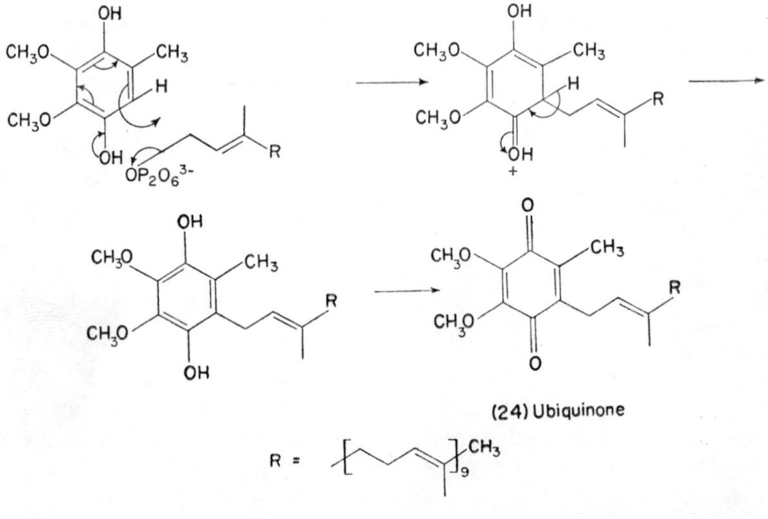

(24) Ubiquinone

These processes can lead to the introduction of a variety of polyisoprenoid residues and further structural modifications of these polyisoprenoid units can be envisaged by biosynthetic processes which are mechanistically acceptable. It has been suggested in the past that either $\beta\beta$-dimethylacrylic acid (25)[26] or the corresponding aldehyde (26)[30] would function as isopentenylating agents by analogy with known chemical reactions. With the exception of $\beta\beta$-dimethylacrylyl derivatives, for example glabra lactone (27),[28] which could be derived from $\beta\beta$-dimethylacrylic acid, it is unlikely that either the

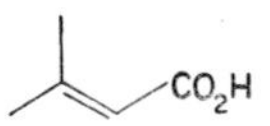

(25) 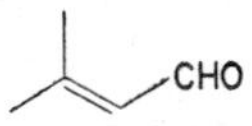   (26)

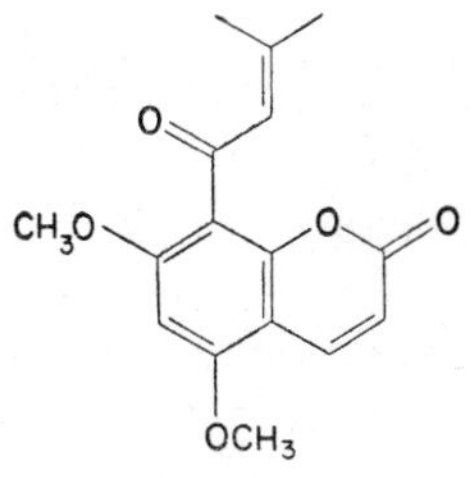

(27) Glabra lactone

acid (25) or the aldehyde (26) is a direct precursor of the isoprenoid side chains in natural products.

αα- and γγ-Dimethylallyl Derivatives

The reaction of γγ-dimethylallyl pyrophosphate with a phenolic compound would be expected to give rise to any of four possible products by the mechanisms indicated in (28) to (31). γγ-Dimethylallyl pyrophosphate, which has actually been isolated from yeast preparations, is probably the

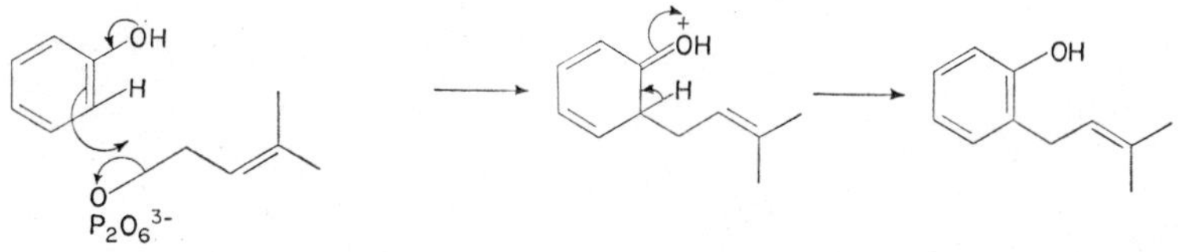

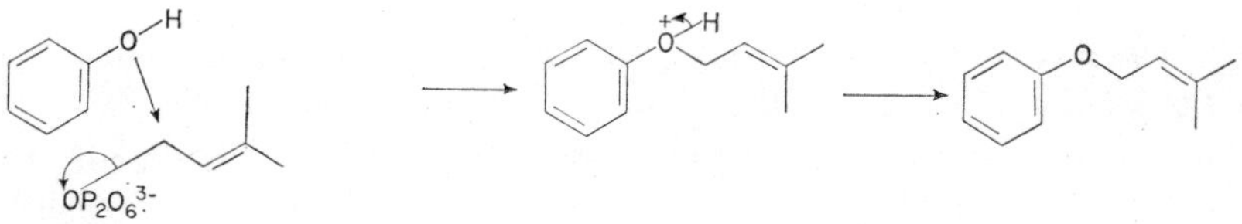

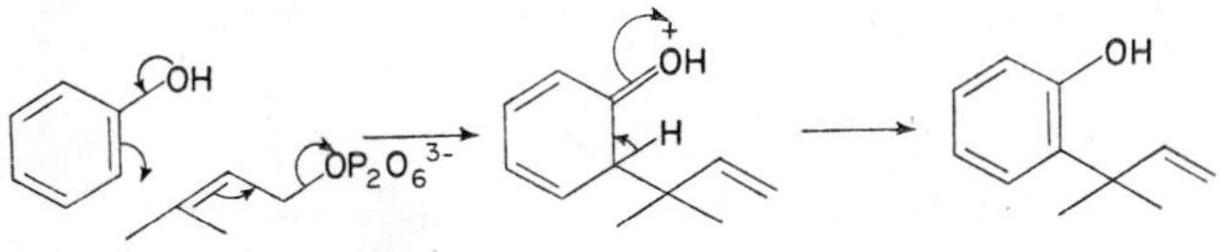

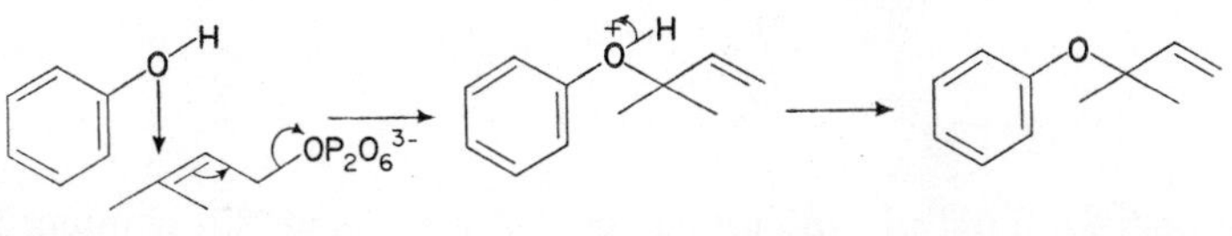

alkylating agent involved in the introduction of C_5 units, but other γγ-dimethylallyl derivatives cannot be excluded, as has been pointed out by Cornforth and Popjak.[21] The first two alkylation reactions, (28) and (29), leading to C-$\gamma\gamma$-dimethylallyl derivatives and $\gamma\gamma$-dimethylallyl ethers are more likely to occur for obvious steric reasons. The close inter-relationships between the structures of a very large number of natural products become obvious when considered from this point of view.

Compounds of all four types have been isolated from natural sources and as expected the products of the first two processes greatly outnumber the rather rare $\alpha\alpha$-dimethylallyl derivatives.

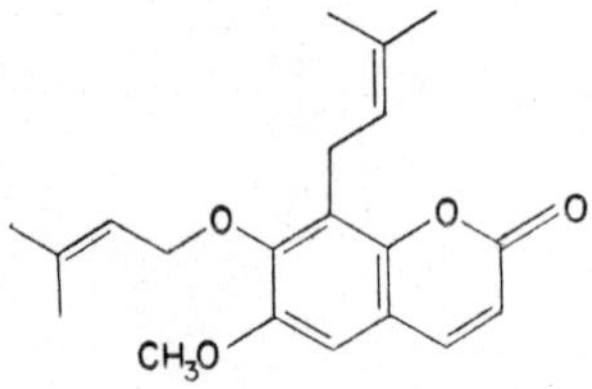

(32) Brayleyanin

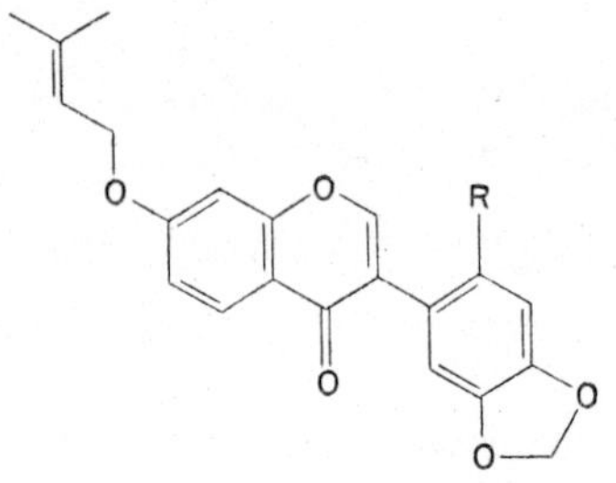

(34) Maxima substance-B, R = H

(35) Maxima substance-C, R = OCH₃

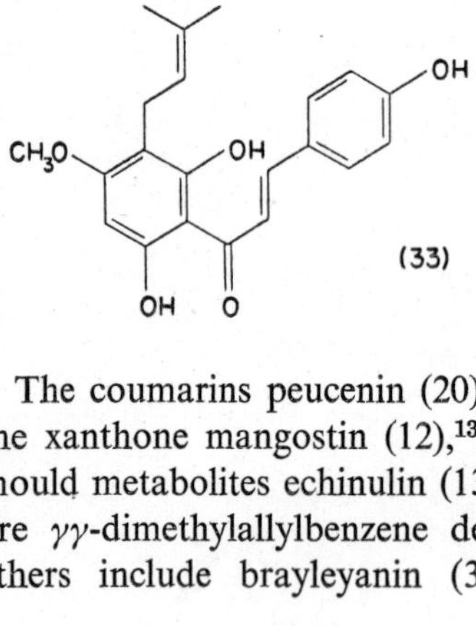

(33) Xanthohumol

The coumarins peucenin (20),[20] brayleyanin (32),[29] and mammein (14);[15] the xanthone mangostin (12),[13] the chalkone xanthohumol (33)[33] and the mould metabolites echinulin (13),[14] novobiocin (9),[10] and auroglaucin (22)[23] are $\gamma\gamma$-dimethylallylbenzene derivatives. The analogous $\gamma\gamma$-dimethylallyl ethers include brayleyanin (32),[29] *Maxima* substance-B (34), *Maxima*

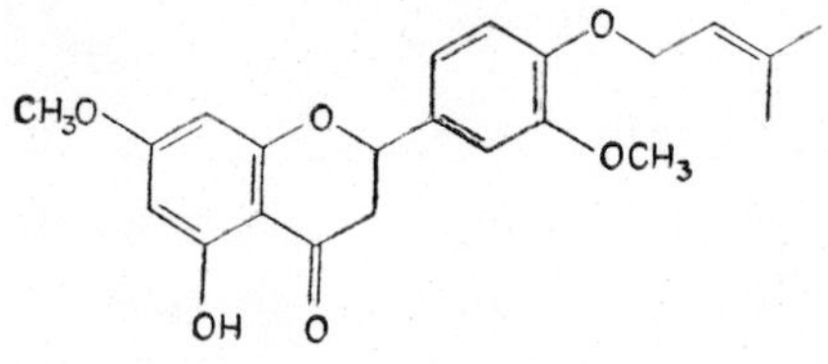

(36)

substance-C (35)[31] and the un-named flavanone (36).[32] Echinulin (13)[14] and the hypothetical precursors (37) and (38) of dunnione[6] and atrovenetin[9] are examples of $\alpha\alpha$-dimethylallyl compounds, although it is not possible to exclude rearrangement of a $\gamma\gamma$-dimethylallyl precursor. Anisoxide (39)[34] may be formed from the precursor (40) during its isolation; the αα-dimethyl-allyl ether (40) could be identical with the anisoxide isomer isolated by Takens.[35]

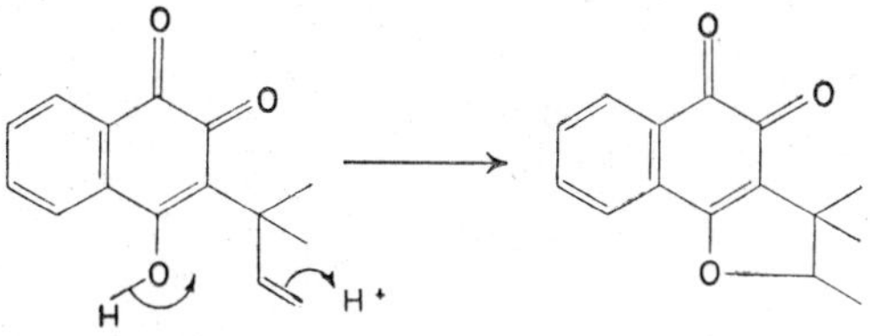

(37)   Dunnione

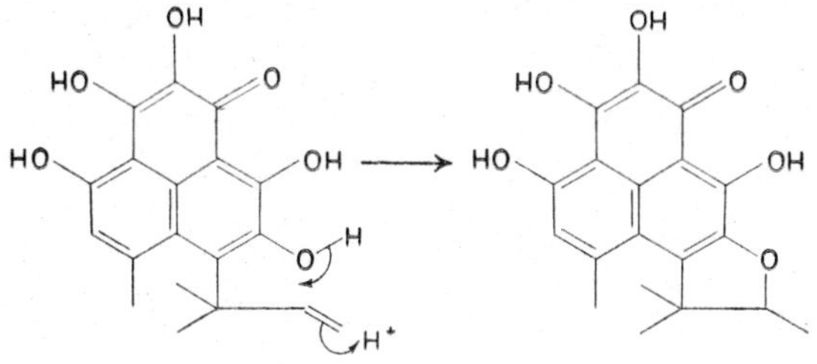

(38)   Atrovenetin

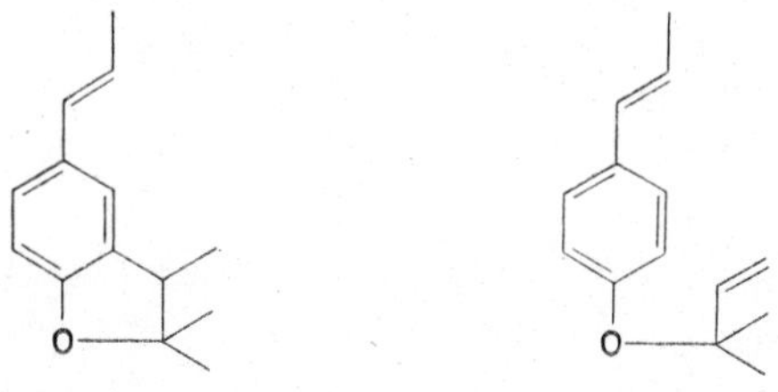

(39) Anisoxide   (40)

Similar alkylations, either of phenolic oxygen or of the aromatic ring, by a chain of two or more isoprene units as the appropriate allyl pyrophosphates, for example, farnesyl (41) and geranyl (42) pyrophosphates, could lead to the coumarins collinin (43),[36] ostruthin (44),[37] marmin (45),[38] 5-geranyloxy-7-methoxycoumarin (46),[39] umbelliprenin (47),[40] bergamottin (48),[41] and ammoresinol (49).[42] This group also includes the more complex quinones, vitamins K_1 (50)[46] and K_2 (51),[43] the various ubiquinones (52)[44] and Kofler's quinone (6).[7]

The γγ-dimethylallyl substituent also appears in a number of other compounds, but it has been modified by hydration giving a hydroxyisopentanyl derivative. Examples include the flavonols icariin (53)[45] and amurensin (54),[18] the flavanol phellamurin (18),[18] and the coumarin marmin (45),[38] the latter being formed by the hydration of both double bonds of a geranyloxy precursor.

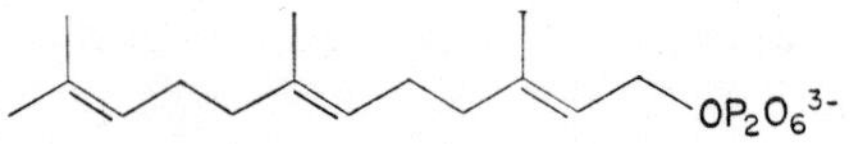

(41)

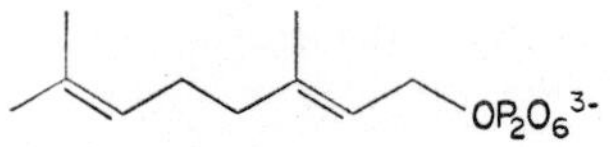

(42)

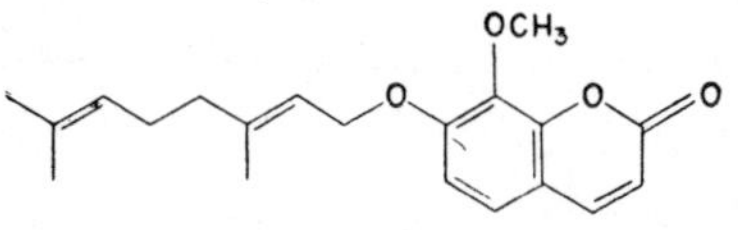

(43) Collinin

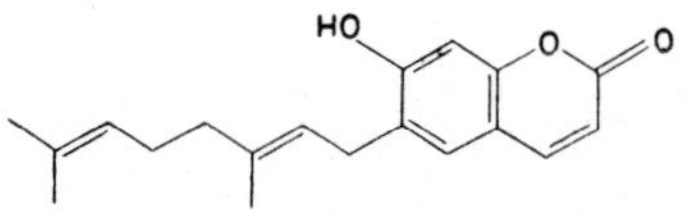

(44) Ostruthin

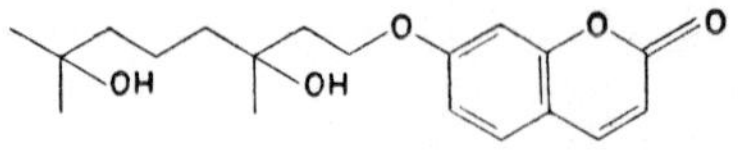

(45) Marmin

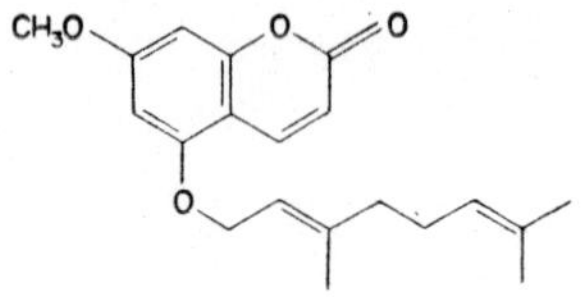

(46)

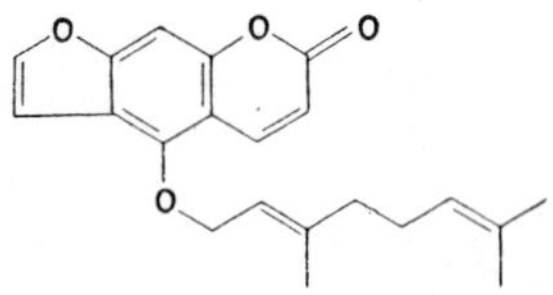

(48) Bergamottin

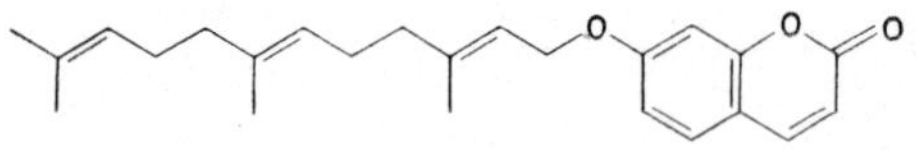

(47) Umbelliprenin

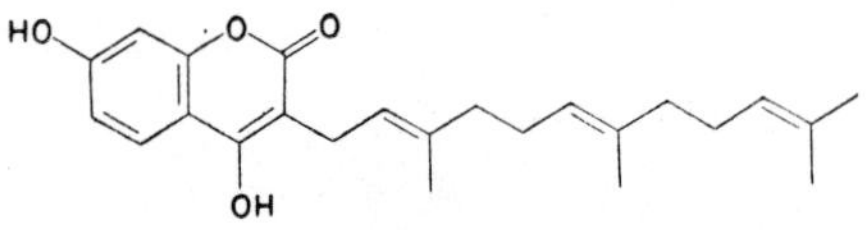

(49) Ammoresinol

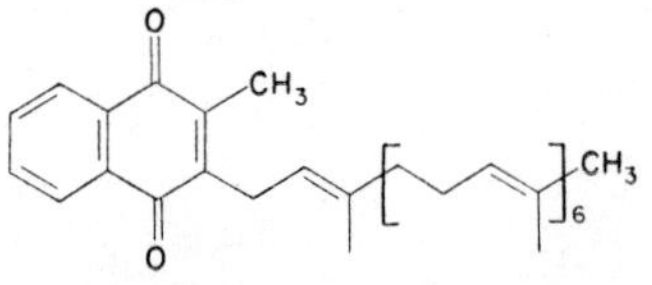

(51) Vitamin K_2

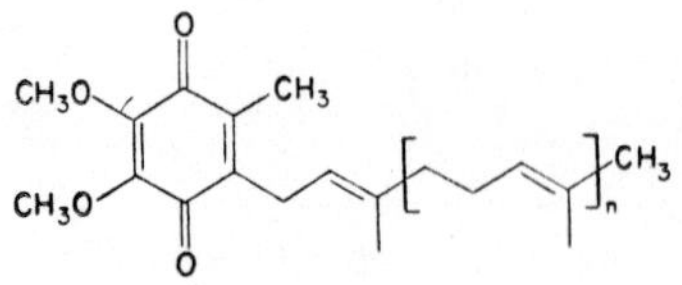

(52) Ubiquinones (n = 4–9)

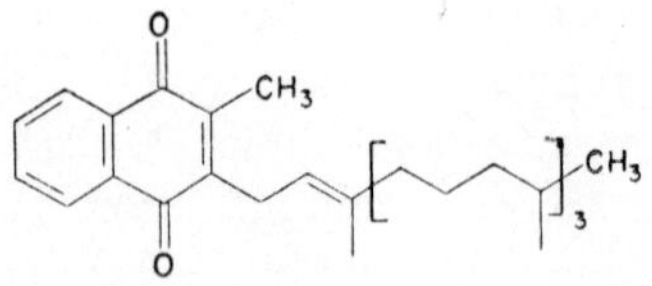

(50) Vitamin K_1

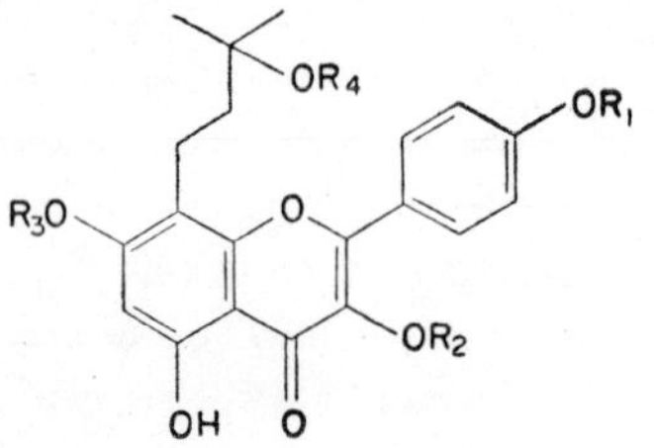

(53) Icariin, R_1 = Me; R_2 = rhamnosidyl; R_3 = H; R_4 = glucosidyl

(54) Amurensin, R_1 = H; R_2 = H; R_3 = glucosidyl; R_4 = H

Further structural variations can be recognized. The double bond of a
γγ-dimethylallyl precursor may be modified by oxidation to the corresponding isopentenyl epoxide which in turn may be hydrolysed to an iso-
pentane-diol. The coumarins oxypeucedanin (55),[47] aculeatin (56),[48] auraptene (57),[49] and byakangelicol (58)[50] are examples of dimethylallyl epoxides.

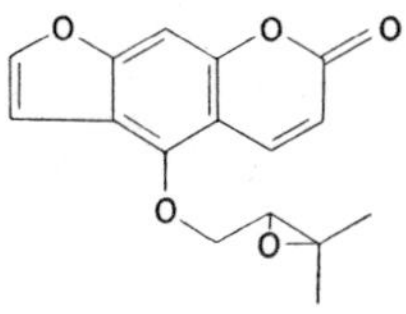

(55) Oxypeucedanin

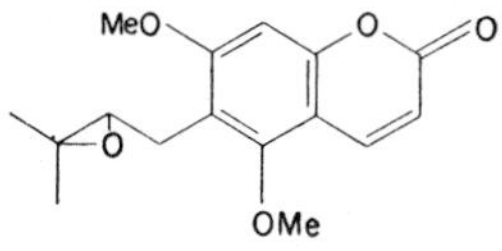

(56) Aculeatin

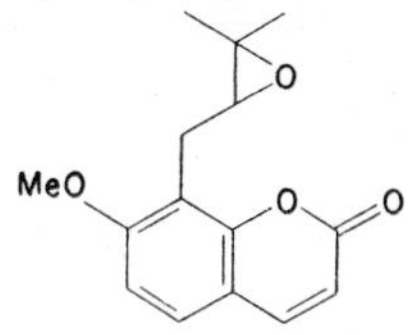

(57) Auraptene

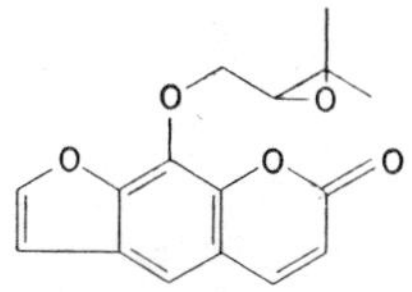

(58) Byakangelicol

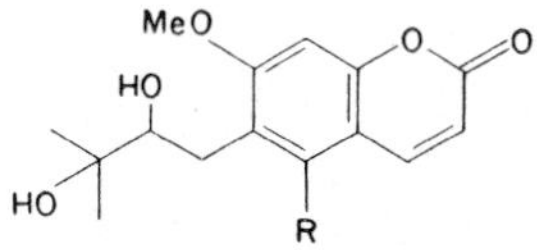

(59) Toddalolactone ,R =OMe

(60) Osthol,R =H

The coumarins toddalolactone (59),[51] osthol (60),[52] byakangelicin (61),[50]
and ostruthol (62)[54] and the alkaloid evoxine (63)[55] are 2,3-dihydroxyiso-
pentanyl derivatives.

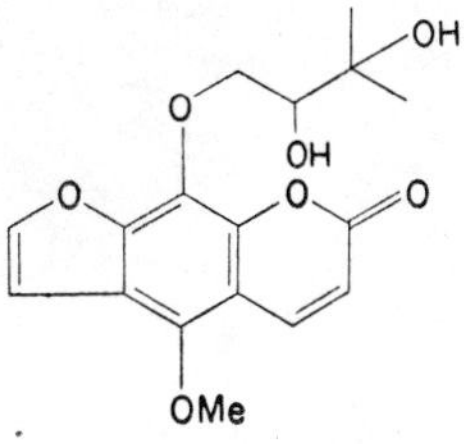

(61) Byakangelicin

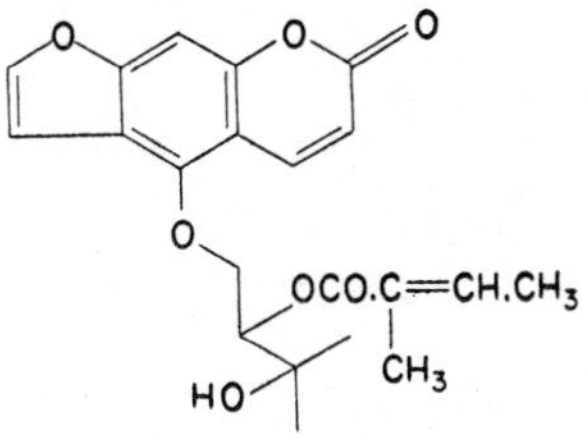

(62) Ostruthol

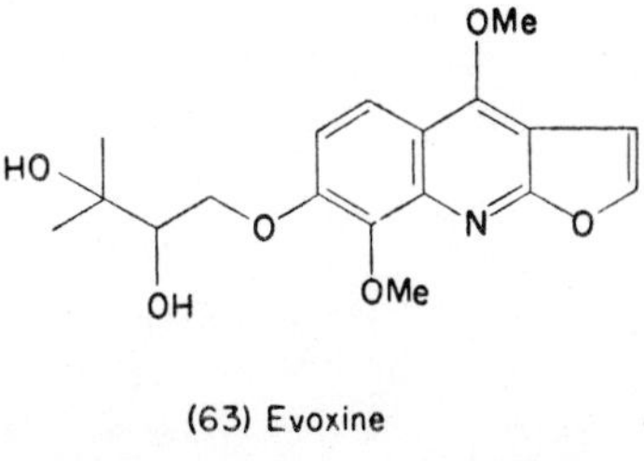

(63) Evoxine

It is difficult to be precise about the stage at which alkylation occurs in
the biogenesis of these compounds. It is reasonable to assume that O-
alkylation occurs at a late stage. It is likely that C-alkylation also occurs at

a late stage, for those aromatic rings which are derived from carbohydrate.[56] The poly-β-keto acid precursors of many aromatic compounds would, however, be systems which would undergo facile alkylation by a cationoid reagent, and it has been suggested[57] that in this case introduction of a C_5 unit is akin to methylation. The isolation of the rotenoid munduserone (64)[58] suggests that in the case of the rotenoids alkylation of the (probably) acetate derived aromatic A ring occurs at a late stage in its biosynthesis. This may

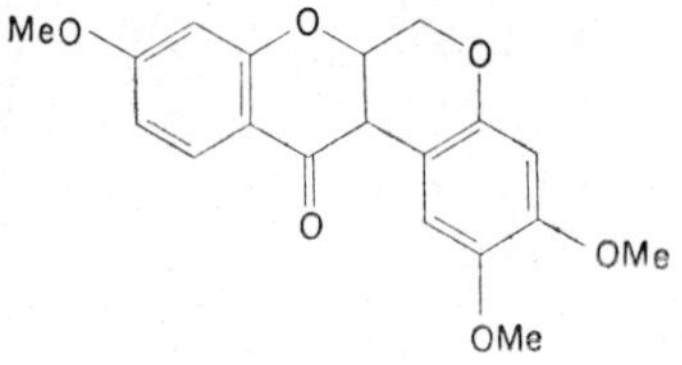

(64) Munduserone

well apply more generally, but alkylation of the poly-β-keto-precursors of aromatic compounds is certainly an acceptable alternative biosynthetic process. Biochemical evidence is not yet available to show the order in which these processes can occur.

2,2-Dimethylchromenes and Derivatives

The most frequently occurring arrangement of the C_5-unit in aromatic natural products is in derivatives of 2,2-*dimethylchromene*. The formation of a 2,2-dimethylchromene from a C-dimethylallyl-phenol precursor involves

(65)

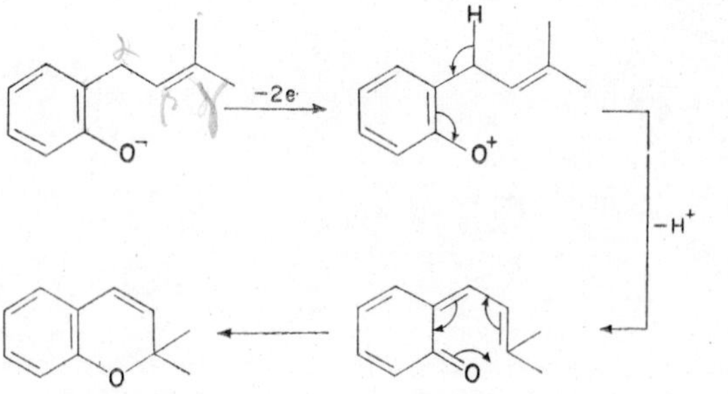

oxidation, and it is suggested that the scheme indicated above (see 65) provides a suitable mechanism for such a transformation. The reaction is initiated by the oxidation of the phenol anion, followed by the loss of the benzylic proton to give an o-methylenequinone intermediate, which can then cyclize to a 2,2-dimethylchromene.

This is similar to the mechanism proposed[59] for the biosynthetic transformation of dopamine (66) to norepinephrine (67). In this case, however, the

1,6-addition of water to a *p*-methylenequinone intermediate results in the appearance of a benzylic hydroxyl group.

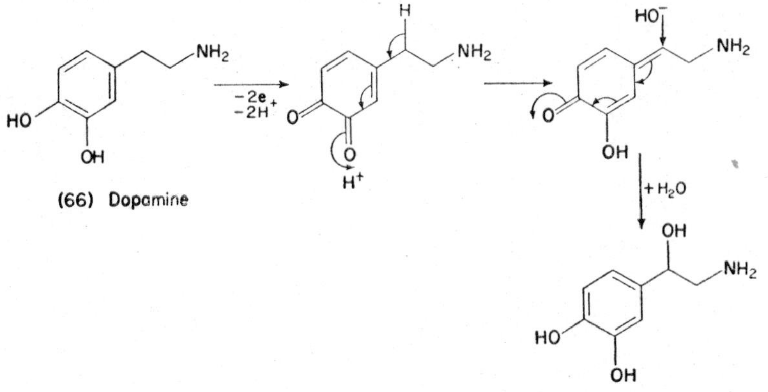

(66) Dopamine

(67) Norepinephrine

The cyclization of the polyisoprenylated quinones, ubiquinone (68)[44] and Kofler's quinone (69)[7] to 2,2-disubstituted chromenes is base-catalysed and the mechanism indicated below for this transformation[60] is closely analogous to the mechanism now proposed for the biosynthesis of 2,2-dimethylchromene systems.

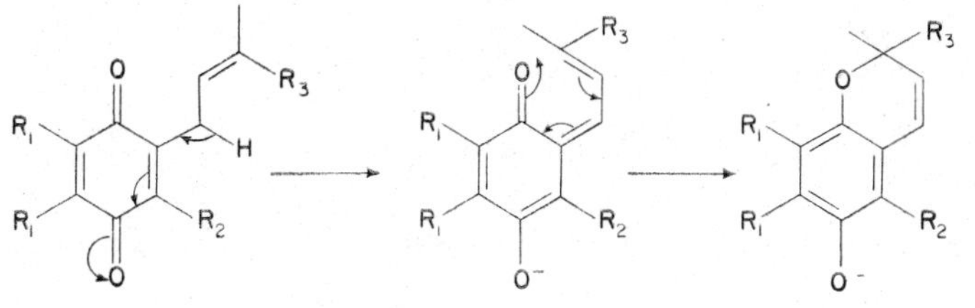

(68) Ubiquinone, R_1 = OMe, R_2 = Me

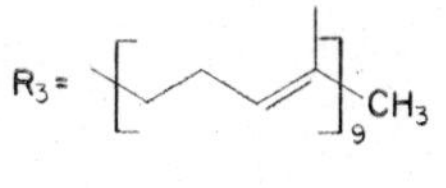

$$R_3 = \left[\begin{array}{c}\\\end{array}\right]_9 CH_3$$

(69) Kofler's quinone, R_1 = Me, R_2 = H

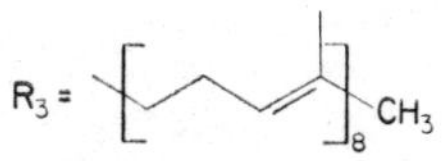

$$R_3 = \left[\begin{array}{c}\\\end{array}\right]_8 CH_3$$

A diagnostic laboratory reaction of $\gamma\gamma$-dimethylallyl-*o*-hydroxybenzene derivatives is their acid-catalysed cyclization to the corresponding 2,2-dimethylchroman (70). The conditions required in the laboratory are generally quite vigorous and it is possible that competing biochemical processes lead to 2,2-dimethylchromenes rather than 2,2-dimethylchromans. Whereas many examples of 2,2-dimethylchromenes are known, the mould metabolite fuscin (71)[61] appears to be the only example of a naturally occurring 2,2-dimethylchroman; the biosynthesis in this case could involve either the reduction of a chromene or the more likely direct cyclization (see 70) of a dimethylallyl precursor.

The variety of natural products which contain 2,2-dimethylchromene

(70)

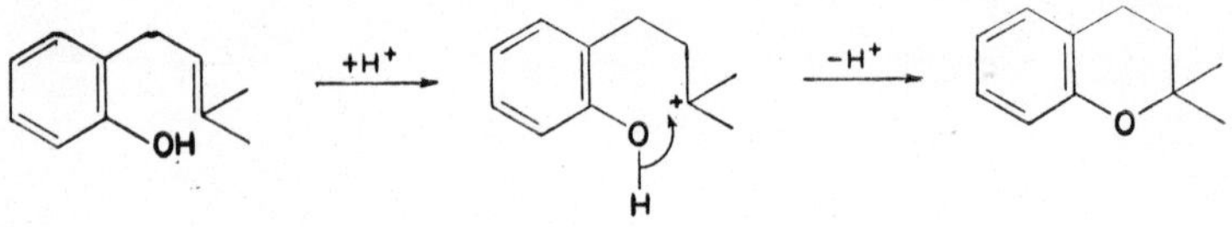

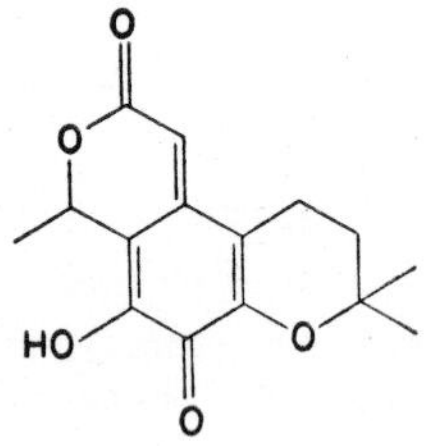

(71) Fuscin

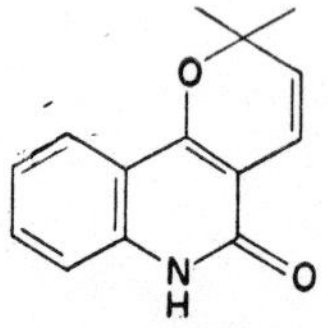

(72) Flindersine

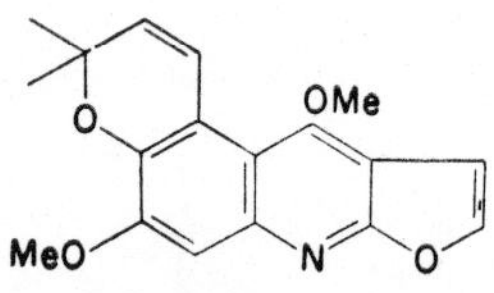

(73) Acronidine

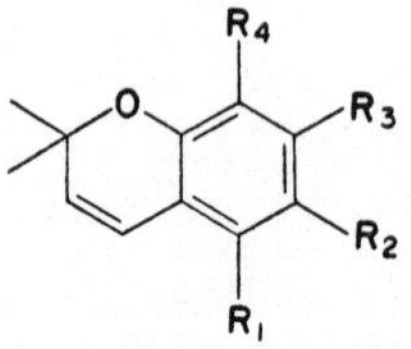

(74) Evodione, $R_1 = R_3 = R_4 = OMe$; $R_2 = COCH_3$
(75) Alloevodione, $R_1 = R_2 = R_3 = OMe$; $R_4 = COCH_3$
(76) Evodionol, $R_1 = OMe$; $R_3 = R_4 = OH$; $R_2 = COCH_3$
(77) Alloevodionol, $R_1 = OMe$; $R_2 = H$; $R_3 = OH$; $R_4 = COCH_3$
(78) Alloevodionol methyl ether, $R_1 = R_3 = OMe$; $R_2 = H$; $R_4 = COCH_3$
(79) Ageratochromene, $R_2 = R_3 = OMe$; $R_1 = R_4 = H$

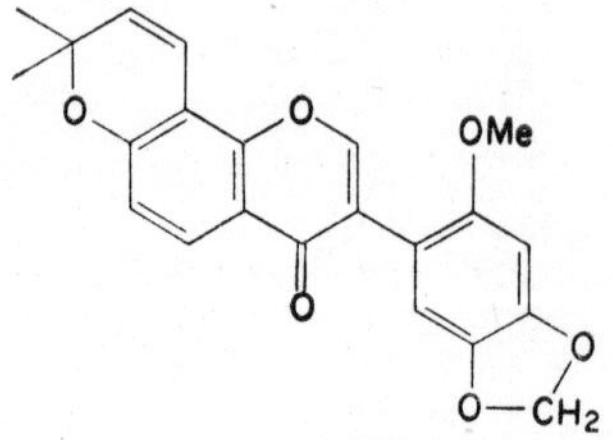

(80) Jamaicin

residues is illustrated by the occurrence of the quinolone (72),[62] the quinolines (73)[63] and (10),[11] the acridone (11),[12] the closely related chromenes (74),[64] (75),[65] (76),[65] (77),[65] (78),[65] and (79),[126] the isoflavones (17),[17] (16),[17] and (80),[66] the rotenoids (81)[67] and (82),[67] the coumarins (83),[69,71] (84),[70] (85),[71] (86),[29] (87),[73] and (88),[74] the naphthalene derivative (3),[4] the xanthone (89),[75] the chalkone (19)[19] and rottlerin (90),[76] calophyllolide (91)[77] and inophyllolide (92).[77]

2,2-Dimethylchromenes are also likely precursors of 3,4-chromandiol derivatives (94). Their formation by an oxidation mechanism involving

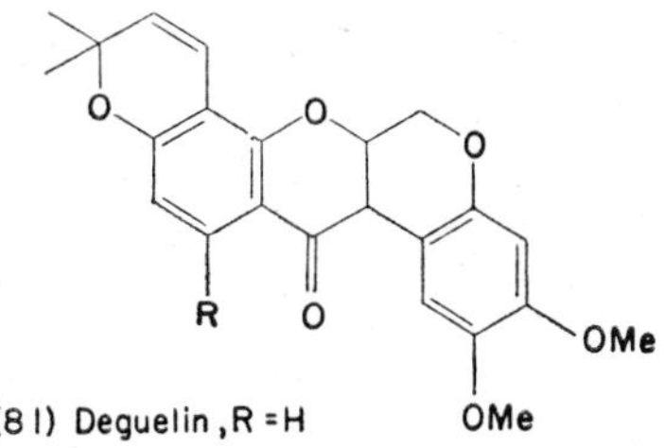

(81) Deguelin, R = H
(82) Toxicarol, R = OH

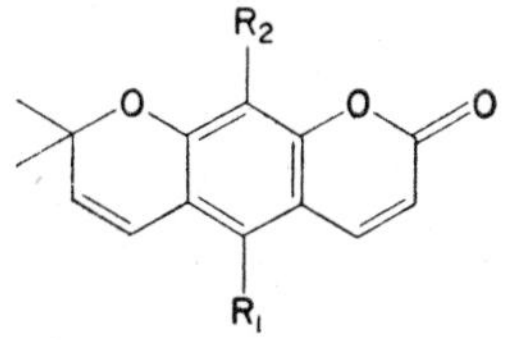

(83) Xanthoxyletin, R_1=OMe; R_2=H
(84) Luvangetin, R_1=H; R_2=OMe
(85) Xanthyletin, R_1=R_2= H

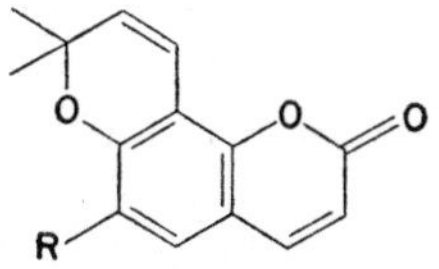

(86) Braylin, R = OMe
(87) Seselin, R = H

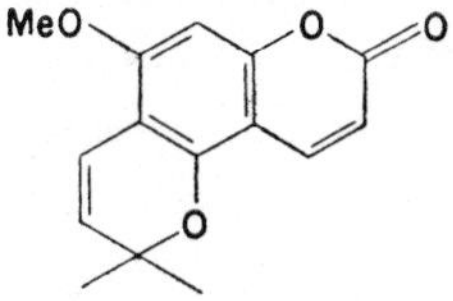

(88) Alloxanthoxyletin

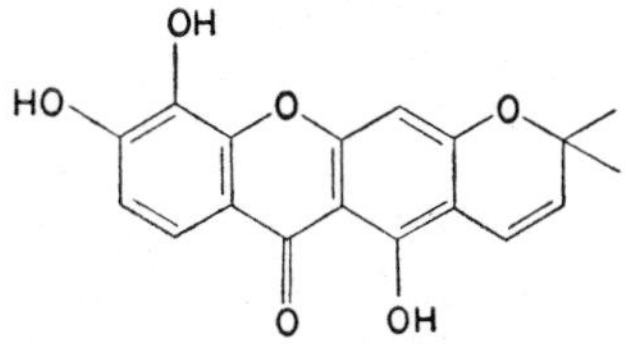

(89) Jacareubin

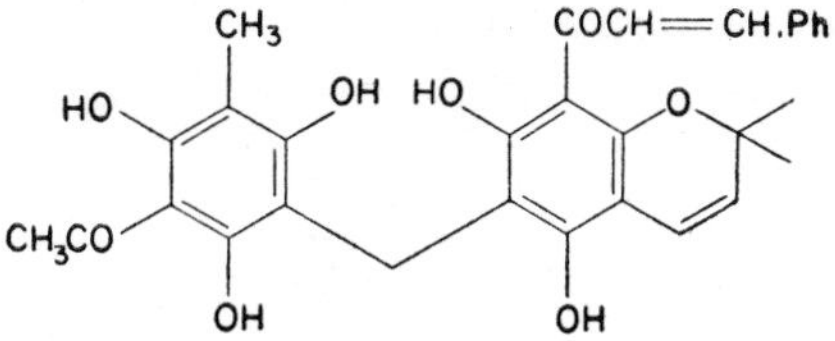

(90) Rottlerin

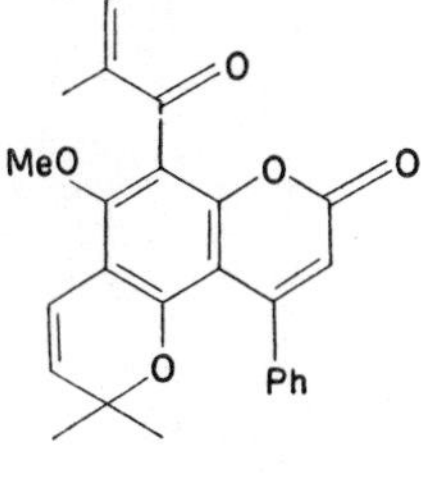

(91) Calophyllolide

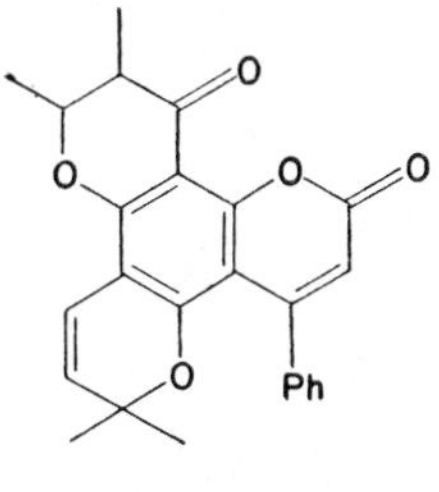

(92) Inophyllolide

intermediate formation of the epoxide (93) or an equivalent reaction would account for the *trans* stereochemistry of the hydroxyl groups. The closely related coumarins dihydrosamidin (95),[78,79] samidin (96),[78,79] and visnadin (97)[78,79] are naturally occurring esters of the diol, khellactone (98), which was synthesized by mild acidic hydrolysis of seselin epoxide.[79]

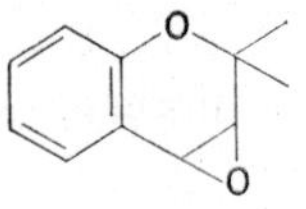

(93)

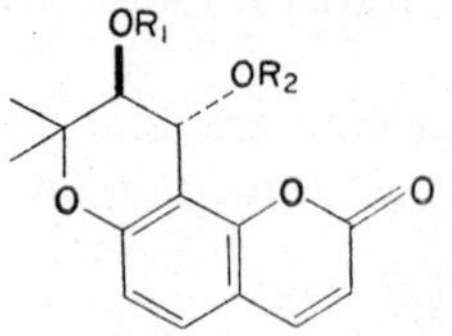

(95) Dihydrosamidin, R_1 = COCH$_2$CHMe$_2$; R_2 = COCH$_3$

(96) Samidin, R_1 = COCH═CMe$_2$; R_2 = COCH$_3$

(97) Visnadin, R_1 = COCH.MeEt; R_2 = COCH$_3$

(98) Khellactone, R_1 = R_2 = H

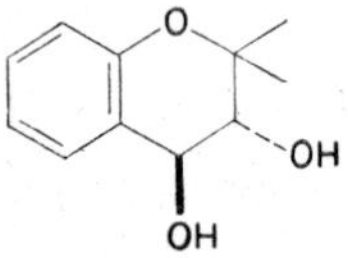

(94)

Hydroxyisopropyl-dihydrobenzfurans and Derivatives

Acid catalysed ring closure of $\gamma\gamma$-dimethylallyl epoxides (99) would be expected to yield hydroxyisopropyl-dihydrobenzfurans (100); dehydration can then lead to isopropenyl-dihydrobenzfurans (101) or to isopropyl-benzfurans (102) by rearrangement.

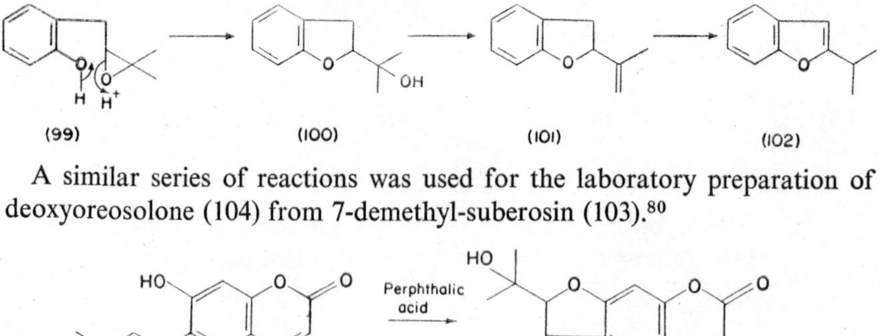

(99)   (100)   (101)   (102)

A similar series of reactions was used for the laboratory preparation of deoxyoreosolone (104) from 7-demethyl-suberosin (103).[80]

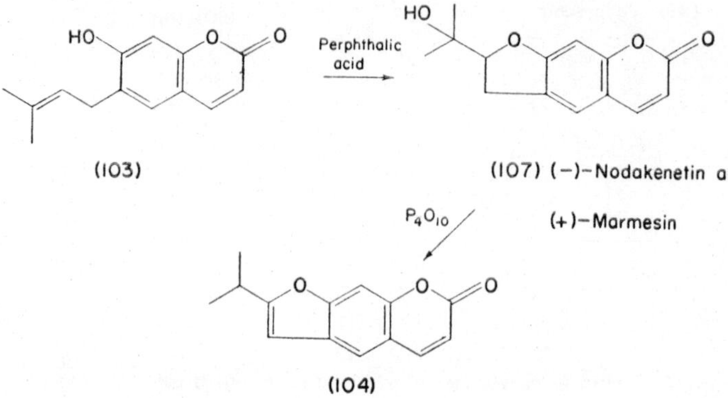

(103)   (107) (−)−Nodakenetin and

(+)−Marmesin

(104)

Examples of hydroxyisopropyl-dihydrobenzfurans and their anhydro-derivatives include rotenone (15),[16] munetone (105),[81] visamminol (106),[82] and the optical isomers nodakenetin (107)[83] and marmesin (107).[84] Further structural variety is produced by oxidation and dehydration of either the hydroxyisopropyl-dihydrofuran, or an acyclic precursor. This leads to compounds such as peucedanin (108),[85] oreoselone (109),[85] oroselone (110),[86] athamantin (111)[86] and euparin (112).[87]

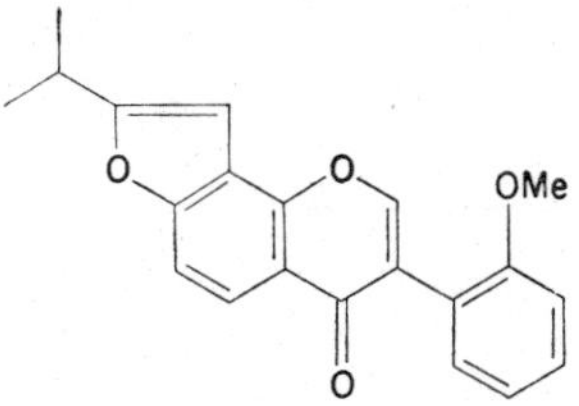

(105) Munetone

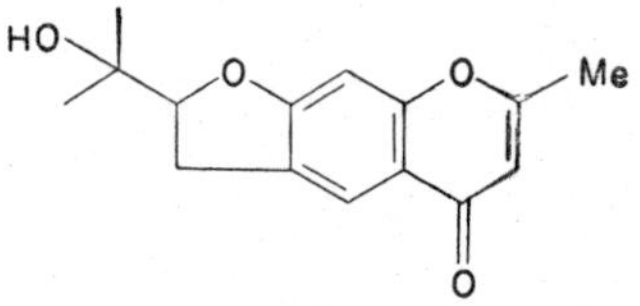

(106) Visamminol

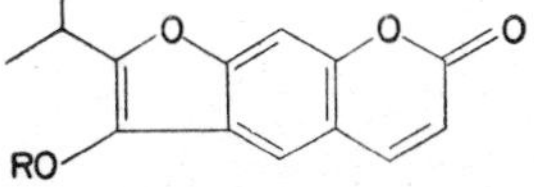

(108) Peucedanin, R = CH₃

(109) Oreoselone, R = H

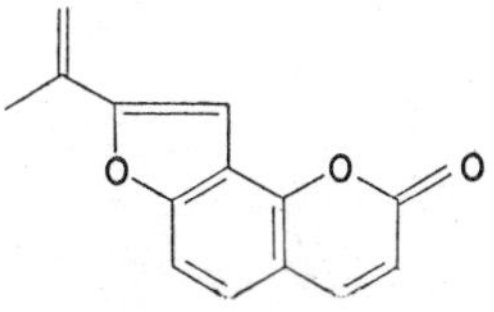

(110) Oroselone

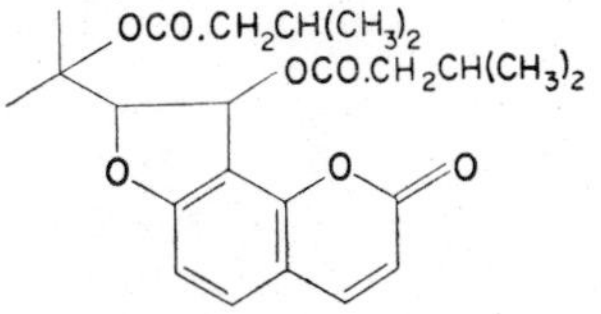

(111) Athamantin

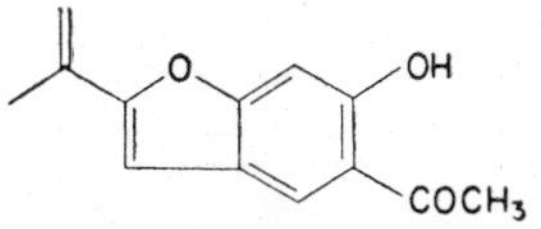

(112) Euparin

It has been suggested by Birch[57] and by Seshadri[30] that the C_2 unit of benzfurans could have been derived originally from a C_5 unit; it was pointed out that the oxidized hydroxyisopropyl-dihydrobenzfuran precursor (113) would readily lose acetone by a reverse aldol reaction, and that the product (114) could be converted into the benzfuran (115) by reduction.

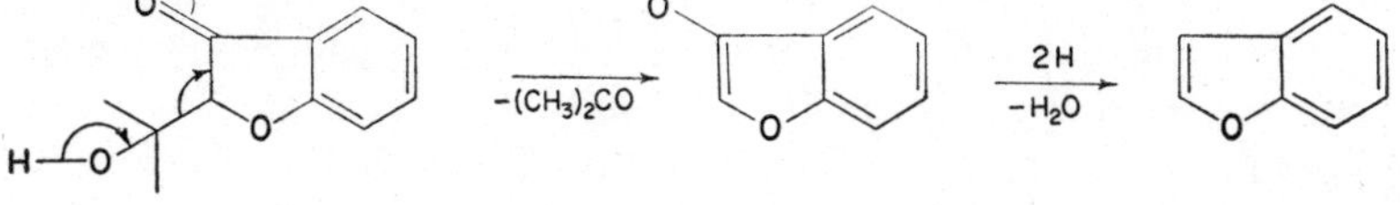

(113)

(114)

(115)

As evidence for this relationship, both authors quote the occurrence of natural products which have C_5 side chains in addition to the C_2 (furan)

7

substituent, as in for example the coumarins oxypeucedanin (55), byakangelicol (58), byakangelicin (61) and ostruthol (62), and the quinolines acronidine (73), evoxine (63) and medicosmine (10). Additional evidence to suggest this relationship is afforded by the co-occurrence in many plants of similar compounds having either a C_2 (furan) group or a C_5 side chain, as in for example the rotenoids rotenone (116), deguelin (117), and elliptone (118) which all

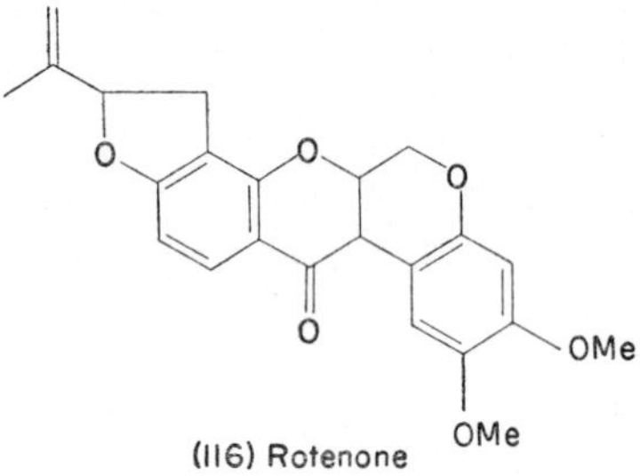

(116) Rotenone

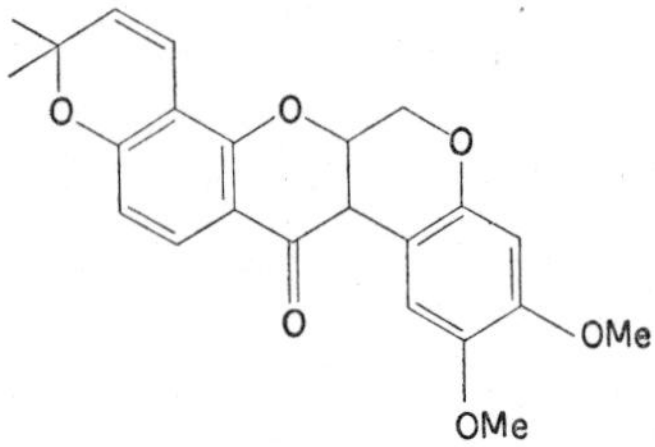

(117) Deguelin

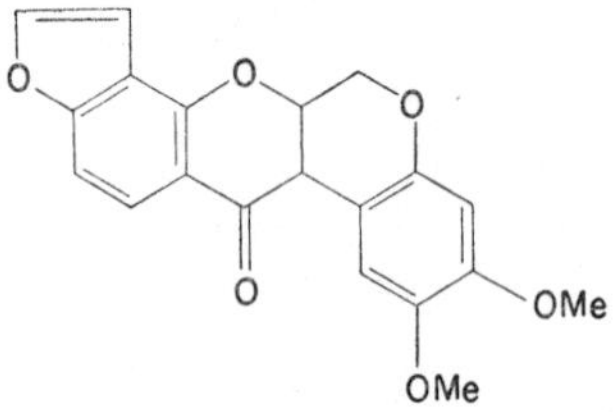

(118) Elliptone

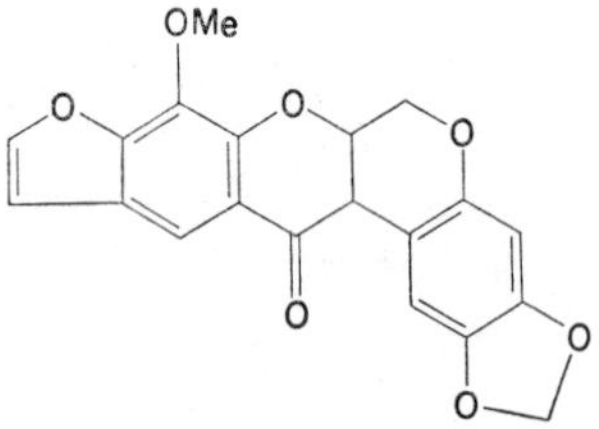

(119) Pachyrrhizone

occur in *Derris elliptica*.[67] Rotenone (116) and pachyrrhizone (119) occur together in the seed of *Pachyrrhizus erosus*.[88]

STRUCTURAL DETERMINATIONS

It is not possible to review all the methods which have been used in the structural elucidation of these compounds, but some of the physical and chemical methods which have been used in the determination of the structures of C_5 units in natural products are illustrated by the examples outlined below. The increasingly important role now played by physical methods in such structural determinations is clearly evident. Frequently complex compounds containing C_5 units may be degraded to compounds of known structure containing the unmodified C_5 unit, as in the degradation of mundulone[89] to β-tubaic acid methyl ether. In other cases it has been necessary to study the reactions of the side chain while it was still attached to the complex molecule. The general reactions of dimethyallyl and 2,2-dimethyl-chromene derivatives are considered, since these are probably the two most frequently occurring types of C_5 unit.

γγ-Dimethylallyl Derivatives

$\gamma\gamma$-Dimethylallyl ethers are easily recognized, since acid catalysed cleavage of the ether linkage occurs readily yielding the corresponding phenol with loss of the C_5 unit. The presence of a double bond in the side chain can be demonstrated by the formation of a dibromide; hydrogenation may result in hydrogenolysis of the allylic ether linkage.

Compounds bearing a $\gamma\gamma$-dimethylallyl substituent on an aromatic ring are recognized by ready hydrogenation of the double bond and by their infrared absorption characteristics which are typical of a trisubstituted ethylene (ν_{max} 790–840 cm^{-1})[90] and of a *gem*-dimethyl group (ν_{max} 1385–1380, 1370–1365 cm^{-1}).[90] Phenols having an o-$\gamma\gamma$-dimethylallyl substituent cyclize to the corresponding isomeric chromans on treatment with strong acid (120).

(120)

It is of interest that alkaline fusion of mangostin (121) produced some 2-methyl-2-hepten-6-ol (122),[91] derivable from the $\gamma\gamma$-dimethylallyl substituent and the phloroglucinol nucleus.[13]

(121) Mangostin   (122)

Novobiocin (123)

The antibiotic novobiocin[10,93] was isolated from *Streptomyces spheroides* (Cathomycin)[94] and *S. niveus* (Streptonivicin).[95] The presence and location of an $Me_2C=CH-CH_2-$ group was established in the following way. Cleavage of the amide linkage of novobiocin (123) by acetic anhydride followed by alkaline hydrolysis of the acetyl compound (125) yielded the substituted benzoic acid, $C_{12}H_{14}O_3$ (126), which was identified as a *p*-hydroxy-benzoic acid (C_7) with a C_5 substituent. The ultraviolet spectrum of this acid, $C_{12}H_{14}O_3$ showed that the double bond, known to be in the side chain from hydrogenation studies, was unconjugated. Infrared absorption (ν_{max} 842 cm^{-1}) suggested that the double bond was trisubstituted, and oxidation with osmium tetroxide followed by periodic acid yielded acetone demonstrating the presence of the $Me_2C{<}$group. Finally, acid-catalysed cyclization of (126) yielded the isomeric chroman (124) which could also be obtained from novobiocin by acidic cleavage of the glycosidic linkage followed by acetic anhydride rupture of the amide linkage.

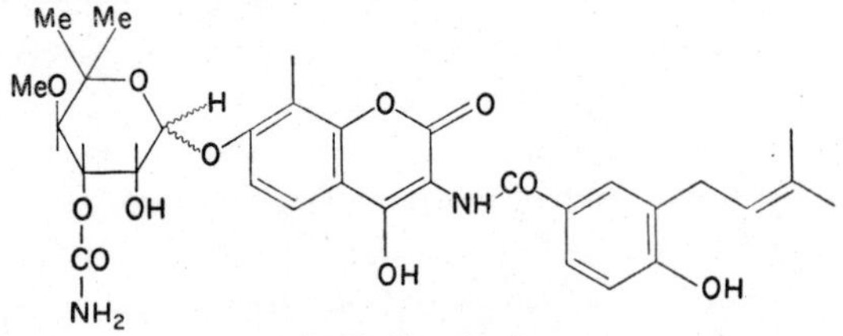

(123) Novobiocin

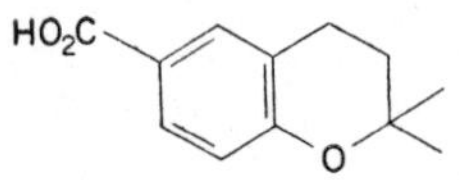

(124)

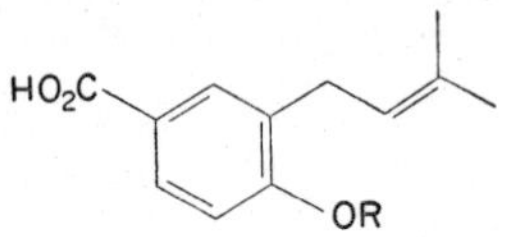

(125) R = COCH₃

(126) R = H

5-Hydroxy-3',7-dimethoxy-4'-γγ-dimethylallyloxyflavanone (127)

This flavanone (127) was isolated by Geissman from the bark of the rutaceous tree, *Melicope sarcococca*.[32] The compound $C_{20}H_{18}O_4(OMe)_2$ was shown to be a 5-hydroxyflavanone derivative by its ultraviolet spectrum and

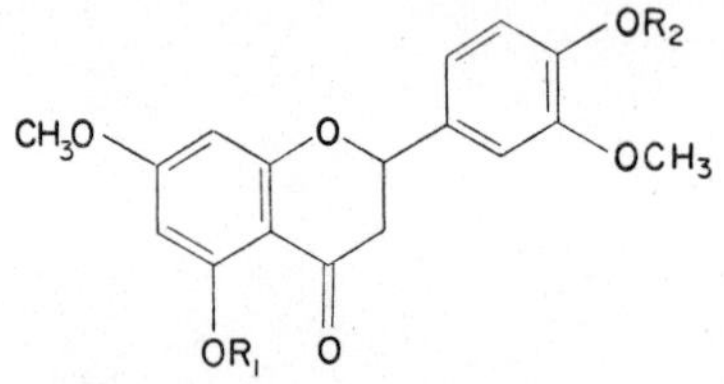

(127) R₁ = H, R₂ = CH₂CH═CMe₂
(128) R₁ = R₂ = Me
(129) R₁ = R₂ = H

by colour tests, and to contain ethereal oxygen substituents on the 7, 3', and 4' positions by conversion to luteolin tetramethyl ether (128). Mild acidic hydrolysis of the flavanone (127) yielded the dihydroxy compound (129) with a loss of a C_5 fragment. Since the flavanone (127) did not yield veratric acid on oxidation it was concluded that the C_5 substituent was located on either the 3'- or 4'-oxygens, and the 4'-position was favoured by colour tests.

The facility of the acid-catalysed removal of the C_5 residue suggested that the cleavage of an allylic ether was involved. The natural product was further characterized as (127) by the formation of acetone on chromic acid oxidation, the preparation of a dibromide and by a Kuhn-Roth oxidation which yielded rather less than one molecule of acetic acid.

Brayleyanin (130)

Extraction of *Flindersia brayleyana* yielded brayleyanin (130)[29] which was shown to be a 6-methoxy coumarin with two C_5 substituents. One of these C_5 units was shown to be a $\gamma\gamma$-dimethylallyl group linked *via* oxygen to the

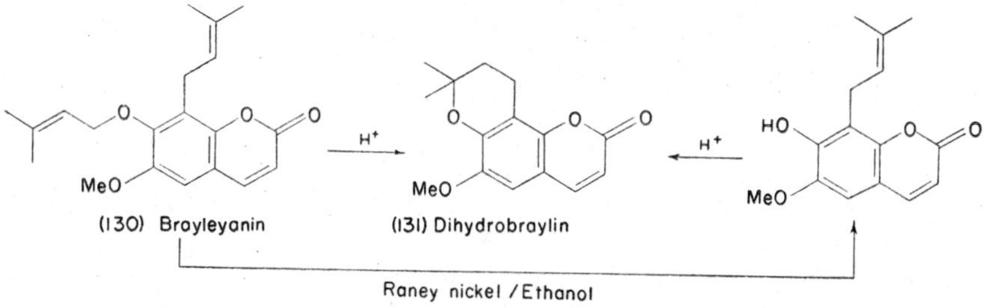

(130) Brayleyanin   (131) Dihydrobraylin

Raney nickel / Ethanol

aromatic ring since it was readily removed by hydrogenation or by acidic hydrolysis. The latter reaction yielded dihydrobraylin (131) from which it follows that the second C_5 unit was a C-$\gamma\gamma$-dimethylallyl substituent at the 8 position of the coumarin. This structural proposal for brayleyanin was shown to be correct by an unambiguous synthesis of the natural product.

Evoxine (132)

The furoquinoline alkaloid evoxine was extracted from the leaves of the rutaceous tree *Evodia xanthoxyloides*.[55] Evoxine, $C_{17}H_{18}O_6N.OCH_3$, (132) was shown to be a 4-methoxyquinoline derivative by the ease of its acid-catalysed

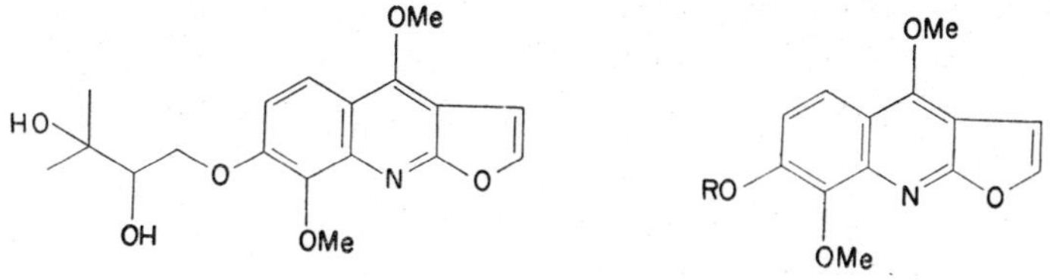

(132) Evoxine

(133) R = H

(134) Skimmianine, R = Me

(135) R = Et

demethylation. Alkaline fusion of evoxine yielded a phenol (133) which gave skimmianine (134) on methylation. Ethylation of the phenol (133) gave a product identical with the synthetic compound (135), thus locating the $C_5H_{11}O_3$ group in evoxine. The remaining problem was to determine the nature of this $C_5H_{11}O_3$ group which must be linked ethereally to the 7-position of the quinoline nucleus since evoxine did not contain a free phenolic hydroxyl group. Evoxine yielded a diacetate, characterizing the two unlocated oxygens as alcoholic, and acetone on periodate oxidation.

The other product of periodate oxidation, the aldehyde (136), was readily converted to the phenol (133) by alkaline peroxide oxidation. These reactions proved the $C_5H_{11}O_3$ residue to be a 2,3-dihydroxyisopentanyloxy unit and evoxine to be (132).

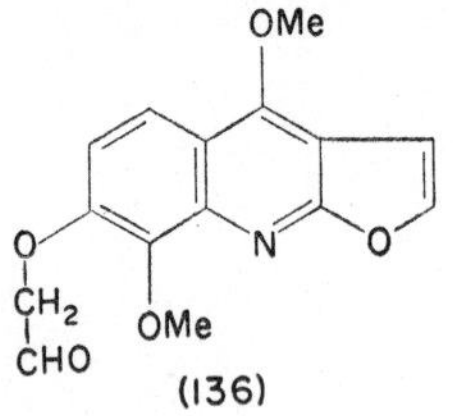

2,2-*Dimethylchromenes and Derivatives*

2,2-Dimethylchromenes are readily reduced to chromans with a corresponding change in their ultraviolet spectra. Such compounds on vigorous oxidation yield α-hydroxyisobutyric acid and milder oxidation cleaves the

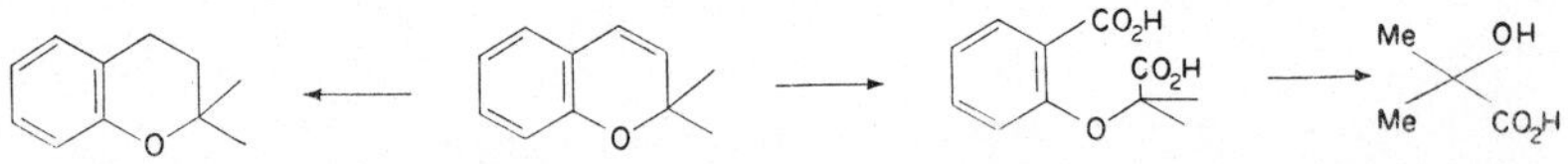

chromene double bond to give a dicarboxylic acid which yields α-hydroxyisobutyric acid on pyrolysis. These reactions are illustrated by the general degradative scheme (137). Vigorous alkaline hydrolysis of 2,2-dimethylchromenes yields acetone and acetaldehyde,[53,96] but this reaction can only occur if a phenolic hydroxyl group is suitably located on the benzene ring to permit the cleavage reaction which is of the reverse aldol type [see (138)].

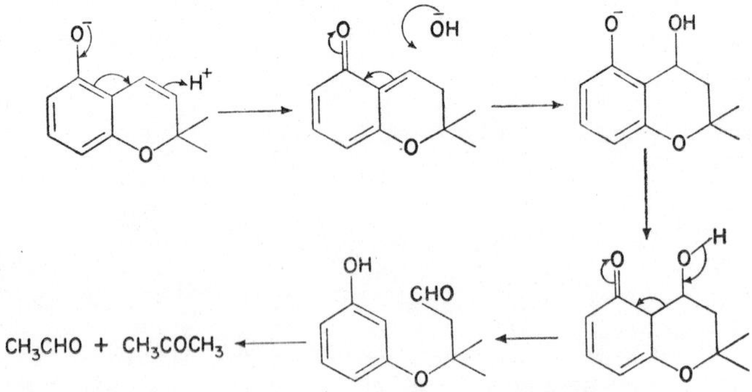

Lapachenole (140)

The factor in the wood of *Paratecoma alba* (Brazilian white peroba) which causes dermatitis was identified as lapachenole,[4] $C_{15}H_{13}O.OCH_3$. Lapachenole was neutral and inert to lithium aluminium hydride reduction, so it was concluded that both oxygen atoms were ethereal. Lapachenole was readily converted to a dihydro-derivative which had an ultraviolet spectrum resembling that of 1,4-dimethoxynaphthalene (139) and was distinct from that of lapachenole. Permanganate oxidation of lapachenole (140) yielded the dicarboxylic acid (141), which on lithium aluminium hydride reduction gave the diol (142). This diol (142) by a pinacolic transformation gave isobutyralde-hyde on treatment with sulphuric acid. The structure (140) for lapachenole was further confirmed by the presence of an infrared absorption band (ν_{max} 684 cm^{-1}) characteristic of a cis-CH=CH group.

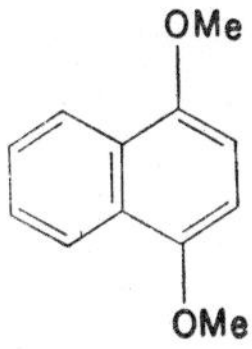

(139)

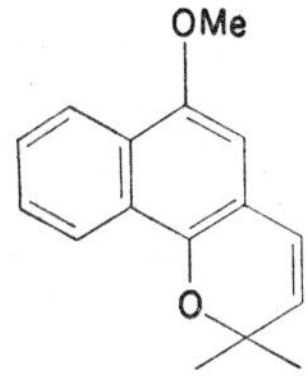

(140) Lapachenole

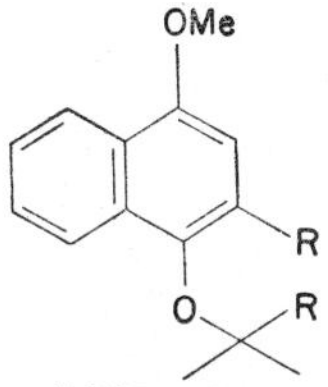

(141) R=CO$_2$H

(142) R=CH$_2$OH

Lapachenole was unstable to acids yielding a dimer (143) containing no ethylenic double bonds. The indirect acid-catalysed dimerization of 2,2-dimethylchromene itself has been reported to yield an analogous dimer (144).[97]

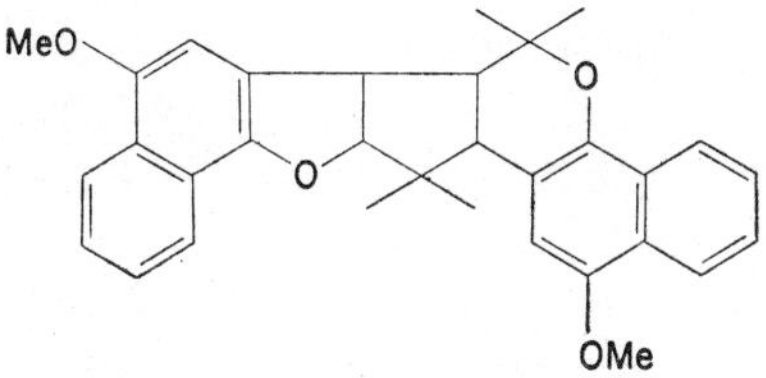

(143)

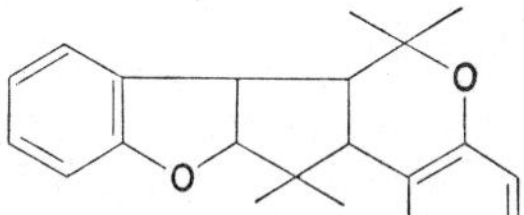

(144)

Braylin (145)

Flindersia brayleyana yielded the coumarin braylin, $C_{14}H_{11}O_3 \cdot OCH_3$,[29] in addition to brayleyanin. Braylin (145) was shown to be a methoxy coumarin with a C_5-substituent which contained a reducible double bond. Alkaline

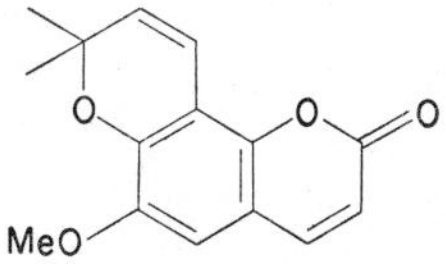

(145) Braylin

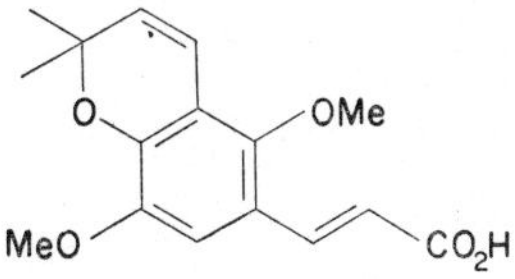

(146)

hydrolysis of braylin yielded acetone and 4-methoxyresorcinol. Permanganate oxidation of the dimethoxy cinnamic acid (146) derived from braylin gave α-hydroxyisobutyric acid. These reactions indicated that braylin was a derivative of 2,2-dimethylchromene. The position of the C_5-substituent was established by the chemical relationship between braylin and brayleyanin (130) which involved the conversion of brayleyanin to dihydrobraylin (see p. 93).

Acronycine (147)

The alkaloid acronycine, $C_{18}H_{13}OCH_3.NCH_3$, was obtained from the rutaceous plant *Acronychia baueri*.[21,92] Nitric acid oxidation of acronycine (147) yielded the carboxylic acid (148), the structure of which was proved

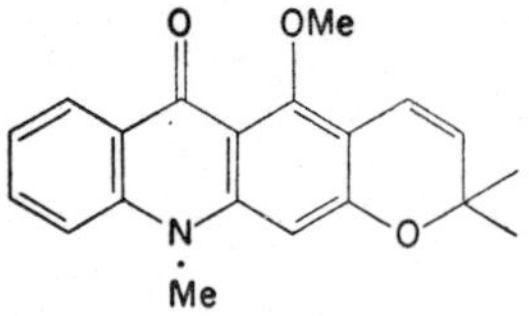

(147) Acronycine

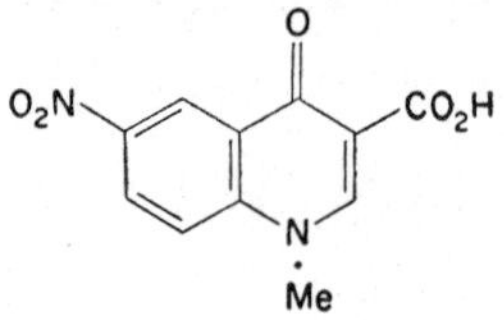

(148)

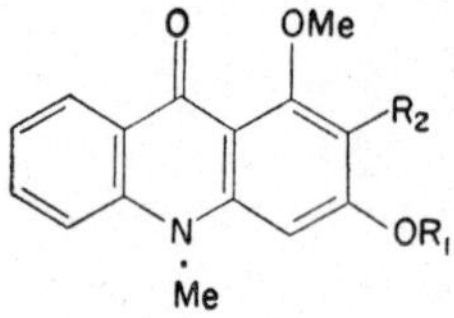

(149) $R_1 = CMe_2.CO_2H; R_2 = CO_2H$
(150) $R_1 = CMe_2.CO_2H; R_2 = H$
(151) $R_1 = R_2 = H$
(152) $R_1 = H; R_2 = CHO$
(153) $R_1 = Me, R_2 = CO_2H$

by comparison with the synthetic compound. Permanganate oxidation of acronycine yielded the dicarboxylic acid (149) which readily lost carbon dioxide to give acronycinic acid (150). Pyrolysis of acronycinic acid yielded the phenol (151) and α-hydroxyisobutyric acid. These reactions established the presence of a 2,2-dimethylchromene system in acronycine. The methoxyl group was shown to be in the 4-position by the easy demethylation of acronycine on treatment with acid, and structure (147) for acronycine then follows. Further confirmation of this structure was provided by ozonolysis of acronycine to give the aldehyde (152), which was converted by methylation, oxidation, and decarboxylation of the resulting acid (153) to 2,4-dimethoxy-10-methylacridone.

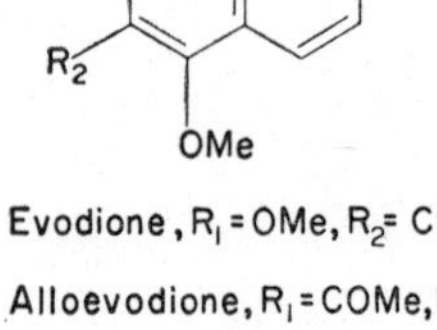

(154) Evodione, $R_1 = OMe, R_2 = COMe$
(157) Alloevodione, $R_1 = COMe, R_2 = OMe$

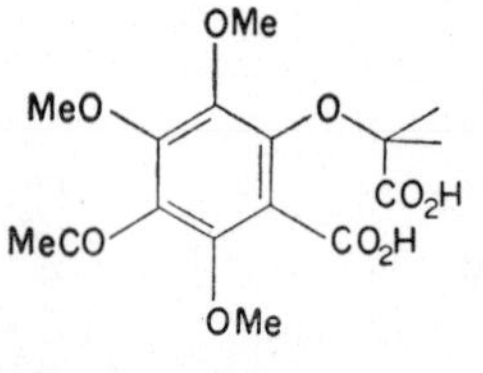

(155)

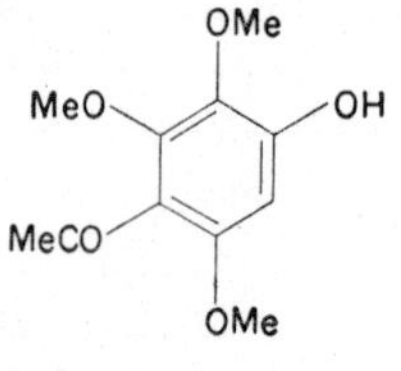

(156)

Evodione (154) and Alloevodione (157)

Evodione, $C_{13}H_{11}O_2(OCH_3)_3$,[64] was shown to contain one double bond and a reactive carbonyl group. Oxidation of evodione (154) with permanganate yielded the dicarboxylic acid (155) which gave α-hydroxyisobutyric acid and the phenol (156) on pyrolysis. The structure of the phenol was confirmed by synthesis. By a similar series of reactions the compound alloevodione[65] was shown to possess the isomeric structure (157).

Mundulone (158)

The isoflavone mundulone, $C_{25}H_{23}O_5.OCH_3$, was obtained by extraction of the root bark of *Mundulea sericea*.[89] Mundulone (158) was shown to be an isoflavone since alkaline hydrolysis readily yielded the deoxybenzoin munduletone (159) which could be converted back into mundulone by the action of ethylorthoformate in pyridine-piperidine. Mundulone contained an alcoholic hydroxyl group and a reducible double bond. Alkaline peroxide

(158) Mundulone

(159) Munduletone, R = H
(160) R = Me

(161) R₁ = Me, R₂ = R₃ = H
(165) R₁ = R₂ = R₃ = H
(167) R₁ = R₂ = Me, R₃ = SO₂.Me

oxidation of munduletone methyl ether (160) yielded munduloxic acid methyl ether (161) and β-tubaic acid methyl ether (162); the latter was identified by comparison with the synthetic compound. Oxidation of dihydromunduletone (163) yielded a product having the composition and expected properties of dihydrohomo-β-tubaic acid methyl ether (164), and oxidation of demethylated mundulone gave munduloxic acid (165). Thus, the part structure (166) was deduced for mundulone and the remaining problem was the identification of the C_5 unit present in munduloxic acid.

Munduloxic acid was shown to be a salicylic acid with an ethereal oxygen substituent in the 4-position. Alkaline hydrolysis of the mesyl derivative of methyl munduloxate methyl ether (167) yielded anhydromunduloxic acid methyl ether (168) in which the double bond was clearly styrenoid from its ultraviolet spectrum. Permanganate oxidation of munduloxic acid gave acetone and chromic oxide oxidation of munduloxic acid methyl ether (161)

gave an unconjugated ketone (169). The only structures for anhydromunduloxic acid methyl ether consistent with these reactions were the
isomeric chromenes (168) and (162). Anhydromunduloxic acid methyl ether
was different from β-tubaic acid methyl ether (162) and it therefore has
structure (168). The reaction of methyl β-resorcylate with 2-methylbut-3-yn-
2-ol yielded the two isomeric chromenes (170) and (171) which after

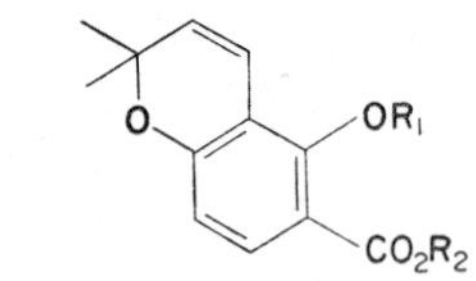

(162) R₁ = Me, R₂=H

(170) R₁= H , R₂= Me

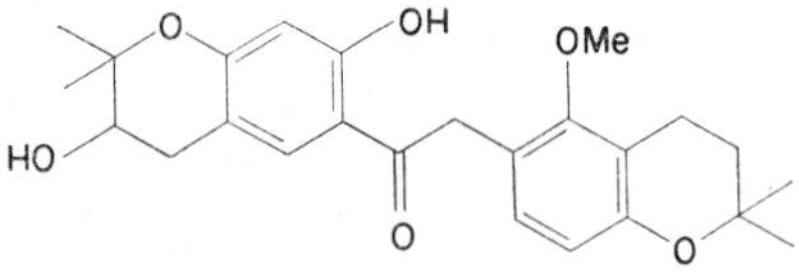

(163)

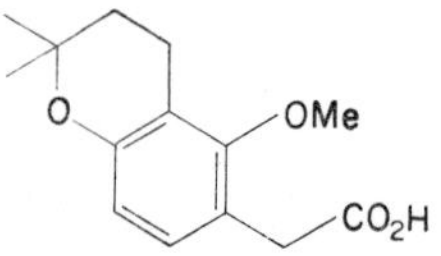

(164)

C₅H₁₁O (OH)

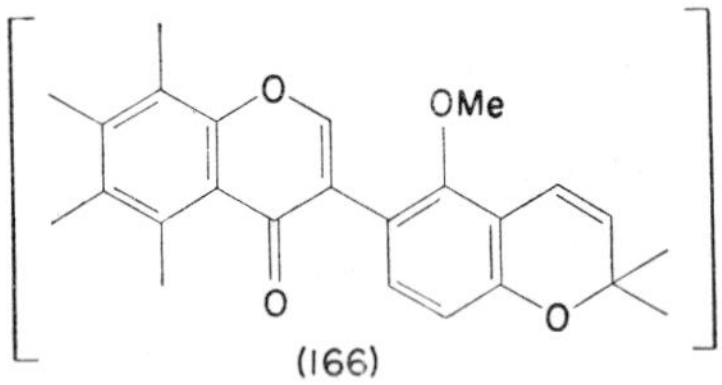

(166)

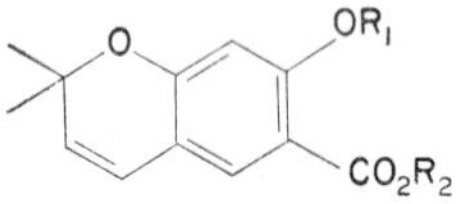

(168) R₁=Me, R₂=H

(171) R₁=H, R₂=Me

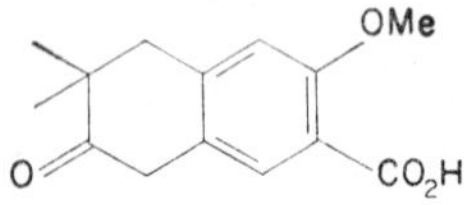

(169)

hydrolysis and methylation yielded β-tubaic acid methyl ether (162) and
anhydromunduloxic acid methyl ether (168). Thus, munduloxic acid has
the structure (165) and mundulone the structure (158). Mundulone is the
first recognized example of a naturally occurring 2,2-dimethylchroman-3-ol
and is possibly derived biogenetically by hydration of a chromene precursor.

Sericetin (173 or 174)

The flavonol sericetin, $C_{25}H_{24}O_5$, was obtained from the root bark of
Mundulea sericea.[98] Sericetin could be converted into two series of derivatives, a monoacetate, a monomethyl ether, and a monobenzoate, and a
diacetate, a dimethyl ether and a monoacetate-monomethyl ether. The ultraviolet and infrared spectra of sericetin and its derivatives indicated that it
was a 5,7-dioxygenated-flavonol derivative (172). Since alkaline fusion and
alkaline peroxide oxidation of sericetin yielded benzoic acid, the sericetin
molecule could be divided into a flavonol (C_{15}) nucleus plus two C_5 units
($C_5H_8 + C_5H_9 = C_{10}H_{17}$), both situated on ring A of the flavonol.

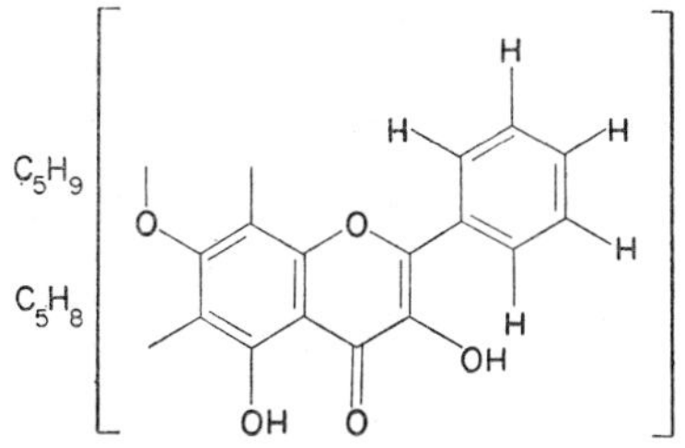

(172)

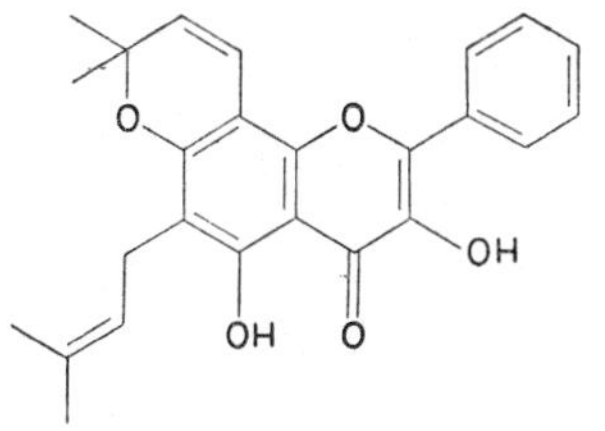

(173)

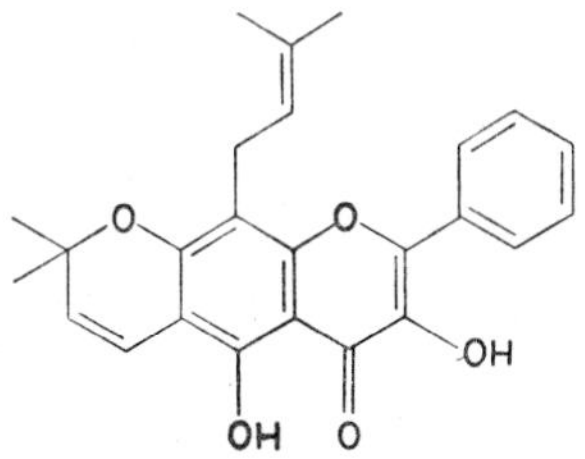

(174)

The infrared spectrum of sericetin included bands which were assigned as follows: C=C (1630 cm^{-1}); aromatic C=C (1598, 1563, 1493 cm^{-1}); Me$_2$C (1375, 1361 cm^{-1}); (Ar)O—C (tertiary) (1123 cm^{-1}); and Me$_2$CR—O (1375, 1361, 896 cm^{-1}). Sericetin and its derivatives, excluding benzoates, showed absorption in the 225–230 mμ region characteristic of a 2,2-dimethyl-chromene part structure. Kuhn-Roth oxidation of sericetin gave 1.25 equivalents of acetic acid indicating two Me$_2$C< units. These facts suggested that the C$_5$H$_8$ unit could be assigned to a 2,2-dimethylchromene residue, and the C$_5$H$_9$ unit to a $\gamma\gamma$-dimethylallyl side chain leading to either structure (173) or (174) for sericetin.

A nuclear magnetic resonance spectrum of sericetin in deuterochloroform confirmed these proposals. The spectrum at 56.4 Mcs. exhibited bands [τ values relative to benzene (relative number of protons)] which were assigned as follows: Me$_2$C [8·55 (6)]; Me$_2$C=C [8·33(3), 8·18(3)]; >CH$_2$ [6·52(2), doublet J $\sim$ 7·0 c/s]; cis-CH=CH[4·40(1), 3·29(1) doublets J $\sim$ 10·0 c/s]; chelated phenolic OH [–1·87(1)]; phenolic or enolic OH [3·20(1)]; C$_6$H$_5$ [2·57 (2), 1·85(3)].

The two possible structures (173 and 174) for the flavonol, sericetin, bear a close similarity to the structures of the isoflavones, osajin and pomiferin (175).

Fuscin (176)

Fuscin, C$_{15}$H$_{16}$O$_5$, was obtained from the mould *Oidiodendron fuscum*;[100] it was shown to be a methylene quinone with one phenolic hydroxyl group.[61,101] Alkaline fusion of fuscin (176) yielded isovaleric acid and

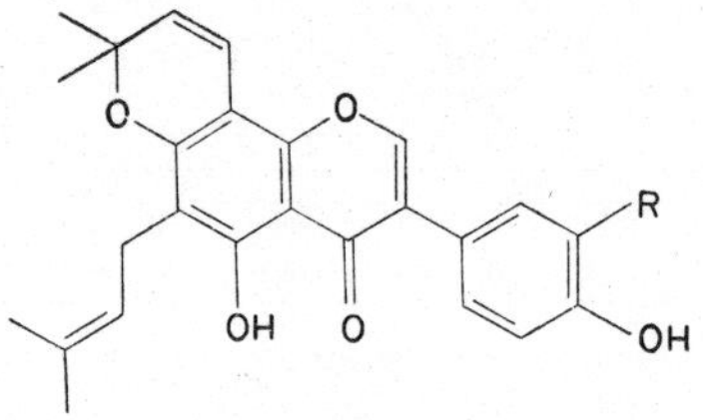

(175) Osajin, R = H

Pomiferin, R = OH

3,4,5-trihydroxyphenylacetic acid (177), and milder alkaline hydrolysis gave fuscinic acid (178) and acetaldehyde. Oxidation of fuscinic acid dimethyl ether (179) yielded the compounds (181), (182), and (183) by the changes indicated, together with α-hydroxyisobutyric acid. Pyrolysis of fuscinic acid yielded 2,2,5-trimethyl-7,8-dihydroxychroman (180). Structure (176) proposed for fuscin on the basis of these reactions was confirmed by synthesis.[61]

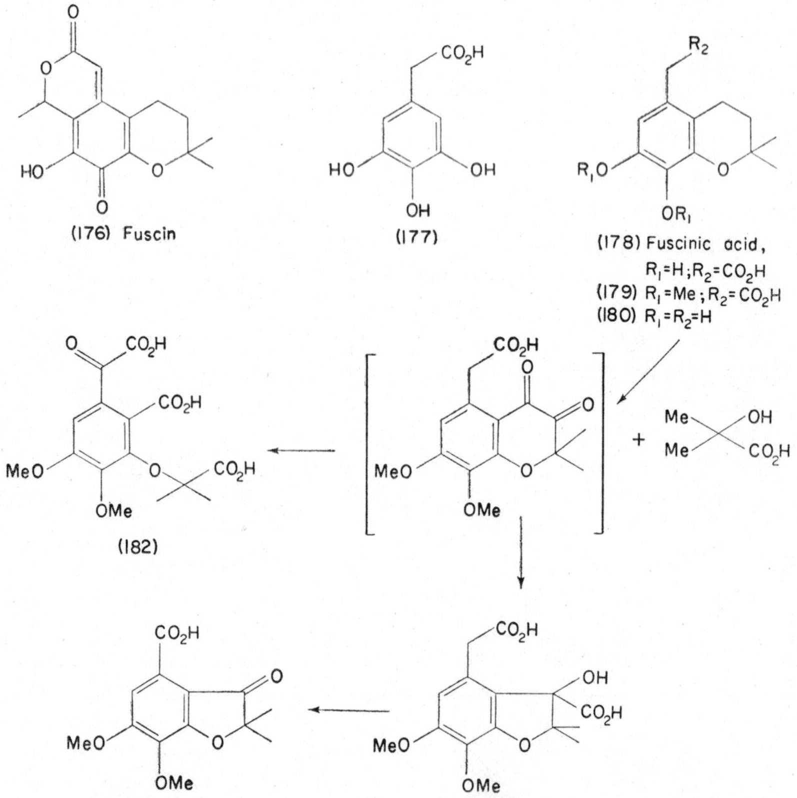

(176) Fuscin

(177)

(178) Fuscinic acid,
$R_1 = H; R_2 = CO_2H$
(179) $R_1 = Me; R_2 = CO_2H$
(180) $R_1 = R_2 = H$

(182)

(181)

(183)

Samidin (184) and Visnadin (185)

The closely related compounds samidin, visnadin, and dihydrosamidin were isolated in low yields after careful purification of *Ammi visnaga* extracts (Bishop's weed),[78,79] and were identified as 7-hydroxycoumarin derivatives by their ultraviolet spectra. On mild alkaline hydrolysis samidin yielded one equivalent of acetic acid and one equivalent of $\beta\beta$-dimethylacrylic acid. Similarly, visnadin yielded acetic acid and methylethylacetic acid. Aqueous alkaline hydrolysis of samidin (184) and visnadin (185) yielded the corresponding diol, khellactone (186), which does not occur naturally, whereas

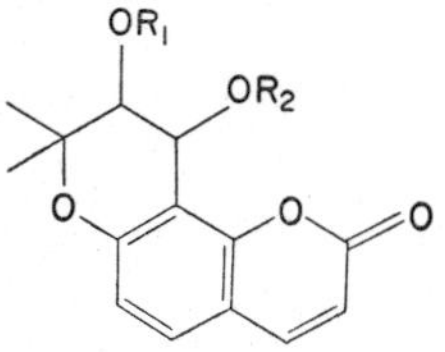

(184) Samidin, R_1 = COMe, R_2 = COCH=CMe$_2$
(185) Visnadin, R_1 = COMe, R_2 = COCHMe Et
(186) Khellactone, R_1 = R_2 = H
(187) R_1 = H, R_2 = Et
(188) R_1 = COCH=CMe$_2$, R_2 = Et

ethanolic alkaline or acidic hydrolysis gave the ethyl ether of khellactone (187). Khellactone ethyl ether (187) gave acetone on oxidation with potassium permanganate, and after reduction to the corresponding dihydrocoumarin nitric acid oxidation yielded succinic acid indicating that carbon atoms 3 and 4 of the coumarin bore hydrogen atoms only. Khellactone (186) did not liberate volatile aldehydes on oxidation with periodic acid. The only structures for samidin and visnadin in accordance with these reactions were the diesters derived from the cyclic diol (186).

The relative positions of the two acyl residues in samidin were indicated by partial hydrolysis with ethanolic potash at room temperature giving the ethyl ether (188), which on further alkaline hydrolysis yielded $\beta\beta$-dimethyl acrylic acid. The results of this partial hydrolysis could be rationalized by locating the acetyl residue on the benzylic hydroxyl group, and mechanism (189) was suggested. The hydroxyl groups in khellactone were proved to be in

(189)

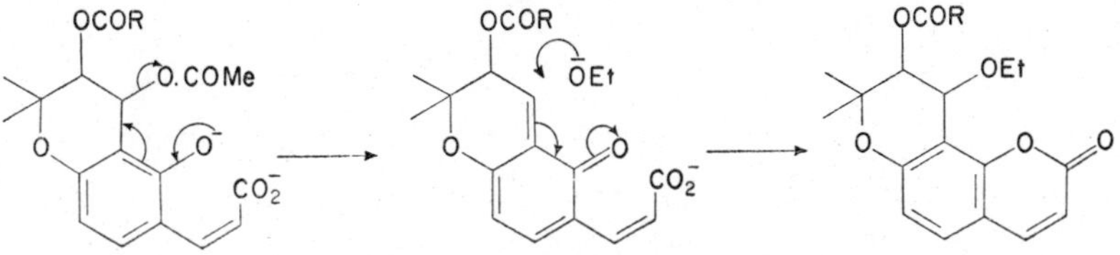

the *trans*-configuration by showing its structural identity with synthetic ($\pm$)-*trans*-khellactone obtained by aqueous oxalic acid hydrolysis of the corresponding chromene epoxide.[79]

NATURAL PRODUCTS WITH UNUSUAL C_5 RESIDUES

Atrovenetin

The mould metabolite atrovenetin, $C_{19}H_{18}O_6$, from *Penicillium Atrovenetum*[102] was shown to be identical with the deoxynorherqueinone obtained by zinc–acetic acid reduction of the related pigment nor-herqueinone, $C_{19}H_{18}O_7$[103] obtained from *Penicillium herquei*. Herqueinone,[103] $C_{20}H_{20}O_7$, also obtained from *P. herquei*, appears to be a methyl ether of nor-herqueinone. Clearly atrovenetin, herqueinone, and nor-herqueinone are structurally related.

All three compounds were optically active and both herqueinone and nor-herqueinone were converted into optically inactive xanthoherquein and norxanthoherquein by acidic hydrolysis with the loss of a C_5 fragment as methyl-isopropyl ketone. Norxanthoherquein, $C_{14}H_{10}O_7$, (191) was identified spectroscopically as a derivative of 9-hydroxyperinaphthenone (190), and since it yielded nitrococussic acid (192) on nitric acid oxidation, it was assigned the structure shown to account for the seven oxygen atoms indicated by analysis.

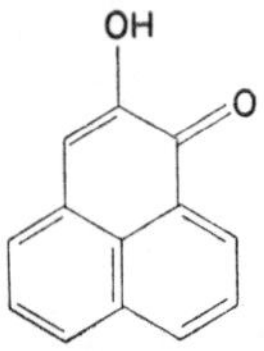

(190) 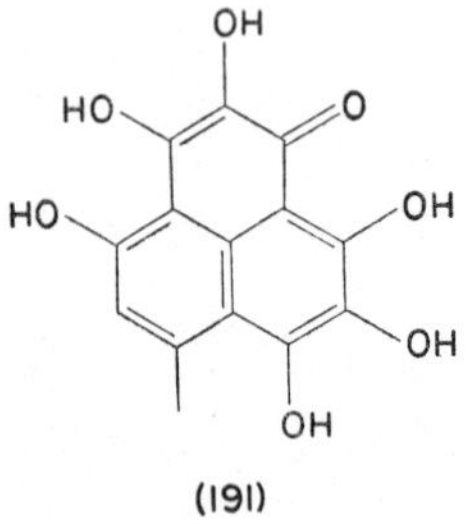   (191) 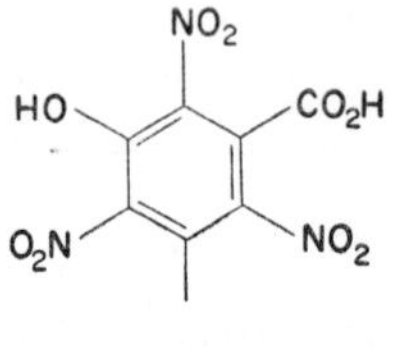   (192)

Alkaline peroxide oxidation of atrovenetin (193) yielded the perinaphthalic anhydride (194) which was optically active and formed a diacetyl derivative. Both (194) and the diacetate had infrared absorption typical of 2,7-dihydroxynaphthalic anhydride (195) and its diacetate.

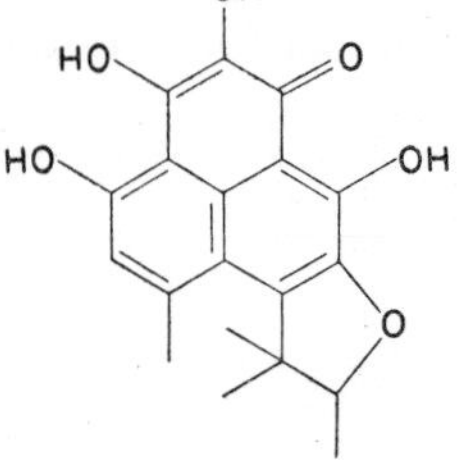

(193) Atrovenetin 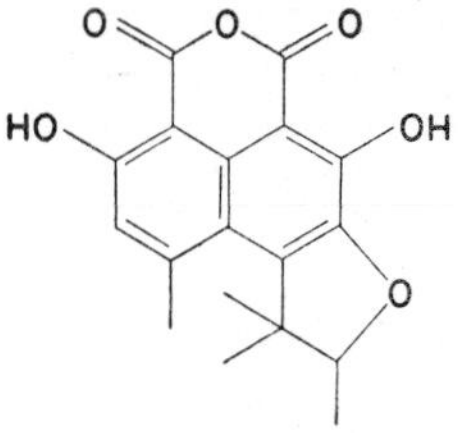   (194) 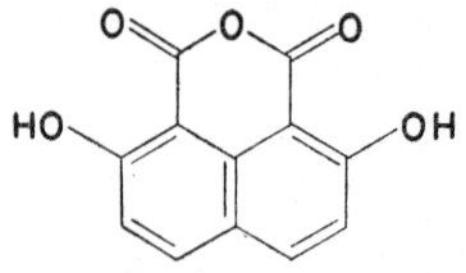   (195)

Nitric acid oxidation of atrovenetin gave, in addition to nitrococussic acid (192), the dilactone (196) which was optically active and contained the intact C_5-substituent which was originally located on the perinaphthenone nucleus of atrovenetin. Chemical and spectroscopic evidence showed that the dilactone could be formulated as shown (196) or as its isomer (197), which differed only in the arrangement of the three methyl substituents on the lactone ring.

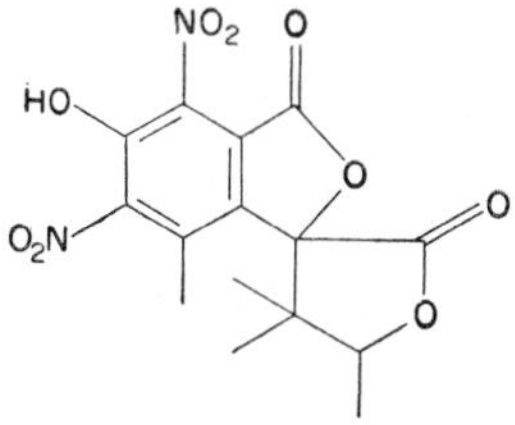

(196) 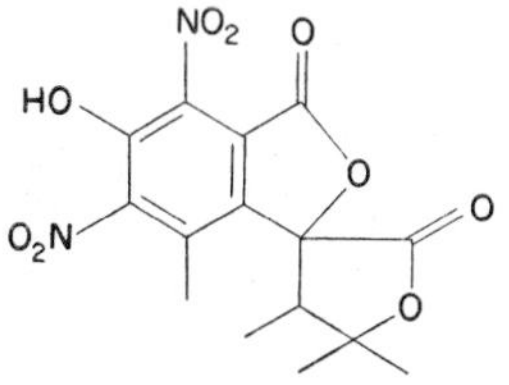   (197)

The decision between the structures (196) and (197) was taken after examining the nuclear magnetic resonance spectrum which contains bands assignable to various structural features as indicated in the figure below. The values are given relative to aromatic protons of toluene (arbitrary value, 1000 c/s).

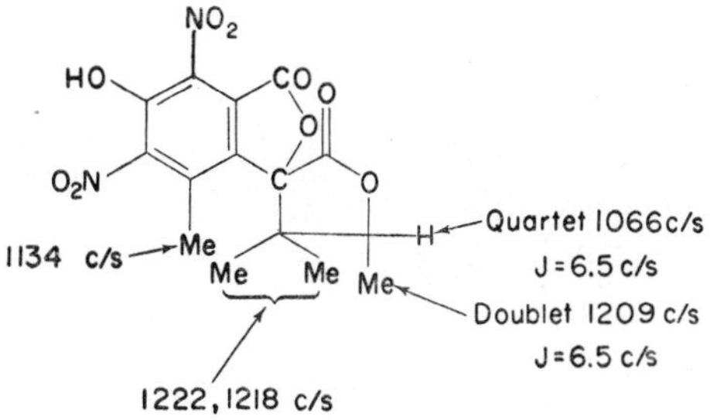

This result, which is a striking demonstration of the n.m.r. method, indicated that the dilactone had the structure (196) and atrovenetin was therefore given the structure (193).

Professor Barton has recently informed us that a modified structure for atrovenetin should still be considered as it is possible that the formation of the dilactone (196) from atrovenetin could involve a molecular rearrangement. This alternative structure for atrovenetin is also suggested by speculation regarding its biosynthesis.

The biosynthesis of atrovenetin probably involves the polyacetic acid precursor shown below and from this, by an introduction of a C_5 unit, the alternative structure for atrovenetin may be derived.

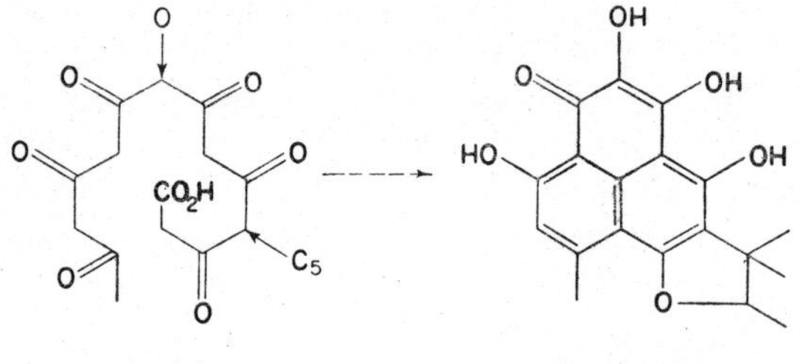

Atrovenetin?

This different structural proposal for atrovenetin is of interest in that it is obviously biosynthetically acceptable. However, it may be pointed out that a biosynthesis of the structure (193) may be proposed which is equally plausible if it is accepted that the type of rearrangement represented schematically can occur. These reactions have analogues in the chemistry of hop resin acids.

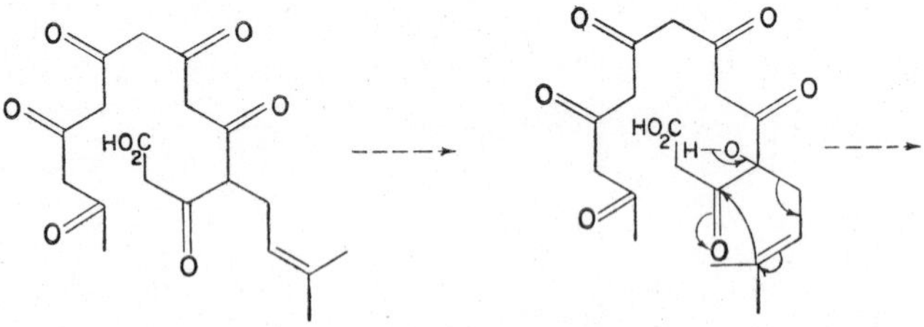

Further work is clearly necessary to settle the constitution of atrovenetin, but this analysis illustrates the value of subjecting structural proposals to scrutiny in terms of current views regarding biosynthesis. We thank Professor Barton for informing us of his views regarding atrovenetin. It is our understanding that similar views are held by Professor R. B. Woodward and by Dr. J. B. Hendrickson.

Munetone (198)

The isoflavone munetone, $C_{20}H_{15}O_3.OCH_3$, was extracted from the root bark of *Mundulea suberosa*.[81] Munetone (198) was shown to be a methoxyiso-flavone (C_{16}) with a C_5 substituent. Alkaline hydrolysis of munetone yielded the deoxybenzoin (199) and formic acid; the deoxybenzoin was reconverted into munetone by heating with ethyl orthoformate in pyridine-piperidine. Alkaline fusion of the deoxybenzoin yielded isobutyric acid and oxidation with alkaline hydrogen peroxide gave o-anisic acid, locating the methoxyl group on the 2'-position of the isoflavone nucleus. Oxidation of munetone yielded a salicylic acid (200), shown to be identical with isotubaic acid (200), and o-methoxybenzoic acid from which the structure (198) for munetone is established.

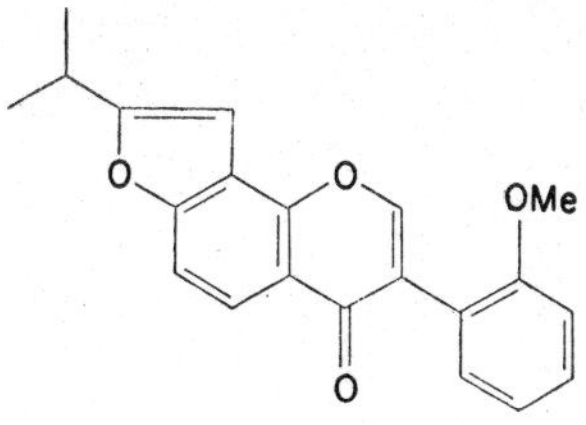

(198) Munetone

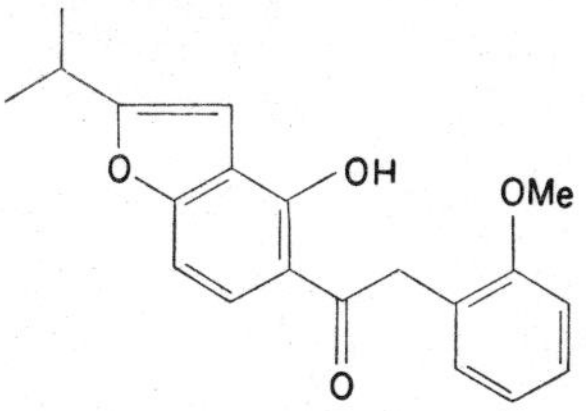

(199)

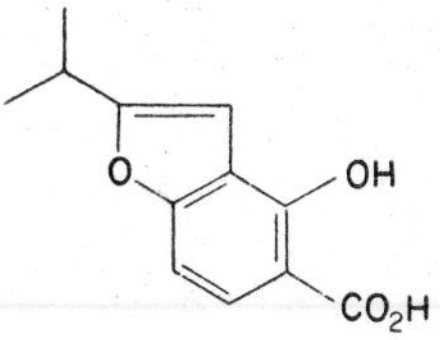

(200)

Euparin (201)

Euparin (201) $C_{13}H_{12}O_3$., obtained as yellow crystals from the roots of *Eupatorium purpureum* (gravel root), was shown to be an *o*-hydroxy-aromatic ketone,[87] containing two reducible double bonds. Euparin methyl ether (202) was oxidized to the salicylic acid (203), whose structure was established by methylation or demethylation to the known compounds (204) and (205).

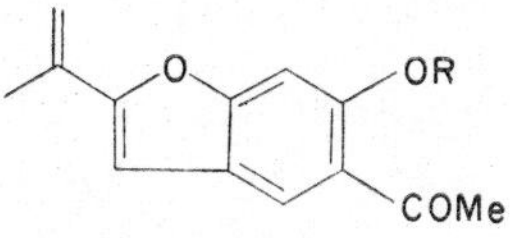

(201) Euparin, R = H
(202) R = Me

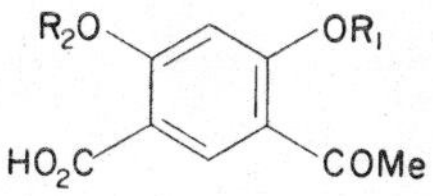

(203) R_1 = Me, R_2=H
(204) R_1 = R_2= Me
(205) R_1 = R_2= H

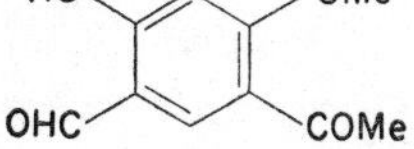

(206)

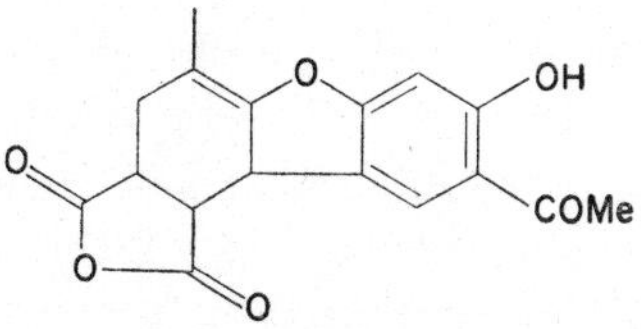

(207)

This indicated that euparin contained a C_5 substituent linked both directly and *via* an oxygen atom to the benzene ring. Ozonolysis of euparin methyl ether (202) yielded formaldehyde and the aldehyde (206). This was

8

further oxidized to the benzoic acid (203), which had previously been obtained by permanganate oxidation of euparin methyl ether. Finally, euparin formed a maleic anhydride adduct (207). The preferred structure, (201), of the three possible structures for euparin containing two conjugated double bonds in the side chain was shown to be correct by the alkaline degradation of tetrahydroeuparin to isobutyric acid. This conclusion was confirmed by the synthesis of tetrahydroeuparin.

Visamminol (210)

The optically active compound, visamminol, $C_{15}H_{16}O_5$, was obtained from *Ammi visnaga*.[82] Visamminol contained two hydroxyl groups, one of which was phenolic. The presence of a *gem*-dimethyl group was shown by the

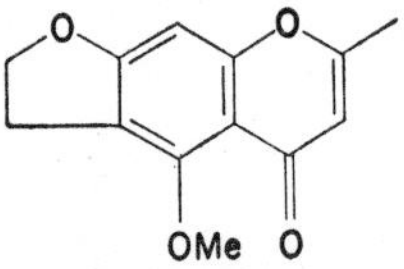

(208) Dihydrovisnagin 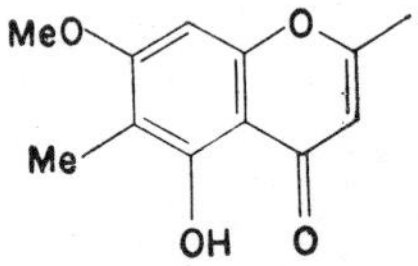   (209) Eugenetin 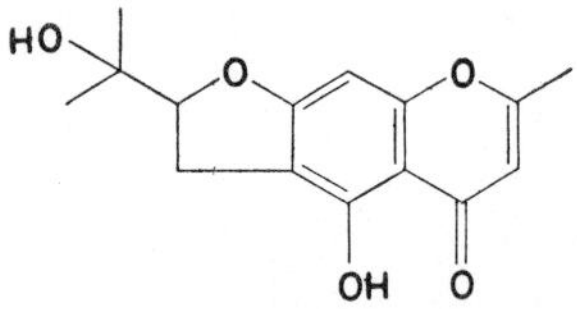   (210) Visamminol

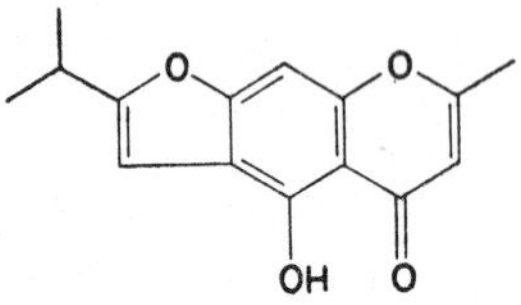

(211) 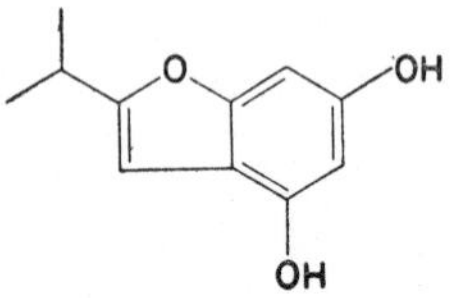   (212) 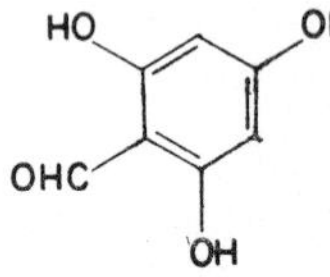   (213)

formation of acetone on chromic acid oxidation. Alkaline fusion yielded phloroglucinol. Visamminol was identified as a 2-methylchromone by comparison of the ultraviolet spectrum of its methyl ether with that of dihydrovisnagin (208), and as a 5-hydroxychromone by a similar comparison of the ultraviolet spectra of eugenetin (209) and visamminol. Dehydration of visamminol (210) readily yielded the optically inactive chromone (211), which after alkaline hydrolysis to the resorcinol derivative (212) gave isobutyric acid and phloroglucinaldehyde (213) on ozonolysis, thus establishing the structure of the side chain. The alcoholic hydroxyl group of visamminol placed as in (210) accounts for the formation of acetone on oxidation.

Reaction of visamminol with acetic anhydride–sodium acetate yielded a mono-acetyl derivative which has been presumed to involve the relatively unusual acetylation of the tertiary hydroxyl group. A similar mono-acetyl derivative was obtained from marmesin (107).[84]

SYNTHETICAL STUDIES

The syntheses of natural products bearing isoprenoid substituents are of two types. The C_5 unit may be introduced in one step, possibly with subsequent minor modifications, or, less commonly, the isoprenoid substituent is built up from an existing substituent in the starting material. The former type of synthesis frequently yields a complex mixture of products. The methods of synthesis which have been used for the preparation of $\gamma\gamma$-dimethylallyl derivatives, 2,2-dimethylchromenes and some benzfuran derivatives are discussed below.

$\gamma\gamma$-Dimethyl Derivatives

The $\gamma\gamma$-dimethylallyl unit is always introduced by alkylation of a suitable aromatic precursor with $\gamma\gamma$-dimethylallyl bromide, a reaction closely analogous to the proposed biosynthetic alkylation with $\gamma\gamma$-dimethylallyl pyrophosphate. This process is frequently referred to as "prenylation", particularly in the German literature.

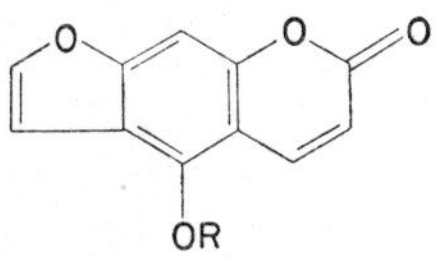

(211) R = CH₂CH=CMe₂
(212) R = H
(215) R = CH₂CH—CMe₂

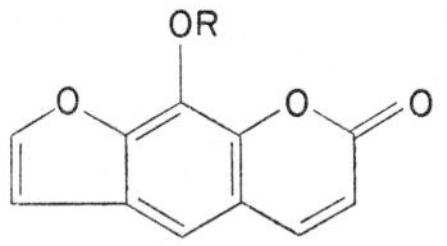

(213) R = CH₂CH=CMe₂
(214) R = H
(216) R = CH₂CH—CMe₂

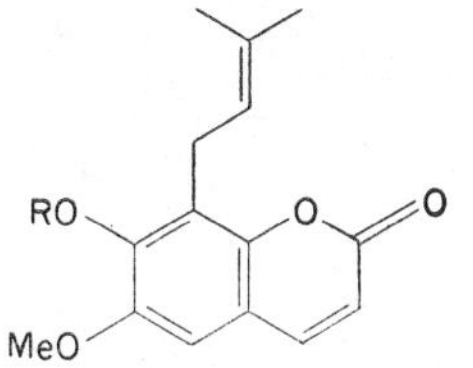

(217) R = CH₂CH=CMe₂
(218) R = H

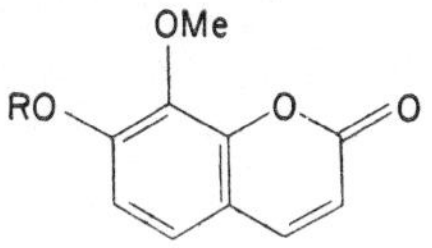

(219) R = CH₂CH=CMe.CH₂CH₂CH=CMe₂
(220) R = H

O-Alkylation of a suitable phenol by $\gamma\gamma$-dimethylallyl bromide has been used in the synthesis of isoimperatorin (211)[104] from bergaptol (212) and imperatorin (213)[105] from xanthotoxol (214). Both isoimperatorin and imperatorin were converted into the corresponding epoxides oxypeucedanin (215)[104,106] and oxyimperatorin (216)[105] by the action of perbenzoic acid in chloroform. By similar reactions brayleyanin (217)[29] was obtained from the phenol (218) and collinin (219) from daphnetin-8-methyl ether (220), geranyl chloride being used in the latter synthesis. Ether formation is generally achieved by the treatment of a methanolic solution of the phenol sodium salt with $\gamma\gamma$-dimethylallyl bromide. With phloroglucinol derivatives,

C-alkylation tends to predominate over O-alkylation under these conditions, but $\gamma\gamma$-dimethylallyl ethers of such compounds may conveniently be prepared by using solid potassium carbonate as the base in acetone.[107] C-Alkylation with $\gamma\gamma$-dimethylallyl bromide is for the most part illustrated by the preparation of phloroglucinol derivatives, but an early example of this type of reaction is the preparation of osthol (222).[108] The mono-sodium salt of resorcylaldehyde-4-methyl ether was heated with dimethylallyl bromide in benzene to yield the C-alkylated derivative (221), which was converted into osthol by the Perkin coumarin synthesis.

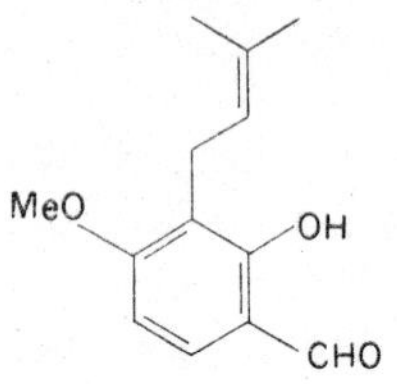

(221) 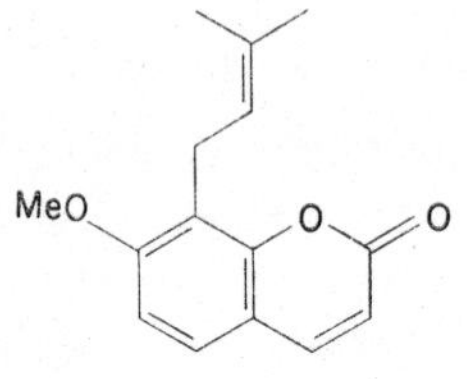   (222) Osthol

The work of Riedl and his collaborators concerning the synthesis of humulone (223),[109] lupulone (224), and their analogues [(223) and (224); R = CHO, COMe, COEt, COCH$_2$Ph, COPh, etc.][110,111] has indicated that, in general, the reaction of $\gamma\gamma$-dimethylallyl bromide with acyl-phloroglucinols can yield any of the products of the general types (224–227). Reaction

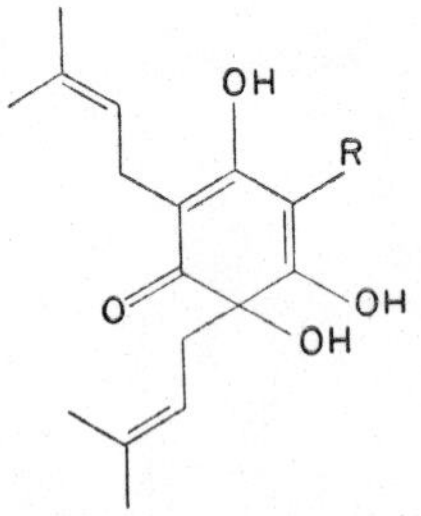

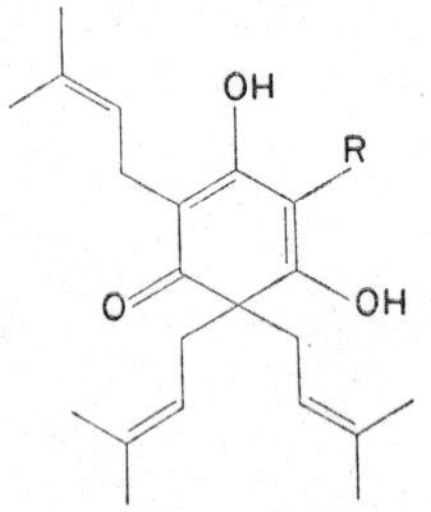

(223) Humulone, R = COCH$_2$CHMe$_2$ (224) Lupulone, R = COCH$_2$CHMe$_2$

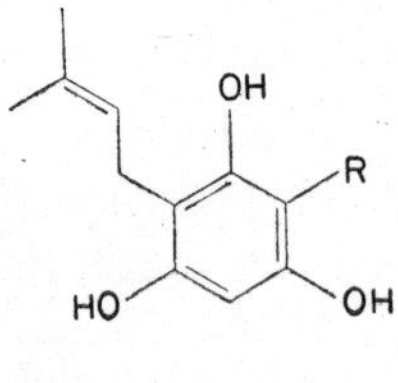

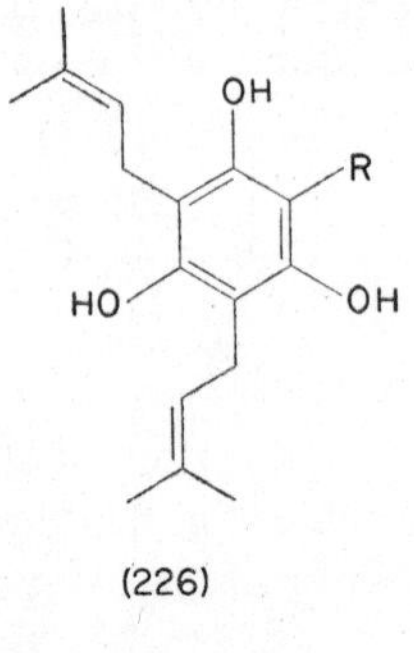

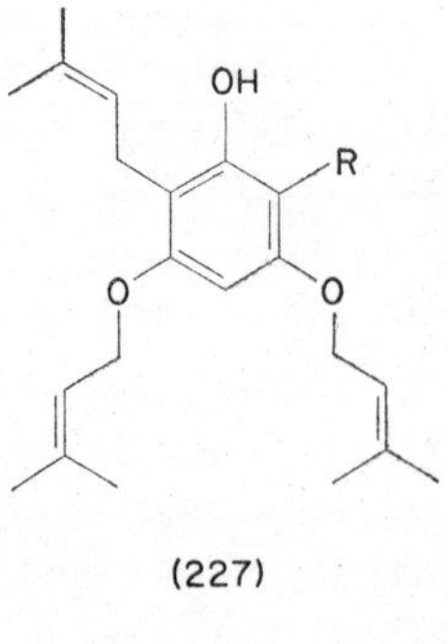

(225)   (226)   (227)

conditions may be arranged to give yields of up to 20% or more of the mono-, di-, or tri-C-alkylated product.

An ingenious use of this type of synthesis to prepare methyl ethers of 2-$\gamma\gamma$-dimethylallyl phloroglucinol enabled Riedl and Mitteldorf to determine the relative positions of substituents in the chalkone xanthohumol (228).[33]

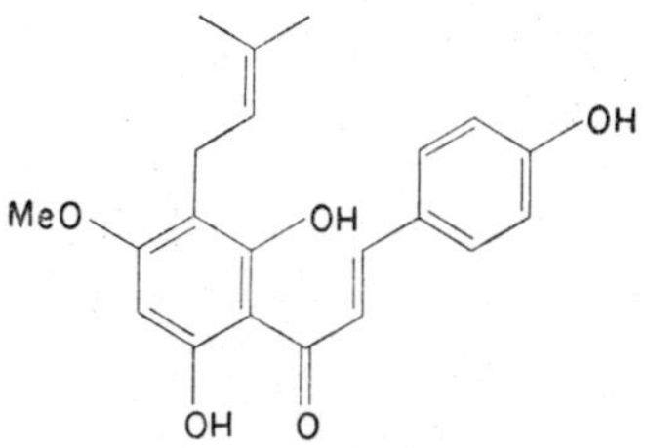

(228) Xanthohumol

Schmid and co-workers[107] observed that the reaction of the monosodium salt of 2-methyl-5,7-dihydroxychromone (229) with dimethylallyl bromide in benzene yielded heteropeucenin (231) and isoheteropeucenin (232) in addition to the required product, peucenin (230).

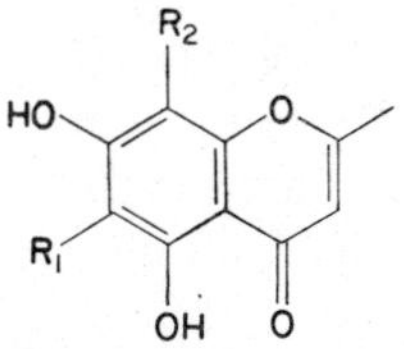

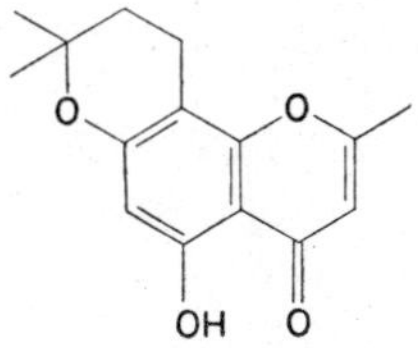

(229) $R_1 = R_2 = H$
(230) $R_1 = CH_2CH=CMe_2, R_2 = H$ (232)
(231) $R_1 = H, R_2 = CH_2CH=CMe_2$

The examples of C-alkylation by $\gamma\gamma$-dimethyl bromide quoted above refer to alkylation of phloroglucinol and resorcinol derivatives; this reaction has recently been extended to a phenol derivative. 3-$\gamma\gamma$-Dimethylallyl-4-hydroxybenzoic acid (233), a degradation product of novobiocin, was

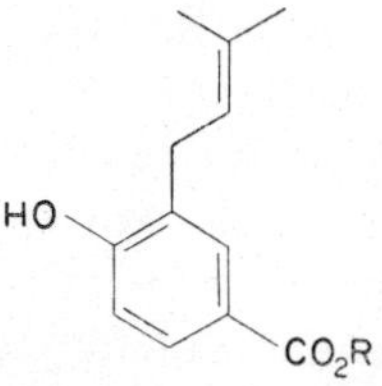

(233) R = H
(234) R = Et

synthesized[68] by the reaction of the mono-sodium salt of ethyl 4-hydroxy-benzoate with dimethylallyl bromide in toluene followed by alkaline hydrolysis of the ethyl ester (234).

Finally, mention should be made of the synthetic work in connection with vitamins K_1 and K_2 and related quinones with polyisoprene side chains which has recently been adequately reviewed.[72] Reference may also be made to the synthesis of lapachol, which is mentioned later (see p. 113).

2,2-*Dimethylchromene Derivatives*

2,2-Dimethylchromenes may be prepared in one step from the corresponding phenols by reaction with 2-methylbut-3-yn-2-ol (235) and zinc chloride. By means of this reaction, Späth and his co-workers[113] prepared a mixture of xanthyletin (236) and seselin (237) from umbelliferone (238), and luvangetin (239) was obtained from daphnetin 8-methyl ether (240).

(235)   (236) R=H   (237)   (238) R = H
             (239) R=OMe   (240) R = OMe

This method was further extended by Nickl[114] to the synthesis of β-tubaic acid (244) from methyl β-resorcylate and of lonchocarpin (241) from resaceto-phenone after condensation of the initial product (242) with benzaldehyde.

(241)   (242)   (243)

The direct synthesis of 2,2-dimethylchromenes is not satisfactory as low yields are obtained and an alternative method employing 2,2-dimethyl–chromanone intermediates has been studied. Robertson and co-workers[115] showed that a Friedel-Crafts reaction between resorcinol and $\beta\beta$-dimethyl-acrylyl chloride gave a good yield of the chromanone (243). Although this could not readily be converted into the corresponding chromene by methods then available, reduction of chromanones by sodium borohydride or lithium aluminium hydride now makes this a useful method for chromene synthesis. Nickl[116] has described a synthesis of β-tubaic acid (244) from methyl resorcylate and $\beta\beta$-dimethylacrylyl chloride involving borohydride reduction of the intermediate chromanone, and acid-catalysed dehydration of the 4-chromanol (245) to β-tubaic acid. The chromanone (246) was isolated in addition to the isomer (247) and was similarly converted into the acid (248).

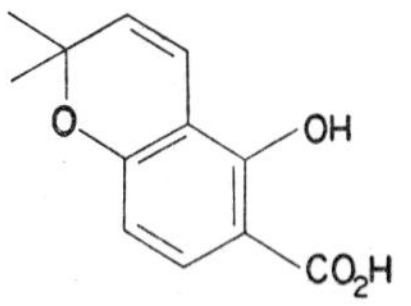

(244) 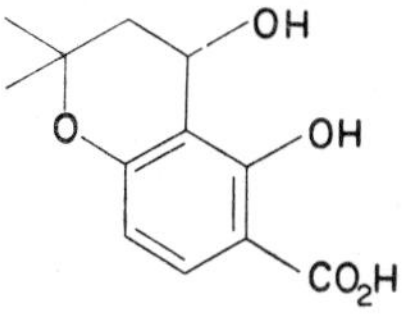   (245) 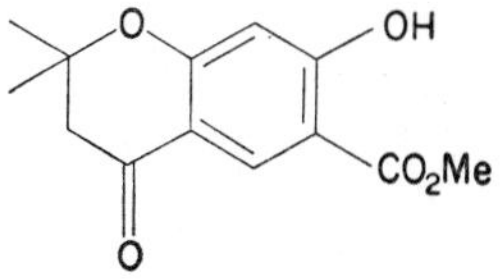   (246)

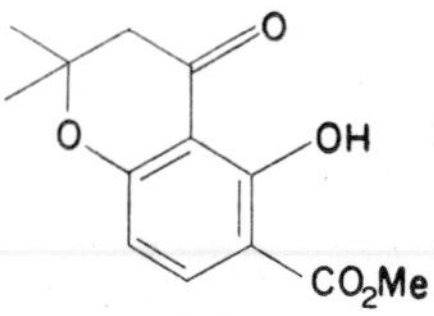

(247) 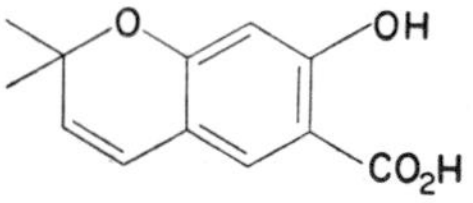   (248)

For the synthesis of lapachenole (249),[117] the ester (250) was converted to the chromanone (251) by the Fries rearrangement. Lithium aluminium hydride reduction followed by pyrolysis of the acetyl derivative of the chromanol yielded lapachenole. Acid-catalysed dehydration of the chromanol yielded only lapachenole dimer.

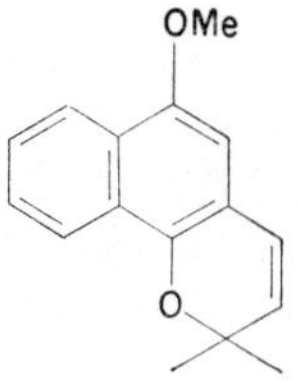

(249) 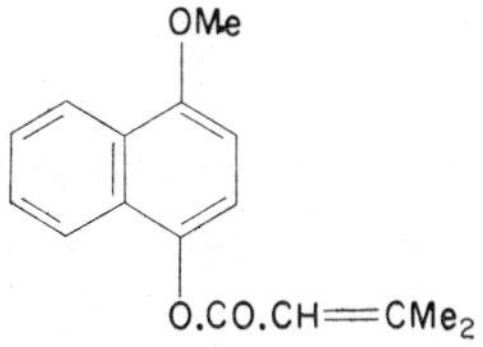   (250) 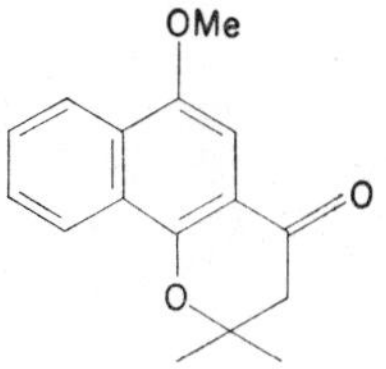   (251)

An interesting synthesis of (±)-samidin has been achieved.[79] Seselin, synthesized by the condensation of 2-methylbutyn-2-ol with umbelliferone in o-dichlorobenzene at 160°, was converted into trans-khellactone (252) by

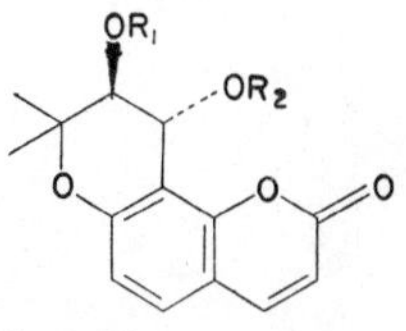

(252) R$_1$=R$_2$=H   (253)   (256)
(254) R$_1$=H, R$_2$=COMe
(255) R$_1$=COCH=CMe$_2$,
       R$_2$=COMe

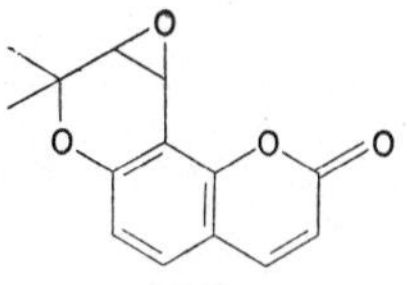

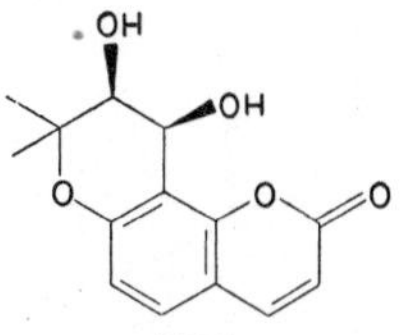

hydrolysis of seselin epoxide (253) with aqueous oxalic acid. Seselin epoxide and acetic acid yielded the *trans*-mono-acetate (254) which was converted into (±)-samidin (255) by esterification with $\beta\beta$-dimethylacrylyl chloride. Osmium tetroxide oxidation of seselin yielded *cis*-khellactone (256).

Isopropenyldihydrofurans

Kierstead *et al.*[118] observed that the condensation of butadiene-1,4-dibromide with sodio-malonic ester yielded the cyclopropane derivative (257) rather than the expected product (258). Similar reactions occurred with ethyl acetoacetate and ethyl cyanoacetate. Nickl[119] extended this reaction to isoprene-1,4-dibromide and showed that similar products could be obtained (see 259).

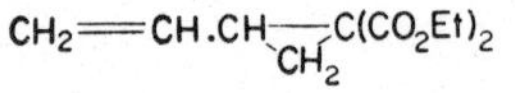

$$CH_2{=\!=}CH.CH{\!-\!}C(CO_2Et)_2$$
$$\underset{CH_2}{\quad}$$

(257)

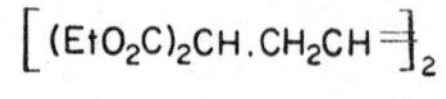

$$\left[(EtO_2C)_2CH.CH_2CH{=}\right]_2$$

(258)

(259)

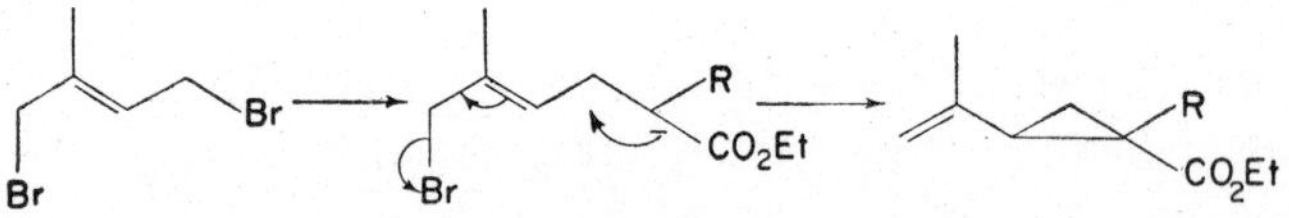

R = CO₂Et, CN

R = CO_2Et, CN

Dimedone, however, yielded the isopropenyldihydrofuran (260) rather than (261), and this result caused Nickl to investigate the reaction of isoprene-1,4-dibromide with the disodium salt of phloroacetophenone, which in fact gave the structurally analogous compound (262). This reaction has not yet been extended to other compounds, but it could be useful in

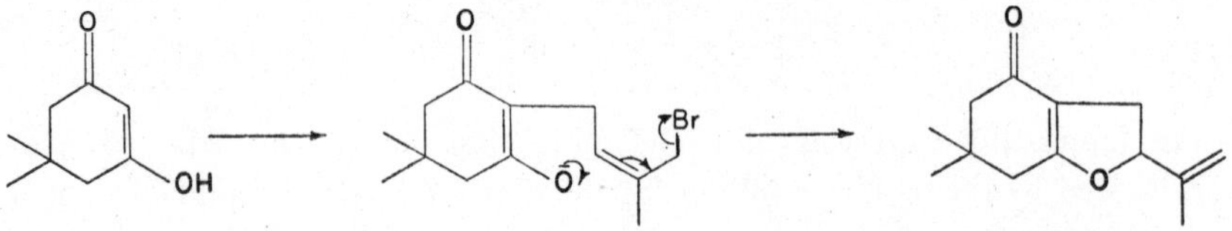

(260)

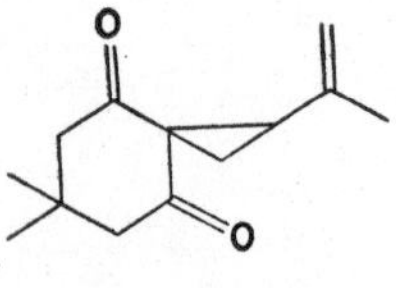

(261)

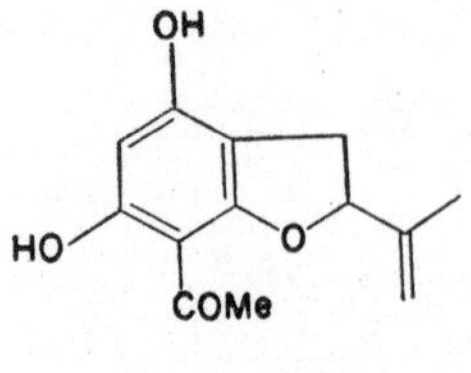

(262)

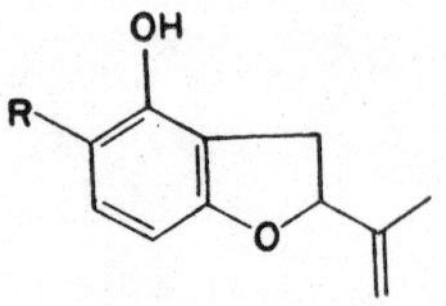

(263) R = H

(264) R = CO₂H

synthetical approaches to rotenone. The isopropenyldihydrofurans, tubanol (263) and tubaic acid (264), had previously been prepared by Shamshurin[120] by a synthesis involving several stages.

Benzfuran Derivatives

The first synthesis of a benzfuran derivative containing an isoprenoid substituent on an aromatic ring was of oreoselone from umbelliferone-6-carboxylic acid (265).[121] This acid gave the acid chloride (266) which was converted by successive treatments with diazomethane and hydrogen chloride–acetic acid to the coumaranone (267). Condensation of (267) with acetone followed by reduction yielded oreoselone (268).

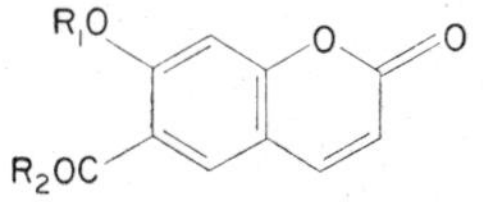

(265) $R_1 = H, R_2 = OH$

(266) $R_1 = COEt, R_2 = Cl$

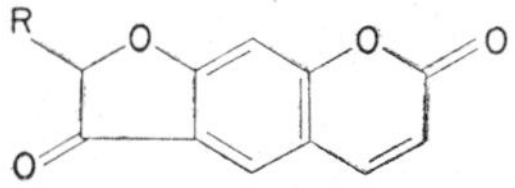

(267) $R = H$

(268) $R = Me_2CH$

The preparation of deoxyoreoselone by acid-catalysed cyclization and dehydration of 7-demethylsuberosin epoxide has already been discussed[80] (see p. 88).

The unusual trimethyldihydrofuran systems of dunnione[122] and anisoxide[30] have been synthesized by two very different methods. Reaction of the potassium salt of 2-hydroxy-1,4-naphthoquinone (269) with $\gamma\gamma$-dimethylallyl bromide in acetone yielded almost equal amounts of the required ether (270) and lapachol (271).[122,123] Claisen rearrangement of (270) in refluxing ethanol yielded the $\alpha\alpha$-dimethylallyl naphthoquinone (272) in high yield. This was converted by the action of concentrated sulphuric acid to DL-dunnione (273) which was not resolved.

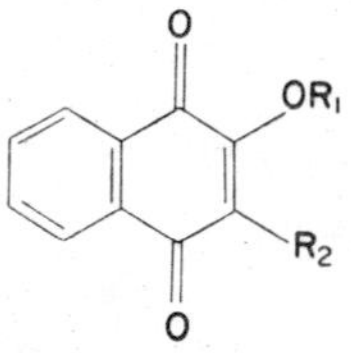

(269) $R_1 = H, R_2 = H$

(270) $R_1 = CH_2 CH = CMe_2, R_2 = H$

(271) $R_1 = H, R_2 = CH_2 CH = CMe_2$

(272) $R_1 = H, R_2 = CMe_2 CH = CH_2$

(274) $R_1 = H, R_2 = CH_2CMe = CMe_2$

(275) $R_1 = CH_2CMe = CMe_2, R_2 = H$

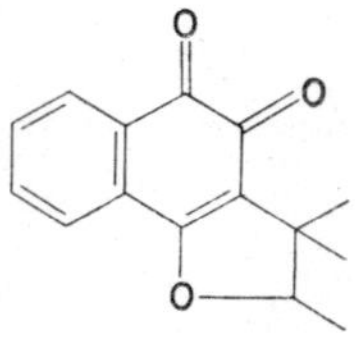

(273)

The dunnione rearrangement products, α- and β-isodunnione, were synthesized by an ingenious method[124] employing the Hooker oxidation reaction.[125] Reaction of the silver salt of 2-hydroxy-1,4-naphthoquinone with

$\beta\gamma\gamma$-trimethylallyl bromide yielded a mixture of the C-alkylated (274) and O-alkylated (275) products. The trimethylallyl naphthaquinone (274) was cyclized to the corresponding trimethylpyrano derivative (276) which yielded the alcohol (277) by the action of alkali. Oxidation of (277) by alkaline permanganate[125] gave hydroxyisodunniol (278) identical with the compound obtained from dunnione. Acid-catalysed cyclization of hydroxyisodunniol (278) under the appropriate conditions[6] yielded α- and β-isodunnione [(279) and (280) respectively].

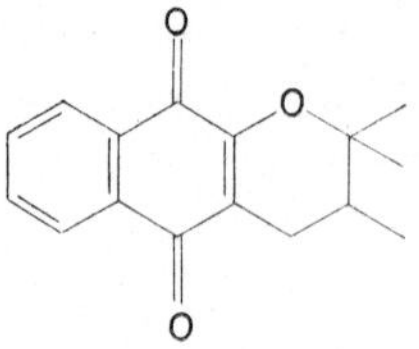

(276)

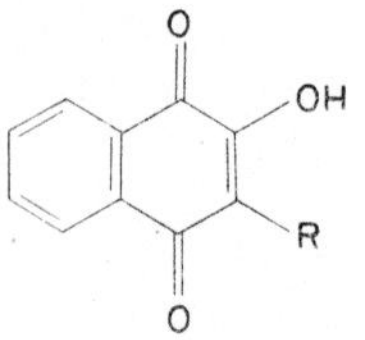

(277) R=CH$_2$CHMe.CMe$_2$OH
(278) R=CHMe.CMe$_2$OH

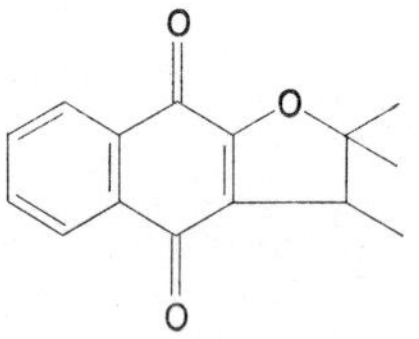

(279)

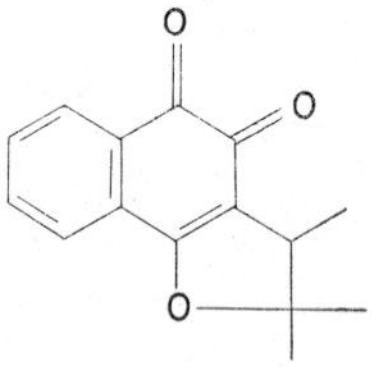

(280)

Anisoxide as isolated was a racemate[34] and the structure (281) proposed on the basis of degradation reactions was confirmed as follows. Reaction of 2-hydroxy-5-methylisobutyrophenone with methylmagnesium iodide yielded the tertiary alcohol (282); acid-catalysed cyclization of (282)

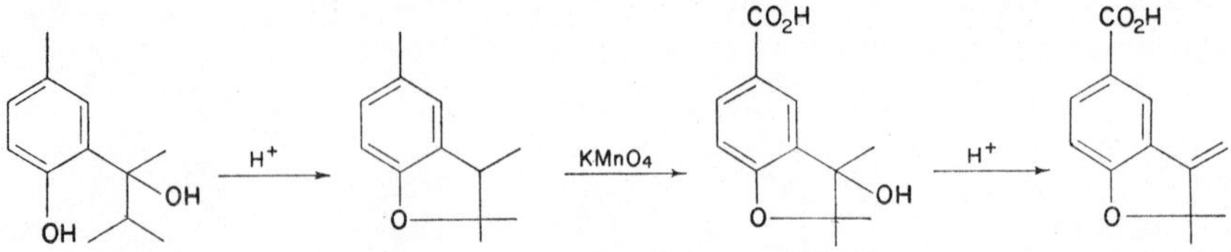

(282)

(283)

(284)

(285)

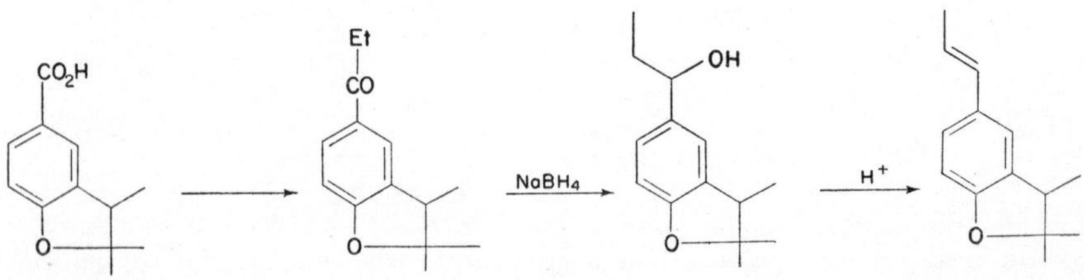

(286)

(287)

(281) Anisoxide

yielded the tetramethyldihydrobenzfuran (283). Compound (283) was oxidized by permanganate to the hydroxy-acid (284), which was dehydrated to the unsaturated acid (285), and reduced catalytically to the acid (286). The benzoic acid derivative (286) was converted into the ethyl ketone (287) by the action of diazoethane on the acid chloride followed by treatment with hydriodic acid and with zinc in acetic acid. Finally, the ketone (287) was reduced by borohydride to the corresponding alcohol which was dehydrated to ($\pm$)-anisoxide (281) by ethanolic hydrochloric acid.

(288) R=H
(289) R=Me

(290)

Derivatives of benzfuran have also been prepared[30] by ozonolysis of o-allyl- (288) or o-dimethylallyl- (289) phenols followed by cyclodehydration of the resulting o-hydroxyphenylacetaldehyde derivatives (290).

REFERENCES

1. T. A. GEISSMAN and E. HINREINER, *Bot. Rev.* 1952, **18**, 17.
2. T. A. GEISSMAN and E. HINREINER, *Bot. Rev.* 1952, **18**, 82.
3. A. QUILICO and C. CARDANI, *Gazz. Chim. Ital.* 1953, **83**, 1088.
4. R. LIVINGSTONE and M. C. WHITING, *J. Chem. Soc.* 1955, 3631.
5. S. C. HOOKER, *J. Amer. Chem. Soc.* 1936, **58**, 1168.
6. J. R. PRICE and R. ROBINSON, *J. Chem. Soc.* 1939, 1522; 1940, 1493.
7. M. KOFLER, A. LANGEMANN, R. RUEGG, L. H. CHOPARD-DIT-JEAN, A. RAYROUD and O. ISLER, *Helv. Chim. Acta* 1959, **42**, 1283; M. KOFLER, A. LANGEMANN, R. RUEGG, U. GLOOR, U. SCHWIETER, J. WURSCH, O. WISS and O. ISLER, *Helv. Chim. Acta* 1959, **42**, 2252; N. R. TRENNER, B. H. ARISON, R. E. ERICKSON, C. H. SHUNK, D. E. WOLF and K. FOLKERS, *J. Amer. Chem. Soc.* 1959, **81**, 2026.
8. H. BROCKMANN and H. ROTH, *Naturwiss*, 1935, **23**, 246; H. BROCKMANN, *Liebigs Ann.* 1936, **521**, 1.
9. D. H. R. BARTON, P. DE MAYO, G. A. MORRISON and H. RAISTRICK, *Tetrahedron*, 1959, **6**, 48.
10. C. H. SHUNK, C. H. STAMMER, E. A. KACZKA, E. WALTON, C. F. SPENCER, A. N. WILSON, J. W. RICHTER, F. W. HOLLY and K. FOLKERS, *J. Amer. Chem. Soc.* 1956, **78**, 1770; J. W. HINMAN, E. L. CARON and H. HOEKSEMA, *J. Amer. Chem. Soc.* 1957, **79**, 3789; E. WALTON, J. O. RODIN, C. H. STAMMER, F. W. HOLLY and K. FOLKERS, *J. Amer. Chem. Soc.* 1958, **80**, 5168.
11. J. A. LAMBERTON and J. R. PRICE, *Austral. J. Sci. Res.* 1953, **6**, 173.
12. L. J. DRUMMOND and F. N. LAHEY, *Austral. J. Sci. Res.* 1949, **2**, 622, 630.
13. P. YATES and G. H. STOUT, *J. Amer. Chem. Soc.* 1958, **80**, 1691.
14. C. CARDANI, G. CASNATI, F. PIOZZI and A. QUILICO, *Tetrahedron Letters* 1959, **16**, 1.
15. C. DJERASSI, E. J. EISENBRAUN, R. A. FINNEGAN and B. GILBERT, *Tetrahedron Letters* 1959, **1**, 10.
16. F. B. LA FORGE, H. L. HALLER and L. E. SMITH, *Chem. Rev.* 1933, **12**, 181.
17. M. L. WOLFROM, W. D. HARRIS, G. F. JOHNSON, J. E. MAHAN, S. M. MOFFETT, and B. WILDI, *J. Amer. Chem. Soc.* 1946, **68**, 406.
18. M. HASEGAWA and T. SHIRATO, *J. Amer. Chem. Soc.* 1953, **75**, 5507.

19. J. BAUDRENGHIEN, J. JADOT and R. HULS, *Bull. Acad. Belg. Cl. Sci.* 1953, **39**, 105; *Chem Abs.* 1955, **49**, 2430.
20. E. SPÄTH and K. EITER, *Ber. dtsch. chem. Ges.* 1941, **74**, 1851.
21. For leading references see G. POPJAK, *Ann. Rev. Biochem.* 1958, **27**, 533; J. W. CORNFORTH and G. POPJAK, *Tetrahedron Letters*, 1959 **19**, 29; H. C. RILLING and K. BLOCH, *J. Biol Chem.* 1959, **234**, 1424; F. LYNEN, H. EGGERER, U. HENNING and I. KESSEL, *Angew. Chem.* 1958, **70**, 739.
22. F. LYNEN, B. W. AGRANOFF, H. EGGERER, U. HENNING, and E. M. MÖSLEIN, *Angew. Chem.* 1959. **71**, 657.
23. A. J. BIRCH, J. SCHOFIELD and H. SMITH, *Chem. and Ind.* 1958, 1321.
24. A. J. BIRCH, P. ELIOT and A. R. PENFOLD, *Austral. J. Chem.* 1954, **7**, 169. A. J. BIRCH, *Fortschr. Chem. Org. Naturstoffe*, 1957, **14**, 186.
25. A. R. TODD, personal communication.
26. R. ROBINSON, *The Structural Relations of Natural Products*, Clarendon Press, Oxford, 1955.
27. U. GLOOR and O. WISS, *Experientia*, 1958, **14**, 410.
28. K. Hata and A. Nitta, *J. Pharm. Soc. Japan*, 1957, **77**, 941. K. HATA, *J. Pharm. Soc. Japan*, 1956, **76**, 666.
29. F. A. L. ANET, G. K. HUGHES and E. RITCHIE, *Austral. J. Sci. Res.*, 1949, **2**, 608.
30. R. ANEJA, S. K. MUKERJEE and T. R. SESHADRI, *Tetrahedron*, 1958, **4**, 256.
31. S. RANGASWAMI and B. V. SASTRY, *Curr. Sci.* 1955, **24**, 13, 337; *Archiv. Pharm.* 1959, **292**, 171.
32. T. A. GEISSMAN, *Austral. J. Chem.* 1958, **11**, 376.
33. H. HÜBNER and W. RIEDL, *Chem. Ber.* 1960, **93**, 312.
34. D. H. R. BARTON, A. BHATI, P. DE MAYO and G. A. MORRISON, *J. Chem. Soc.* 1958, 4393.
35. E. TAKENS, *Reichstoff*, 1929, **4**, 8.
36. F. A. L. ANET, F. R. BLANKS and G. K. HUGHES, *Austral. J. Sci. Res.* 1949, **2**, 127.
37. E. SPÄTH and K. KLAGER, *Ber. dtsch. chem. Ges.* 1934, **67**, 859.
38. A. CHATTERJEE and A. CHOUDHURY, *Naturwiss.* 1955, **42**, 512.
39. A. G. CALDWELL and E. R. H. JONES, *J. Chem. Soc.* 1945, 540.
40. E. SPÄTH and F. VIERHAPPER, *Ber. dtsch. chem. Ges.* 1938, **71**, 1667.
41. E. SPÄTH and E. KAINRATH, *Ber. dtsch. chem. Ges.* 1937, **70**, 2272.
42. E. SPÄTH, A. F. J. SIMON and J. LINTNER, *Ber. dtsch. chem. Ges.* 1936, **69**, 1656.
43. O. ISLER, R. RÜEGG, L. H. CHOPARD-DIT-JEAN, A. WINTERSTEIN and O. WISS, *Helv. Chim. Acta* 1958, **41**, 786.
44. R. A. MORTON, *Nature, London* 1958, **182**, 1764; R. L. LESTER, F. L. CRANE and Y. HATEFI, *J. Amer. Chem. Soc.* 1958, **80**, 4751.
45. S. AKAI, *J. Pharm. Soc. Japan*, 1935, **55**, 537; S. AKAI, M. IMAIDA and T. MATSUKAWA, *J. Pharm. Soc. Japan* 1935, **55**, 214.
46. E. A. DOISY, S. B. BINKLEY and S. A. THAYER, *Chem. Rev.* 1941, **28**, 477.
47. E. SPÄTH and K. KLAGER, *Ber. dtsch. chem. Ges.* 1933, **66**, 914.
48. P. DUTTA, *J. Ind. Chem. Soc.* 1942, **19**, 425.
49. H. BÖHME and G. PIETSCH, *Ber. dtsch. chem. Ges.* 1939, **72**, 773; H. BÖHME and E. SCHEIDER, *Ber. dtsch. chem. Ges.* 1939, **72**, 780.
50. T. NOGUTI and M. KAWANAMI, *J. Pharm. Soc. Japan* 1939, **59**, 755; *Chem. Abs.* 1940, **34**, 2346.
51. B. B. DEY and P. P. PILLAY, *Arch. Pharm.* 1935, **273**, 223; E. SPÄTH, B. B. DEY and E. TYRAY, *Ber. dtsch. chem. Ges.* 1938, **71**, 1825; 1939, **72**, 53.
52. K. HATA and A. NITTA, *J. Pharm. Soc. Japan*, 1957, **77**, 941.
53. W. BRIDGE, R. G. HAYES and A. ROBERTSON, *J. Chem. Soc.* 1937, 279.
54. E. SPÄTH and A. F. VON CHRISTIANI, *Ber dtsch. chem. Ges.* 1933, **66**, 1150.
55. F. W. EASTWOOD, G. K. HUGHES and E. RITCHIE, *Austral. J. Chem.* 1954, **7**, 87.
56. G. EHRENSVÄRD, Chemical Society (London) Special Publication, 1958, No. 12, 17.
57. A. J. BIRCH, Chemical Society (London) Special Publication, 1958, No. 12, 4.
58. N. FINCH and W. D. OLLIS, *Proc. Chem. Soc.* 1960, 176.
59. J. AXELROD, S. SENOH and B. WITKOP, *J. Biol. Chem.* 1958, **233**, 697; *J. Amer. Chem. Soc.* 1959, **81**, 1768.

60. J. LINKS, *Biochim. Biophys. Acta*, 1960, **38**, 193.
61. D. H. R. BARTON and J. B. HENDRICKSON, *J. Chem. Soc.* 1956, 1028; *Chem. and Ind.* 1955, 682.
62. R. F. C. BROWN, J. J. HOBBS, G. K. HUGHES and E. RITCHIE, *Austral. J. Chem.* 1954, **7**, 348.
63. J. A. LAMBERTON and J. R. PRICE, *Austral. J. Chem.* 1953, **6**, 66.
64. S. E. WRIGHT, *J. Chem. Soc.* 1948, 2005.
65. K. D. KIRBY and M. D. SUTHERLAND, *Austral. J. Chem.* 1956, **9**, 411.
66. O. A. STAMM, H. SCHMID and J. BÜCHI, *Helv. Chim. Acta* 1958, **41**, 2006.
67. H. L. HALLER, L. D. GOODHUE and H. A. JONES, *Chem. Rev.* 1942, **30**, 33.
68. E. A. KACZKA, C. H. SHUNK, J. W. RICHTER, F. J. WOLF, M. M. GASSER and K. FOLKERS, *J. Amer. Chem. Soc.* 1956, **78**, 4125.
69. J. C. BELL, A. ROBERTSON and T. S. SUBRAMANIAM, *J. Chem. Soc.* 1936, 627.
70. E. SPÄTH, P. K. BOSE, H. SCHMID, E. DOBROVOLNY and A. MOOKERJEE, *Ber. Dtsch. Chem. Ges.* 1940, **73**, 1361.
71. J. C. BELL and A. ROBERTSON, *J. Chem. Soc.* 1936, 1828; J. C. BELL, A. ROBERTSON and T. S. SUBRAMANIAM, *J. Chem. Soc.* 1937, 286; J. C. BELL, W. BRIDGE and A. ROBERTSON, *J. Chem. Soc.* 1937, 1542.
72. O. ISLER and O. WISS, *Vitamins and Hormones* 1959, **17**, 51.
73. E. SPÄTH, P. K. BOSE, J. MATZKE and N. C. GUHA, *Ber. Dtsch. Chem. Ges.* 1939, **72**, 821.
74. A. ROBERTSON and T. S. SUBRAMANIAM, *J. Chem. Soc.* 1937, 1545.
75. F. E. KING, T. J. KING and L. C. MANNING, *J. Chem. Soc.* 1957, 563; 1953, 3932.
76. A. McGOOKIN, A. ROBERTSON and E. TITTENSOR, *J. Chem. Soc.* 1939, 1579.
77. J. POLONSKY, *Bull. Soc. Chim.* 1957, **24**, 1079.
78. E. SMITH, N. HOSANSKY, W. G. BYWATER and E. E. VAN TAMELEN, *J. Amer. Chem. Soc.* 1957, **79**, 3534.
79. H. D. SCHROEDER, W. BENCZE, O. HALPERN and H. SCHMID, *Chem. Ber.* 1959, **92**, 2338.
80. F. E. KING, J. R. HOUSLEY and T. J. KING, *J. Chem. Soc.* 1954, 1392.
81. N. L. DUTTA, *J. Ind. Chem. Soc.* 1959, **36**, 165.
82. W. BENCZE and H. SCHMID, *Experientia* 1954, **10**, 12.
83. E. SPÄTH and P. KAINRATH, *Ber. dtsch. chem. Ges.* 1936, **69**, 2062.
84. A. CHATTERJEE and S. S. MITRA, *J. Amer. Chem. Soc.* 1949, **71**, 606.
85. E. SPÄTH, K. KLAGER and C. SCHLÖSSER, *Ber. dtsch. chem. Ges.* 1931, **64**, 2203.
86. E. SPÄTH and H. SCHMID, *Ber. dtsch. chem. Ges.* 1940, **73**, 1309.
    E. SPÄTH, N. PLATZER and H. SCHMID, *Ber. dtsch. chem. Ges.* 1940, **73**, 709.
    H. SCHMID, *Sci. Proc. Roy. Dublin Soc.* 1956, **27**, 145.
87. B. KAMTHONG and A. ROBERTSON, *J. Chem. Soc.* 1939, 933.
88. H. BICKEL and H. SCHMID, *Helv. Chim. Acta*, 1953, **36**, 664; L. B. NORTON and R. HANSBERRY, *J. Amer. Chem. Soc.* 1945, **67**, 1609.
89. B. F. BURROWS, N. FINCH, W. D. OLLIS and I. O. SUTHERLAND, *Proc. Chem. Soc.* 1959, 150.
90. L. J. BELLAMY, *The Infrared Spectra of Complex Molecules*, Methuen, 1958, p. 34.
91. M. MURAKAMI, *J. Chem. Soc. Japan*, 1932, **53**, 150, 162.
92. F. N. LAHEY and W. C. THOMAS, *Austral. J. Sci. Res.* 1949, **2**, 423.
93. E. A. KACZKA, C. H. SHUNK, J. W. RICHTER, F. J. WOLF, M. M. GASSER and K. FOLKERS, *J. Amer. Chem. Soc.* 1956, **78**, 4125.
94. E. A. KACZKA, F. J. WOLF, F. P. RATHE and K. FOLKERS, *J. Amer. Chem. Soc.* 1955, **77**, 6404.
95. H. HOEKSEMA, J. L. JOHNSON and J. W. HINMAN, *J. Amer. Chem. Soc.* 1955, **77**, 6710.
96. J. POLONSKY, *Bull. Soc. Chim.* 1955, **22**, 541; 1956, **23**, 914; 1958, **25**, 929.
97. R. LIVINGSTONE, D. MILLER and S. MORRIS, *J. Chem. Soc.* 1960, 602.
98. B. F. BURROWS, W. D. OLLIS and L. M. JACKMAN, *Proc. Chem. Soc.* 1960, 177.
99. M. L. WOLFROM, F. L. BENTON, A. S. GREGORY, W. W. HESS, J. E. MAHAN and P. W. MORGAN, *J. Amer. Chem. Soc.* 1939, **61**, 2832.
100. J. E. MICHAEL, *Biochem. J.* 1948, **43**, 528; J. H. BIRKINSHAW, A. BRACKEN, J. E. MICHAEL and H. RAISTRICK, *Biochem. J.* 1951, **48**, 67.

101. A. J. Birch, *Chem. and Ind.* 1955, 682.
102. K. G. Neill and H. Raistrick, *Biochem. J.* 1957, **65**, 166.
103. F. H. Stodola, K. B. Raper and D. I. Fennell, *Nature, London* 1951, **167**, 773; J. A. Galarraga, K. G. Neill and H. Raistrick, *Biochem. J.* 1955, **61**, 456; R. E. Harman, J. Cason, F. H. Stodola and A. L. Adkins, *J. Org. Chem.* 1955, **20**, 1260.
104. E. Späth and E. Dobrovolny, *Ber. dtsch. chem. Ges.* 1939, **72**, 52.
105. E. Späth and H. Holzen, *Ber. dtsch. chem. Ges.* 1935, **68**, 1123.
106. E. Späth and L. Kahovec, *Ber. dtsch. chem. Ges.* 1933, **66**, 1146.
107. A. Bolleter, K. Eiter and H. Schmid, *Helv. Chim. Acta* 1951, **34**, 186.
108. E. Späth and H. Holzen, *Ber. dtsch. chem. Ges.* 1934, **67**, 264.
109. W. Riedl, *Liebigs. Ann.* 1954, **585**, 38.
110. W. Riedl, *Chem. Ber.* 1952, **85**, 692.
111. W. Riedl, J. Nickl, K. H. Risse and R. Mitteldorf, *Chem. Ber.* 1956, **89**, 1849; W. Riedl, *Liebigs. Ann.* 1954, **585**, 38.
112. W. Riedl and H. Hübner, *Chem. Ber.* 1957, **90**, 2870.
113. E. Späth and R. Hillel, *Ber. Chem.* 1939, **72**, 963, 2093.
114. J. Nickl, *Ber. dtsch. chem. Ges.* 1958, **91**, 1372.
115. W. Bridge, A. Crocker, T. Cubin and A. Robertson, *J. Chem. Soc.* 1937, 1530.
116. J. Nickl, *Ber. Chem.* 1959, **92**, 1989.
117. R. Livingstone and R. B. Watson, *J. Chem. Soc.* 1956, 3701.
118. R. W. Kierstead, R. P. Linstead and B. C. L. Weedon, *J. Chem. Soc.* 1952, 3610; 1953, 1799.
119. J. Nickl, *Chem. Ber.* 1958, **91**, 553.
120. A. A. Shamshurin, *J. Gen. Chem. (U.S.S.R.)*, 1946, **16**, 1877; 1951, **21**, 2068; *Chem. Abs.* 1947, **41**, 6237; 1952, **46**, 6637.
121. F. von Bruchhausen and H. Hoffmann, *Ber. dtsch. chem. Ges.* 1941, **74**, 1584.
122. R. G. Cooke, *Austral. J. Sci. Res.* 1950, **3**, 481.
123. L. F. Fieser, *J. Amer. Chem. Soc.* 1927, **49**, 857.
124. R. G. Cooke and T. C. Somers, *Austral. J. Sci. Res.* 1950, **3**, 466.
125. S. C. Hooker, *J. Amer. Chem. Soc.* 1936, **58**, 1168.
126. A. R. Alertsen, *Acta Chem. Scand.* 1955, **9**, 1725.

CHAPTER 5

SOME RECENT STUDIES RELATING TO THE INTRAMOLECULAR FREE RADICAL COUPLING OF PHENOLS

C. H. HASSALL and A. I. SCOTT

University College of Swansea and University of Glasgow

IT was the work of Pummerer and his collaborators[1] that first drew attention to the role of radicals as intermediates in phenol oxidation. Other extensive studies, among which the investigation by Michaelis[2] on the mechanism of oxidation of hydroquinones is particularly notable, indicate that the formation of a radical is a preliminary step in the majority and perhaps in all phenol oxidation reactions. The phenol radicals which are formed may be converted to stable end-products by several processes. Among these, coupling to form dimers is of particular significance. This may involve carbon–carbon, carbon–oxygen or oxygen–oxygen bonding as illustrated in the following simple examples:

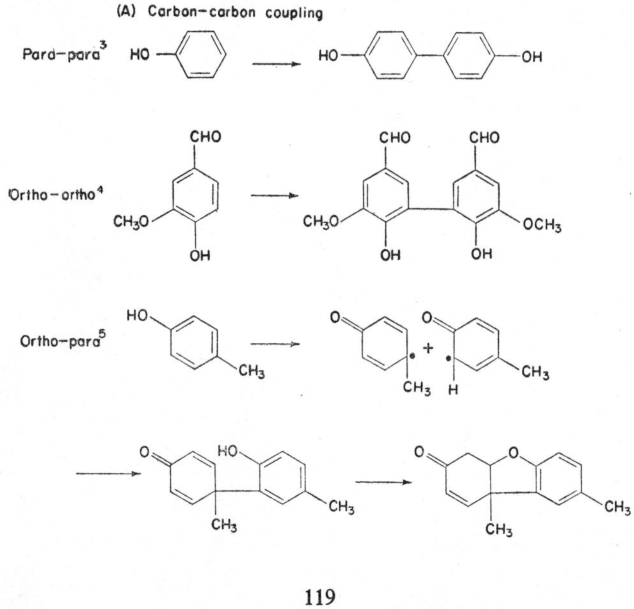

(B) Oxygen–oxygen coupling

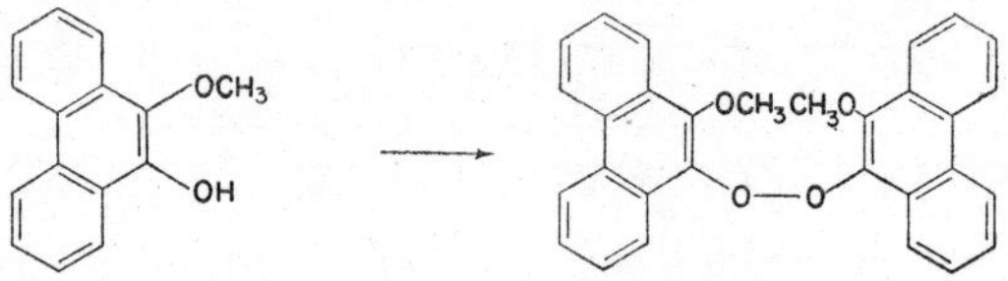

(C) Carbon–oxygen coupling[6]

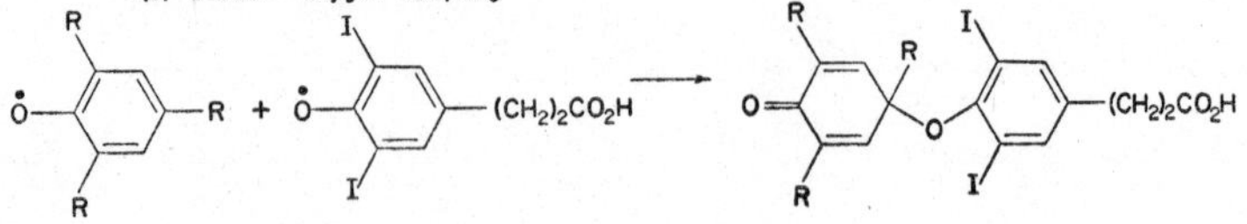

$R = C(CH_3)_3$

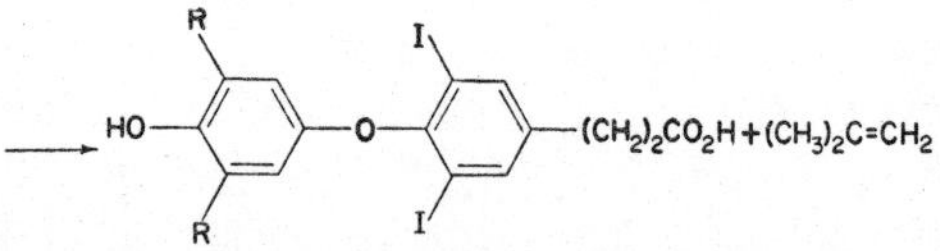

Our knowledge of the structural features which influence the stability of free-radicals is as yet insufficient to make it possible to anticipate in any but a few selected cases the actual course of intramolecular coupling when various alternatives are open.

There is rapidly increasing evidence that free-radical oxidation reactions play an important rôle in the biosynthesis of complex phenols. This topic has been discussed recently by Barton and Cohen[7] and by Erdtman and Wachtmeister[8] in two important reviews. Here, mechanisms involving free-radical intermediates are proposed for the biosynthesis of phenols in a

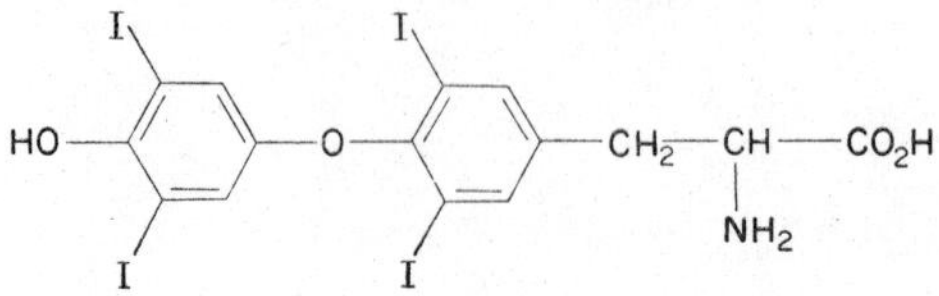

Thyroxine 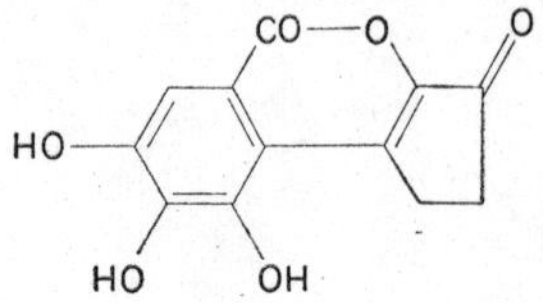   Brevifolin

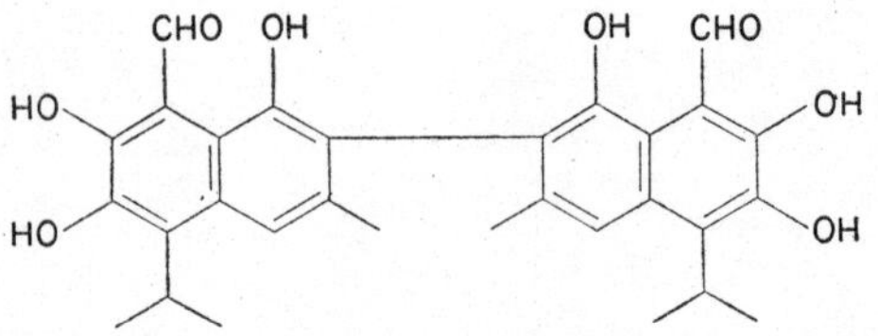

Gossypol

wide range of classes including alkaloids, fungal metabolites, lignin, various plant phenols and other natural products. In the short time since the publication of these reviews, additional studies have appeared which give further evidence of the rôle of free radical phenol coupling in biosynthetic sequences. Among these one may single out the model experiments relating to the biogenesis of thyroxine,[6] gossypol[9] and brevifolin.[20]

In this chapter some recent studies by the authors and their collaborators on intramolecular phenol coupling will be considered. These studies were prompted by the isolation of several compounds with spiran structures from the culture fluids of particular species of *Aspergillus* and *Penicillium*. These structures could evidently be derived by intramolecular coupling illustrated by, for example, the conversion of dihydrogeodin to geodin.

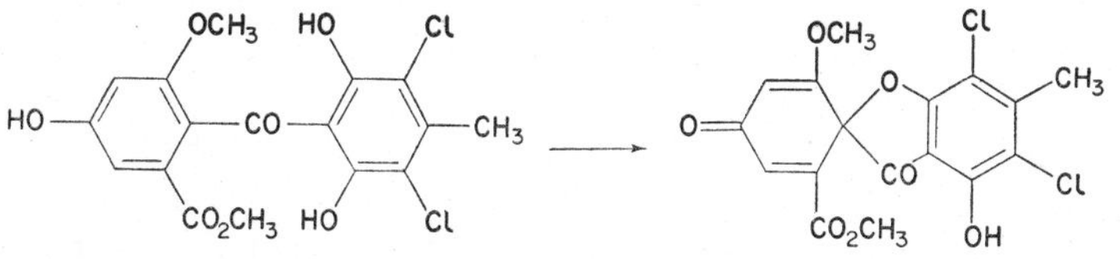

Dihydrogeodin   Geodin

This has led to the development of *in vitro* syntheses of individual metabolites and to the elucidation of some of the steps that are evidently involved in the biogenesis of these spirans. These experiments, we feel, illustrate the general principle that syntheses planned on biogenetic analogy strengthen our views on current biogenetic theory and, at the same time, lead us to predict the natural occurrence of new structures. An early example is

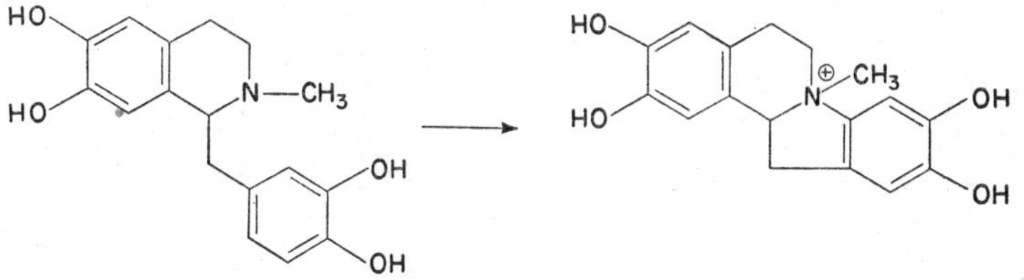

(1)   (2)

provided by Robinson's oxidation of laudanosoline (1), when instead of a morphine or aporphine type structure, the quaternary salt (2) was formed;[11] twenty years later a methyl ether of dehydrolaudanosoline (2) was isolated as a natural product.[12]

Several recent investigations are particularly suitable to illustrate how current views on phenol coupling reactions have been of assistance in structural work and in synthesis.

Griseofulvin.

The structure of the antibiotic griseofulvin, a metabolite of *Penicillium patulum* and *P. griseofulvum,* was assigned on the basis of extensive degradative studies initiated by Raistrick[13] and completed by Grove, Macmillan and their colleagues.[14] No attempt will be made to detail all the arguments for the structure but Fig. 1 summarises the principal reactions involved in these degradative studies.

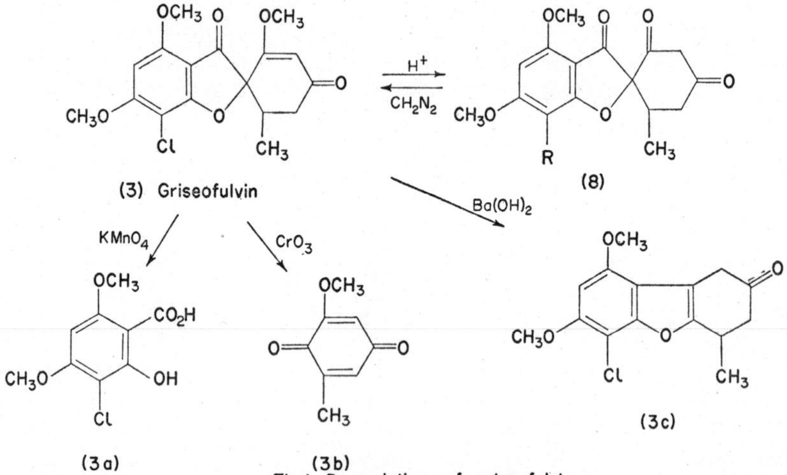

Fig.l. Degradation of griseofulvin

The evidence (see Fig. 1) leads unambiguously to the structure (3) for griseofulvin, as the fragments (3a) and (3b) account for all the atoms of griseofulvin whilst the formation of decarboxygriseofulvic acid (3c) *via* griseofulvic acid (8; R = Cl) is an acceptable process.

The application of current concepts of biogenesis to the case of griseofulvin suggests two distinct stages. In the first stage, condensation of seven acetic acid units in a head-to-tail fashion, possibly through a poly-β-keto-acid (4), followed by methylation and chlorination steps in undetermined sequence, leads to a benzophenone derivative (5). Labelling experiments by Birch and his collaborators[15] have clearly outlined this stage by indicating the head-to-tail incorporation of acetic acid units in griseofulvin while Barton and Cohen[7] first suggested that the second stage is probably a radical pairing step (6 → 7) followed by partial reduction of the dienone (7) giving griseofulvin (3).

Model experiments which simulate the second stage [see Fig. 2 (5) → (7)] of the biogenesis have been carried out *in vitro.*[16] The benzophenone (5), which was obtained quite readily by condensation of 4-methoxycarbonyl-2-methoxy-6-methylbenzoyl chloride and 2-chloro-3,5-dimethoxyphenol using mild Friedel-Crafts conditions, when treated with alkaline potassium ferricyanide at 0° gave a neutral ketone in 60% yield. This compound, exhibited the spectral properties [λ_{max} 238, 292, 330 mμ; ν_{max} 1726 (coumaranone C=O) and 1672 cm^{-1} (enone C=O)] of (±)-dehydrogriseofulvin (7). The solution spectra of the synthetic racemate were identical with those of the (−)-dehydro compound prepared by selenium dioxide dehydrogenation of griseofulvin.[17] The final step, selective reduction of dehydrogriseofulvin (7) to griseofulvin (3), now presented an interesting problem. Hydrogenation

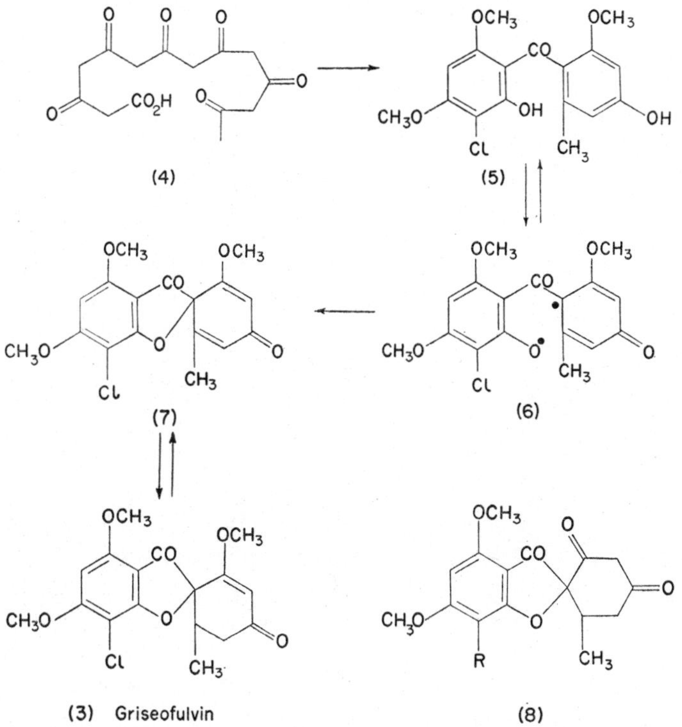

Fig.2 Biosynthesis and synthesis of griseofulvin

studies on (7) revealed that, using a wide variety of catalysts, a retrogression of the crucial biogenetic oxidation step occurred giving back the benzophenone derivative (5) in quantitative yield. A solution to the problem was, however, eventually found by employing a catalyst consisting of rhodium (5%) and selenium (3%) on charcoal. Reduction of (±)-dehydrogriseofulvin (7) in ethanolic solution under carefully controlled conditions in the presence of this catalyst afforded mainly the benzophenone derivative (5), together with a small amount (<10%) of (±)-griseofulvin.

The observation that (−)-dehydrogriseofulvin gave only the natural stereoisomer established that this reduction was stereospecific. The expectation that the synthetic racemate would be stereochemically homogeneous was confirmed when its acid hydrolysis gave ($\pm$)-griseofulvic acid (8; R = Cl) which was resolved *via* the highly crystalline (+)-griseofulvic acid quinine metho-salt. Regeneration of the acid by ion exchange chromatography gave a product identical with (+)-griseofulvic acid derived from the natural material. This constitutes a total synthesis of griseofulvin, as (+)-griseofulvic acid can be transformed into the antibiotic by treatment with diazomethane.

Two further sets of experiments indicated that the *in vitro* and *in vivo* sequences were similar. In the first of these, which was a joint study by Birch and Scott and collaborators, ^{14}C-labelled biosynthetic griseofulvin was converted to the dehydro compound (7). The latter on being fed to *Penicillium patulum* was incorporated into the griseofulvin produced to the extent of 30%, as determined by radio-assay.[18]

In the second series of experiments a careful examination of *P. patulum* mother liquors revealed the presence of several new metabolites of this mould. These were shown to include the benzophenone (5), dehydrogriseofulvin (7), and the compound (8; R = H) which were identified by comparison with material already at hand from synthetic and degradative experiments. In addition a new benzophenone, griseophenone $C_{17}H_{17}O_5Cl$, was isolated and it has been shown to have structure (9). The leading evidence for this proposal was provided by the detailed mass spectrum which clearly defined the groups attached to each aromatic ring. The presence of two methoxyl groups (Zeisel), a free and a bonded aromatic hydroxyl group (ν 3550, 3350 cm^{-1}), and a bonded benzophenone carbonyl group (1610 cm.$^{-1}$) accounted for the five oxygen atoms. Treatment of griseophenone (12) with base afforded a xanthone (13) with loss of methanol. That the xanthone contained the remaining methoxyl grouping at position 1 was shown by hydrolysis with mild acid to a 1-hydroxyxanthone. This leads to the partial structure (12) for griseophenone. The orientation shown in (9) was favoured by analogy with the structure of geodin (see p. 121).

(12)   (13)

Scott and co-workers have also isolated griseoxanthone, $C_{15}H_{12}O_5$, which contains one methoxyl group and shows the spectral characteristics of a 1,6-dihydroxyxanthone. The fact that (10) is a likely intermediate in the biogenesis of griseofulvin suggested that the xanthone is in fact (11; R = H).

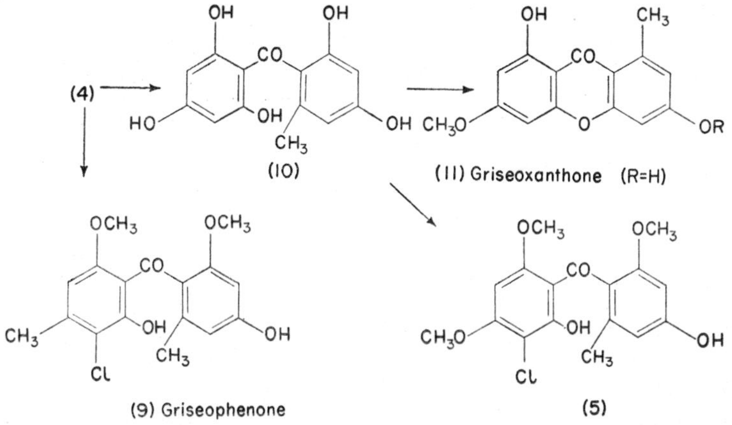

(4) → (10) → (11) Griseoxanthone (R=H)

(9) Griseophenone

(5)

This was verified by its methylation to lichexanthone (11; R = Me), and by the non-identity of griseoxanthone with the synthetic isomer (11; R = Me; OMe = OH). This evidence has led to the suggestion[19] that the biogenesis of griseofulvin may be summarized as shown in Fig. 2.

Sulochrin, Geodin, Asterric acid and Geodoxin.

There is indirect evidence that these four compounds, which have been isolated from different fungi or, in one case, from different strains of a particular species, are involved in a single pathway of biosynthesis.

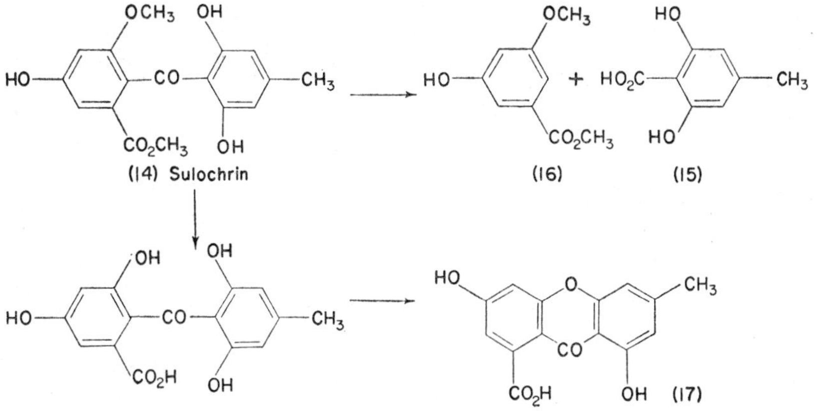

(14) Sulochrin

(16)   (15)

(17)

Reactions of sulochrin

Sulochrin was isolated by Nishikawa[20] in 1936 from the culture fluid of *Oospora sulphurea-ochracea.* It has been assigned the benzophenone structure (14) on the basis of evidence of functional group identification and hydrolysis experiments. Acid-catalysed fission led to *p*-orsellinic acid (15) and the monomethyl ether of α-resorcylic acid methyl ester (16). The point of attachment of the two aromatic nuclei was defined by the fact that demethyl-sulochrin, but not sulochrin itself, was readily converted to the xanthone (17). This leaves no doubt that the structure (14) assigned[20] to sulochrin is correct.

The chemistry of geodin has been the subject of extensive investigation. The initial studies by Raistrick and co-workers[21] were stimulated by the observation that two strains of *Aspergillus terreus*, described as Ac 100 and No 45, were capable of utilising chloride ion in culture solution. This led to the isolation of the chlorinated metabolites geodin and erdin from the culture fluids. Recently Komatsu[22] has shown that geodin is also produced by the species *Penicillium paxilli* var. *echinulatum*. The molecular structures of geodin and erdin are now established. At the outset of the structural studies Raistrick *et al*[21] obtained degradative and synthetic evidence that favoured the constitution (18) for dihydrogeodin. Geodin hydrate, the product of acid hydrolysis was assigned the structure (19). Studies by Barton and Scott[23] defined the orientation of substituents in dihydrogeodin and related compounds. This, together with spectroscopic evidence, led to the structure (20) for geodin. Erdin is the corresponding acid. Some of the reactions of geodin are illustrated below.

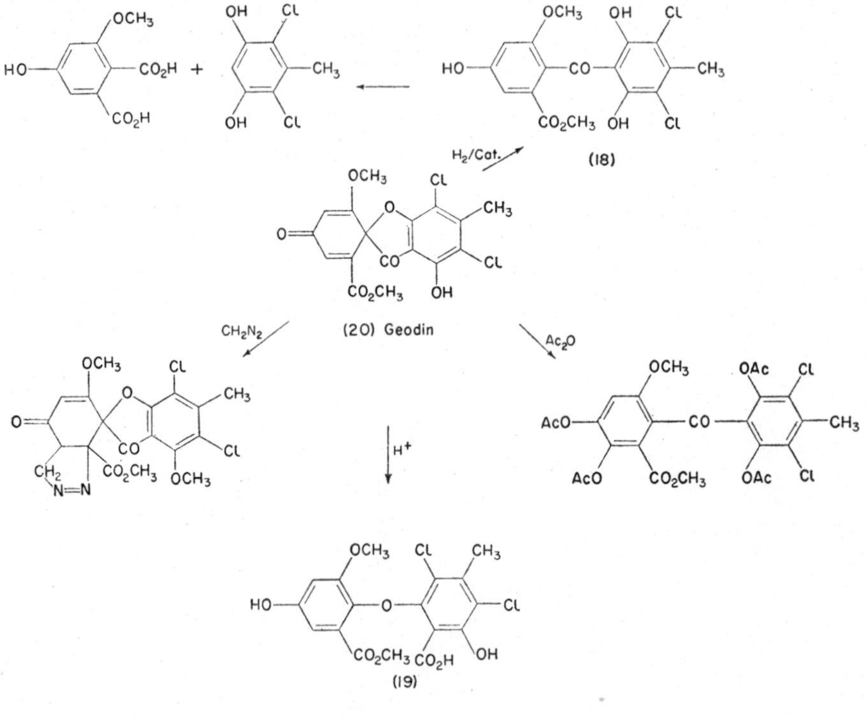

Reactions of geodin

It has been found by Hassall and co-workers that the strains of *A. terreus* which produce geodin and erdin mutate readily, either on irradiation with ultraviolet light or spontaneously in the course of repeated subculturing. The examination of the culture fluids of selected mutants has led to the isolation of compounds which are clearly related in structure to geodin and erdin. Two of these are new metabolites, asterric acid and geodoxin, which deserve particular attention.

Asterric acid, $C_{17}H_{16}O_8$, gives derivatives which indicate that the molecule contains two free phenolic hydroxyl groups, one carboxyl, one methoxycarbonyl, one methoxyl and one C-methyl group. The absence of carbonyl reactivity, resistance to hydrogenation and the nature of the infrared and ultraviolet absorption spectra suggested that it might be a diphenyl ether related to geodin.

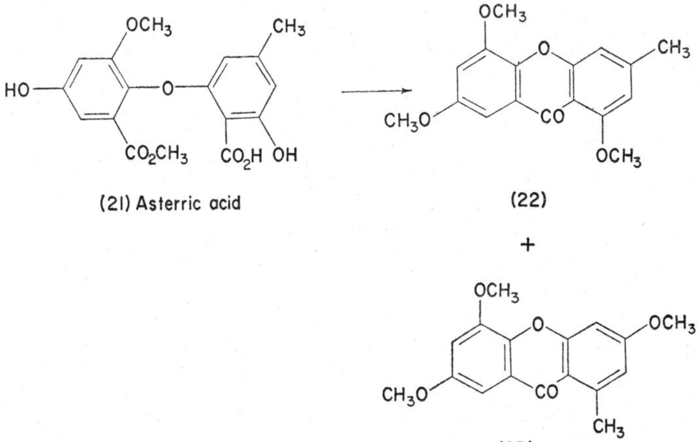

(21) Asterric acid   (22)

+

(23)

This was confirmed and the constitution of asterric acid was established[24] as (21) by showing that the xanthones (22) and (23) obtained by treatment of asterric acid with sulphuric acid followed by methylation, were identical with trimethylnorgeodins A and B.

Geodoxin has been shown to be a spirodienone (24). This structure follows from the definition of functional groups, the formation of the dichloro-*p*-orsellinic acid (25) on oxidation with alkaline hydrogen peroxide, and the production of a monobasic acid, dihydrogeodoxin, on catalytic hydrogenation. This latter compound gives a mixture of products, including methyl 2,5-dihydroxy-3-methoxybenzoate (27) on treatment with 80% sulphuric acid. Spectroscopic evidence, in particular the absorption band at 1670 cm^{-1} indicative of a 5-methoxycyclohexa-1,4-diene-3-one chromophore and the remarkable similarity of the curve obtained when the absorption due to dichloro-orsellinic acid is subtracted from that of geodoxin to the curve

Reactions of geodoxin

similarly obtained from picrolichenic acid (see p. 131) and orsellinic acid, gave support for the structures (24) and (26) which were assigned to geodoxin and dihydrogeodoxin respectively.[25]

Even a casual consideration of the structures of sulochrin, geodin, asterric acid and geodoxin suggests that they are biogenetically related. In the case of the last three compounds this might be expected from the fact that they are produced by closely related mutant strains. Furthermore, it is significant that among the compounds which accompany sulochrin in the culture fluid of *Oospora sulphurea-ochracea* is one (substance A)[20] which has the same properties as asterric acid. Although a direct comparison has not been made, there is strong evidence in favour of this identification. This indicates that sulochrin and the products from *A. terreus* are involved in a common metabolic sequence.

Model *in vitro* experiments[26] support the view that this sequence is as follows. In this scheme no particular significance is attached to the presence of chlorine in geodin and geodoxin; it is assumed that chlorine substitution is a secondary process. This would be analogous to the case of griseofulvin where it has been shown that bromo- and dechloro-analogues are formed when the culture medium of the fungus *Penicillium griseofulvum* is modified.[27].

(28), Sulochrin [R=H]

(29), Geodin [R=Cl]

(31), Geodoxin [R=Cl]

(30), Asterric acid [R=H]

Sulochrin has been converted in good yield to dechlorogeodin (29, R = H) by treatment with alkaline potassium ferricyanide.[26] This is similar to the conversion of dihydrogeodin and *O*-methyldihydrogeodin to geodin[26,29] and *O*-methylgeodin[28] respectively. It is of interest that after the completion of these model experiments, information became available that the intramolecular radical coupling reaction involved in the conversion of dihydrogeodin to geodin has already been achieved by Komatsu using an enzyme preparation from *Penicillium paxilli* var. *echinulatum*.[30]

Asterric acid is obtained in excellent yield from sulochrin through acid-catalysed hydrolysis of the spirodienone (29, R = H).

Consideration of the constitution of geodoxin suggests three possible biosynthetic routes. It could be formed from a corresponding depside (cf. 32) by intramolecular oxidative coupling, by Baeyer-Villiger oxidation[31] of geodin, or from the appropriate chlorinated analogue of asterric acid (30, R = Cl) by oxidative coupling through the carboxy radical (33). Of these possibilities the third is favoured by the fact that it has been achieved

in vitro starting with a known metabolite of *A. terreus*. Hassall and Lewis have found that when geodin hydrate (19) is treated with lead dioxide in an inert solvent, geodoxin is obtained in quantitative yield. A similar coupling reaction using asterric acid has led to dechlorogeodoxin, while 2-carboxy-4 hydroxydiphenyl ether (34) has yielded the simple *spiro*-dienone (35). On the other hand all attempts to oxidize the model compound (32) to (35) have been unsuccessful.

Picrolichenic Acid.

This compound, $C_{25}H_{30}O_7$, a metabolite of the lichen *Pertusaria amara*, has many features of its chemistry that recall the cases of griseofulvin, geodoxin and related compounds. There is evidence that the molecule contains a carboxyl group, a phenolic hydroxyl group, a methoxyl group, a lactone ring and two *n*-amyl groups. Mild alkaline hydrolysis of picro-lichenic acid followed by simultaneous decarboxylation and demethylation with hydrobromic acid gave a phenol which was identified as 2,2'-di-*n*-amyl-4,6,4',6'-tetrahydroxydiphenyl (36). This, together with spectroscopic evidence led Wachmeister[33] to assign the structure (37) to picrolichenic acid.

The unusual spiran system in picrolichenic acid suggests the possibility that it is derived from a depside by carbon–carbon coupling.[33] This could arise through blocking of carbon–oxygen coupling as a result of methylation of the appropriate hydroxyl group. Approaches to a synthesis of picrolichenic

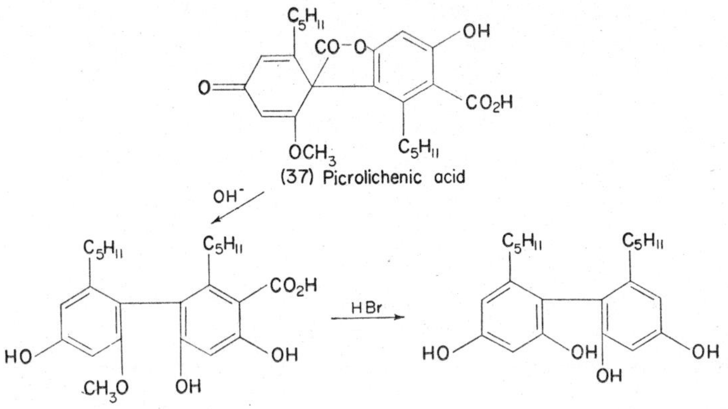

(37) Picrolichenic acid

(36)

acid based upon this proposed biosynthesis have so far led to dihydro-picrolichenic acid (38), but this acid has not been affected by treatment with alkaline potassium ferricyanide under vigorous conditions. The application of alternative oxidative coupling reagents is now receiving attention.[34]

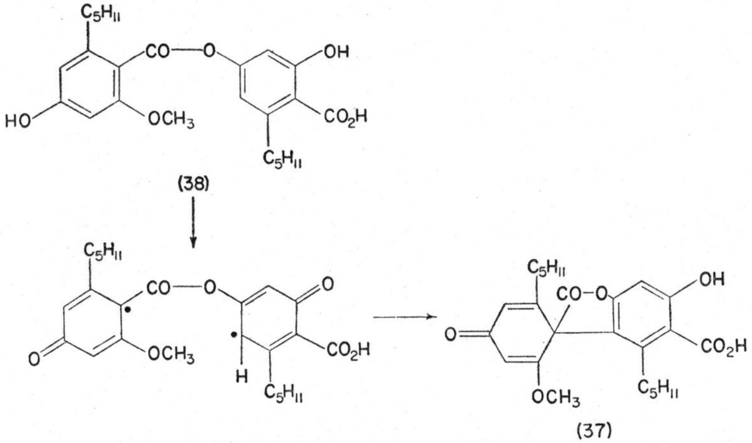

(38)

(37)

Synthesis of picrolichenic acid[35]

Note added in proof: Since this Chapter was written three further examples of the synthesis of natural products by processes involving the oxidative coupling of phenolic precursors have been described.

The synthesis of picrolichenic acid (37) from the ester (38) has been completed using manganese dioxide as the oxidant.[35] The same reagent has also been used in the synthesis of diploicin (40) via the depsides (39; R = H or CH$_2$Ph).[36] This is the first synthesis of a natural product of the depsidone type from a depside precursor and it illustrates their close biogenetic relationship.

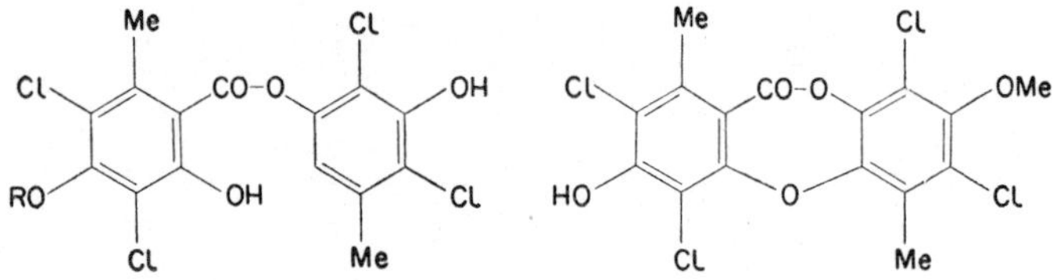

(39)   (40) Diploicin

Barton and Kirby's synthesis of galanthamine[37] (42) *via* the phenolic intermediate (41) illustrates the probable role of oxidative coupling in the biosynthesis of *Amaryllidaceae* alkaloids.

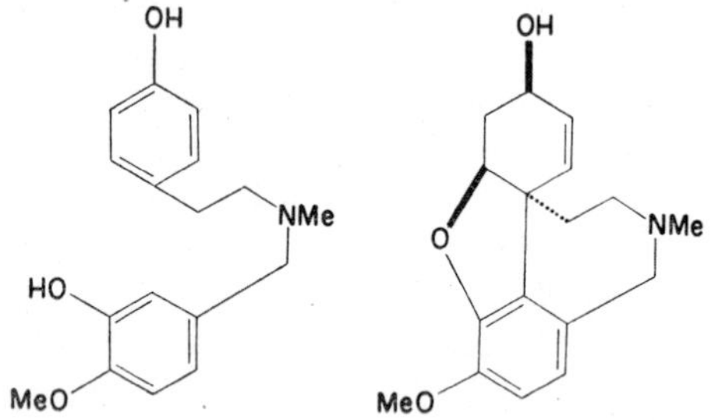

(41)   (42) Galanthamine

REFERENCES

1. R. PUMMERER and F. FRANFURTER, *Ber.* 1914, **47**, 1472; 1919, **52**, 1416; R. PUMMERER and E. CHERBULIEZ, *ibid.* 1914, **47**, 2957; 1919, **52**, 1392; R. PUMMERER, *ibid.* 1919, **52**, 1403; R. PUMMERER, D. MELAMED and H. PUTTFARCKEN, *ibid.* 1922, **55**, 3116; R. PUMMERER, H. PUTTFARCKEN and P. SCHOPFLOCHER, *ibid.* 1925, **58**, 1808; R. PUMMERER and F. LUTHER, *ibid.* 1928, **61**, 1102.
2. L. MICHAELIS, *Cold Spring Harbour Symposium Quant. Biol.* I, 1939, 33; *Ann. N.Y. Acad. Sci.* 1940, **40**, 39.
3. G. W. K. CAVILL, E. R. COLE, P. T. GILHAM and D. J. McHUGH, *J. Chem. Soc.* 1954, 2785.
4. J. M. GULLAND and G. U. HOPTON, *J. Chem. Soc.* 1932, 439.
5. D. H. R. BARTON, A. M. DEFLORIN and O. E. EDWARDS, *Chem. and Ind.* 1955, 1039.
6. T. MATSUURA and H. J. CAHNMANN, *J. Amer. Chem. Soc.* 1960, **82**, 2055.
7. D. H. R. BARTON and T. COHEN, *Festschrift A. Stoll* Birkhauser, Basel, 1957, p. 117.
8. H. ERDTMAN and C. A. WACHTMEISTER, *Festschrift A. Stoll* Birkhauser, Basel, 1957, p. 144.
9. J. D. EDWARDS and J. L. CASHAW, *J. Amer. Chem. Soc.* 1957, **79**, 2283; J. D. EDWARDS, *ibid.* 1958, **80**, 3798.
10. H. W. WANZLICK, *Ber.* 1959, **92**, 3006.
11. R. ROBINSON and S. SUGASAWA, *J. Chem. Soc.* 1932, 789.
12. J. EWING, G. K. HUGHES, E. RITCHIE and W. C. TAYLOR, *Nature* 1952, **169**, 618.
13. A. E. OXFORD, H. RAISTRICK and P. SIMONART, *Biochem. J.* 1939, **33**, 240.
14. J. F. GROVE, J. MACMILLAN, T. P. C. MULHOLLAND and M. A. T. ROGERS, *J. Chem. Soc.* 1952, 3977.
15. A. J. BIRCH, R. A. MASSY-WESTROPP, R. W. RICKARDS and H. SMITH, *ibid.* 1958, 360.

16. A. C. DAY, J. NABNEY and A. I. SCOTT, *Proc. Chem. Soc.* 1960, 284.
17. A. I. SCOTT, *Proc. Chem. Soc.* 1958, 195.
18. A. J. BIRCH, R. W. RICKARDS, J. NABNEY and A. I. SCOTT, unpublished.
19. W. J. MCMASTER, A. I. SCOTT and S. TRIPPETT, *J. Chem. Soc.*, 1960, 4628.
20. H. NISHIKAWA, *Acta Phytochim., Japan* 1939, **11**, 167, and earlier refs.
21. H. RAISTRICK and G. SMITH, *Biochem. J.* 1936, **30**, 1315; P. W. CLUTTERBUCK, W. KÖERBER and H. RAISTRICK, *ibid.* 1937, **31**, 1089; C. T. CALAM, P. W. CLUTTERBUCK, A. E. OXFORD and H. RAISTRICK, *ibid.* 1939, **33**, 579; 1947, **41**, 458.
22. E. KOMATSU, *Nippon Nogei-Kagaku Kaishi*, 1957, **31**, 349.
23. D. H. R. BARTON and A. I. SCOTT, *J. Chem. Soc.* 1958, 1767.
24. R. F. CURTIS, C. H. HASSALL, D. W. JONES and T. W. WILLIAMS, *J. Chem. Soc.*, 1960, 4838
25. C. H. HASSALL and T. C. MCMORRIS, *J. Chem. Soc.* 1959, 2831.
26. R. F. CURTIS, C. H. HASSALL, D. W. JONES and J. LEWIS, unpublished results.
27. J. MACMILLAN, *J. Chem. Soc.* 1954, 2585.
28. A. I. SCOTT, *Proc. Chem. Soc.* 1958, 195.
29. T. A. DAVIDSON and A. I. SCOTT, unpublished results.
30. E. KOMATSU, *Nippon Nogie-Kagaku Kaishi*, 1957, **31**, 698.
31. C. H. HASSALL, *Org. Reactions*, 1957, **9**, 73.
32. K. FRIES and E. BRANDES, *Ann.*, 1939, **542**, 48.
33. H. ERDTMAN and C. A. WACHTMEISTER, *Chem. and Ind.*, 1957, 1042; C. A. WACHTMEISTER, *Acta. Chem. Scand.* 1958, **12**, 147.
34. T. A. DAVIDSON and A. I. SCOTT, unpublished results.
35. T. A. DAVIDSON and A. I. SCOTT, *Proc. Chem. Soc.*, 1960, 390.
36. C. J. BROWN, D. E. CLARK, W. D. OLLIS and P. L. VEAL, *Proc. Chem. Soc.*, 1960, 393.
37. D. H. R. BARTON and G. W. KIRBY, *Proc. Chem. Soc.*, 1960, 392.

CHAPTER 6

RECENT WORK ON THE GALLOTANNINS

(*Summary*)

R. D. HAWORTH

University of Sheffield

EARLY workers, for example Fischer[1], Freudenberg[2] and Karrer[3] and their co-workers, and more recent studies such as those of White[4] and Grassman, Endres and Stiefenhofer[5] have suggested several conflicting structures for Chinese

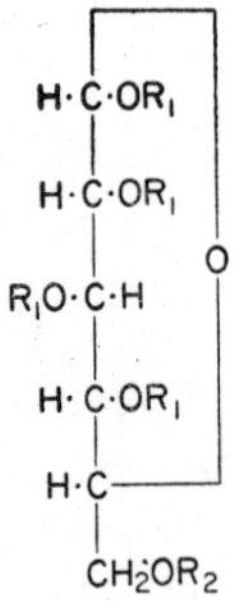

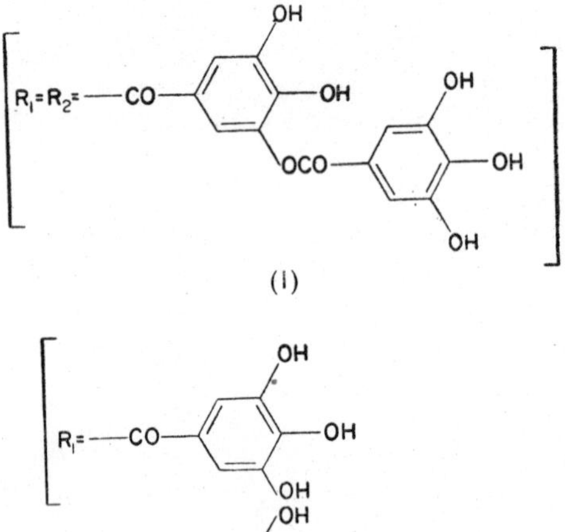

gallotannin (*Rhus semialata*, galls). These structures range from the poly-galloylated glucose types (1) and (2) to the polygalloylated polysaccharide structures advocated by White[4] and Grassman and co-workers[5].

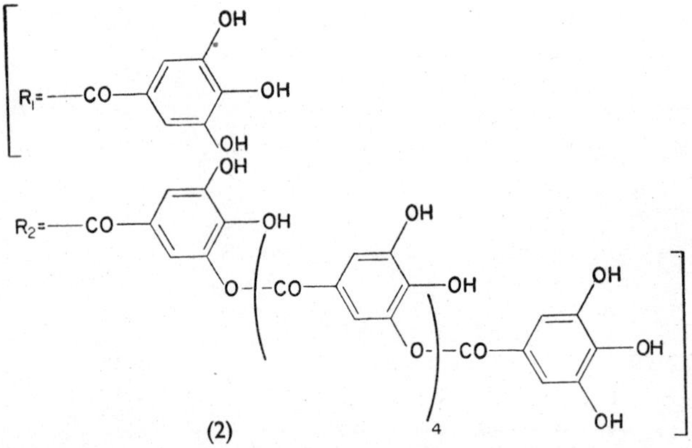

During attempts to clarify these conflicting theories a study has been made of Chinese and Turkish gallotannins (*Rhus semialata* and *Quercus infectoria*, galls) and of Sicilian (*Rhus coriaria*) and Stagshorn Sumach (*Rhus typhina*) tannins.

Two way paper chromatographic analysis of the aqueous extracts of these tannins showed that they consisted of a complex mixture of phenolic substances (e.g. Fig. 1, Chinese gallotannin) and the main component (gallotannin) of the extract was obtained as a white amorphous powder by a number of purification techniques dependent on the particular tannin under examination.

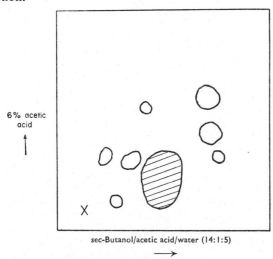

Fig. 1. Two dimensional chromatogram of gallotannin extract.

These products were chromatographically and polarimetrically pure and, except for Turkish gallotannin, indistinguishable. Carbon and hydrogen analyses, and glucose and gallic acid determination suggested the presence of 8–9 galloyl groups for each molecule of glucose. Hydrolysis of Chinese gallotannin, and Sicilian, or Stagshorn Sumach tannin by means of acids or with an esterase obtained by ion-exchange chromatography from tannase,[6] yielded gallic acid and glucose as the only carbohydrate. Methanolic alkaline hydrolysis of the methylated tannin also gave glucose which was isolated and characterized. It is therefore concluded that the carbohydrate core of the tannin is glucose and not a polysaccharide as suggested by White[4] and Grassman and co-workers;[5] these claims have been withdrawn during the course of this work.[7] Turkish gallotannin also yielded glucose and gallic acid on hydrolysis but identity with Chinese gallotannin is unlikely as there are analytical and polarometric discrepancies.

The polygalloylated glucose structure of Chinese gallotannin and of Sumach tannin was confirmed by methanolysis experiments. It was shown using model synthetic compounds that certain depside linkages, particularly those ortho to a phenolic group as in (3; R = OH), are methanolysed to yield in the case of (3; R = OH) methyl benzoate and methyl proto-catechuate, whereas depsides such as (3; R = H) and esters of gallic acid such as trigalloylglycerol and β-pentagalloylglucose were unaffected by methanol. Methanolysis of gallotannin yielded methyl gallate and an amorphous product identical analytically, polarimetrically, and chromato-graphically, with a specimen of β-pentagalloylglucose prepared by condensing

(3)

glucose with tri-O-benzylgalloyl chloride and subsequent hydrogenolysis. This observation indicates a fully galloylated glucose structure for gallotannin, and as interruption of the methanolysis at an intermediate stage yielded methyl m-digallate it is inferred that one of the glucose hydroxyl groups is esterified by a polygallic acid containing at least three galloyl groups. Although the gallotannins used in these experiments were chromato-graphically pure, their homogeneity has not been proved and Fischer's view[1] that they are composed of a mixture of closely related structures may be valid. It is hoped that countercurrent experiments now in progress may throw further light on this problem.

Tara tannin, obtained from *Caesalpinia spinosa*, has previously been classed as a gallotannin in spite of its marked acidic properties[8]. The crude aqueous extract was found to be a complex mixture from which a chromato-graphically pure substance was isolated. Acidic or enzymic hydrolysis of the tannin yielded a mixture of gallic and quinic acids, and preliminary analytical results suggest a tetra- or penta-galloylated quinic acid structure. This was confirmed by methanolysis experiments which also suggest that one of the hydroxyl groups of the quinic acid residue is esterified by a polygallic acid containing at least three galloyl groups.

REFERENCES

1. E. FISCHER, *Ber.* 1919, **52**, 809.
2. K. FREUDENBERG, *Die Chemie der natürlichen Gerbstoffe*, Berlin, 1933, 38.
3. P. KARRER, H. R. SALOMON and J. PEYER, *Helv. Chim. Acta* 1923, **6**, 17.
4. T. WHITE, *The Chemistry of the Vegetable Tannins*, Symposium, Society of Leather Trades' Chemists, 13, (Croydon 1956) *Chem. Abs.* 1958, 2183.
5. W. GRASSMAN, H. ENDRES and G. STIEFENHOFER, *Chem. Ber.* 1956, **89**, 454.
6. R. D. HAWORTH, K. JONES and H. J. ROGERS, *Proc. Chem. Soc.* 1958, 8.
7. T. WHITE and H. G. C. KING, *Chem. and Ind.* 1958, 683; H. ENDRES, private communi-cation at Plant Phenolics Group meeting, April 1960.
8. D. BURTON and H. E. NURSTEN, *The Chemistry of the Vegetable Tannins*, Symposium, Society of Leather Trades' Chemists, 57 (Croydon 1956). *Chem. Abs.* 1958, 2183.

CHAPTER 7

THE BIOSYNTHESIS OF GALLIC ACID

(*Summary*)

E. HASLAM

The University, Sheffield

THE discovery[1] that the gallotannin from pods of *Caesalpinia spinosa* had a polygalloylated quinic acid (1; R_1, R_2, R_2, R_4 galloyl or polygalloyl) instead of the more usual polygalloylated glucose[2] type of structure stimulated our interest in the biosynthesis of gallic acid since the occurrence together of these closely related substances indicated a possible biogenetic relationship.

We used for our initial studies the mould *Phycomyces blakesleeanus*. Earlier reports[3] were confirmed concerning the production of gallic (5) and protocatechuic (6) acids by *Phycomyces blakesleeanus* when grown on glucose media, and both acids were isolated from old media by counter current distribution.

Two routes of biosynthesis of gallic acid in *Phycomyces blakesleeanus* are possible but we have no evidence that its production follows the oxidation of protocatechuic acid [route (a)] in a manner analogous to the latter's formation from p-hydroxybenzoic acid by *Pseudomonas*[4]. The mould when grown on glucose supplemented with [14C]-protocatechuic acid gave no [14C]-gallic acid. Further the action of the widely distributed plant enzyme, polyphenoloxidase, on protocatechuic acid gave no gallic acid, although under similar conditions the former acid was smoothly produced from p-hydroxybenzoic acid.

Dehydrogenation of 5-dehydroshikimic acid (3) [route (b)] is favoured as the mechanism of biogenesis of gallic acid, and growth experiments with *Phycomyces blakesleeanus* have supported this conclusion. These experiments also indicated that 5-dehydroquinic (2) and shikimic (4) acids are near but not immediate precursors of the acid. In addition, both 5-dehydroshikimic (3) and shikimic (4) acids were isolated by ion exchange chromatography from old culture media of *Phycomyces blakesleeanus*, and the former is transformed to gallic acid in good yield by several methods of chemical oxidation.

Other studies have been concerned initially with the identification of both 5-dehydroshikimic (3) and 5-dehydroquinic (2) acids in gallotannin-producing plants. So far this has not been achieved but this is possibly due to their presence in quite low concentrations because they are intermediates which are rapidly metabolised. Further work on this point is in progress.

5-Dehydroshikimic acid (3) has been suggested by Wenkert[6] as being involved in the formation of chebulic acid and similarly it may reasonably be

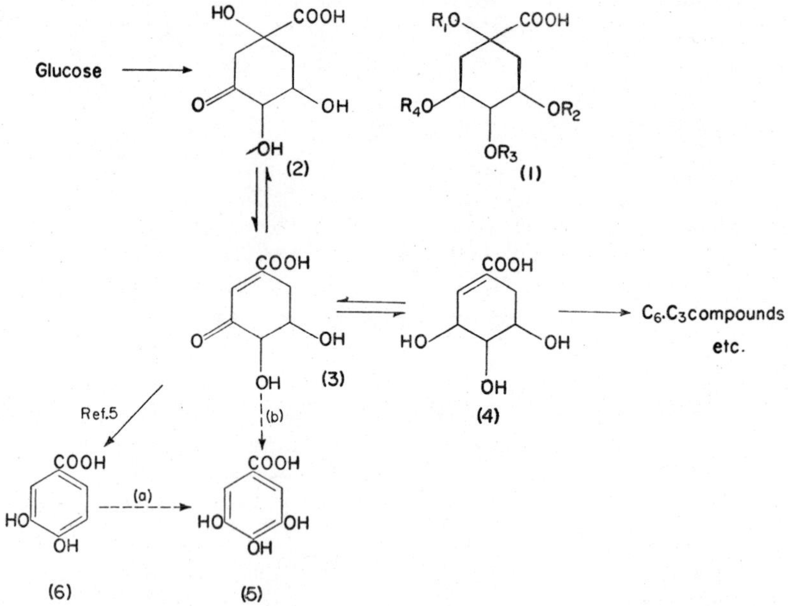

postulated that 5-dehydroshikimic acid (3) is an alternative precursor of C_6C_3 systems which possess a pattern of hydroxylation similar to gallic acid.

The author wishes to express his thanks to Professor R. D. Haworth, F.R.S. and Mr. P. F. Knowles for their help in the preparation of this paper.

REFERENCES

1. R. D. HAWORTH and K. JONES, unpublished results.
2. E. FISCHER, *Ber.* 1919, **52**, 809.
3. K. BERNARD and H. ALBRECHT, *Helv. Chim. Acta* 1947, **30**, 627.
4. W. C. EVANS, *Ann. Rep. Chem. Soc.* 1956, 273.
5. S. R. GROSS, *J. Biol. Chem.* 1958, **233**, 1146.
6. E. WENKERT, *Chem. and Ind.* 1959, 906.

CHAPTER 8

TANNINS FROM ALGAROBILLA

OTTO TH. SCHMIDT

The University, Heidelberg

Algarobilla is the designation of a tanning material obtained from Middle and South America, principally Chile. It consists of the dried and ground fruit pods of a number of *Acacia* species, principally *Caesalpinia brevifolia*. When we began our investigations of the tannins of *Algarobilla*, it was known only that they were derived from glucose, gallic acid, and ellagic acid. Six years ago we discovered two new tannin components in *Algarobilla*[1], namely brevifolin and brevifolin carboxylic acid. This chapter summarizes the earlier structural studies on these two compounds and describes our recent studies on two new components of *Algarobilla* tannin which have been named Brevilagin-I and Brevilagin-II.

Brevifolin, which has been shown to have the constitution (1) is obtained when *Algarobilla* extracts are boiled in water for several days. It is precipitated together with ellagic acid and had previously probably concealed its presence owing to its similarity to ellagic acid and its extremely low solubility.

BREVIFOLIN AND BREVIFOLIN CARBOXYLIC ACID

In order to isolate brevifolin carboxylic acid, the percolate from *Algarobilla* is extracted first at pH 5.8 with ethyl acetate and in this way the phenolic extract is obtained. It is this extract which has yielded Brevilagins I and II (see below). Further ethyl acetate extraction after adjustment to pH 2.7 gives the carboxylic acid extract from which brevifolin carboxylic acid can be isolated in a pure state by countercurrent distribution between ethyl acetate and water. The yield of brevifolin carboxylic acid is variable but it is increased[2] fifty to one hundred times if the percolate is allowed to become contaminated with moulds after separating the phenolic fraction. In these circumstances extraction at pH 2.7 yields brevifolin carboxylic acid directly. It is probable, therefore, that brevifolin carboxylic acid is mainly present initially in the carboxylic acid extract in a bonded form and that it is released by enzymes produced by the growth of the mould.

Brevifolin carboxylic acid is relatively easily decarboxylated giving brevifolin (1). It must therefore have the constitution (2a) or (2b) of which the formula (2a) was initially preferred because the brevifolin carboxylic acid as isolated was optically inactive. We then established, however, by the synthesis of the isomeric trimethyl ether methyl esters of these acids (2a) and (2b), that the formula (2b) is correct[3]. Furthermore, the formula (2b) for brevifolin carboxylic acid would also explain its easy decarboxylation. It could also account for the lack of optical activity of brevifolin carboxylic acid as it is a vinylogous β-keto acid which might be expected to be fairly easily racemised. This, however, as far as I know has never yet been observed in structurally related compounds. This problem has therefore been examined by resolving

(I) Brevifolin

(2a)

(2b)

Brevifolin carboxylic acid

brevifolin carboxylic acid into its antipodes using quinidine. We obtained the pure laevo-rotatory form, $[\alpha]_D$ —73°, and it was found that the compound is not easily racemized as far as we could ascertain, but in view of its facile decarboxylation by, for example, boiling in water, it is not possible to be definitive about its ease of racemisation.

Since we have not yet isolated or examined any composite tannin in *Algarobilla* which could be derived from brevifolin carboxylic acid it is not possible to discuss the form in which this acid exists in the tannin concentrate. Regarding the lack of optical activity in brevifolin carboxylic acid we know that the hexahydroxydiphenic acid occurring in *Myrobolams*[4] and in *Dividivi*[4] is in the dextro-rotatory form whereas that in *Valonea*[5] and in knoppern-nuts[2] in the laevo-rotatory form. It would indeed be rather remarkable if brevifolin carboxylic acid were found to be present in one plant in a racemic form. We consider it possible, therefore, that brevifolin carboxylic acid does not exist in the free state but that it is bonded in some way, possibly to a sugar, in a form which is not yet known but which is associated with racemization either during or after its cleavage. It will therefore be especially interesting to look for tannins derived from brevifolin carboxylic acid in the carboxylic acid extract obtained by extraction at pH 2.7.

BREVILAGIN-I

About six years ago[1] we isolated a beautifully crystalline tannin from the so-called phenolic extract isolated at pH 5.8 and perhaps somewhat hurriedly we named it brevilagin because it yielded ellagic acid on hydrolysis. More recently we have isolated a second crystalline compound and we suggest that the former brevilagin should be named brevilagin-I and that the second tannin should be called brevilagin-II. A third crystalline substance has been isolated quite recently, but it has not yet been studied.

Brevilagin-I

$C_{34}H_{24-28}O_{24}$

Sulphuric acid

Concentrated hydrochloric acid

(3) Ellagic acid

(4) Chloroellagic acid

Acidic degradation of brevilagin-I

Brevilagin-I is yellow and gives a blue-green colour with ferric chloride in methanolic solution. The Griessmayer–Reichel test for ellagic acid[6] is negative giving a brown rather than a red-violet coloration. The reaction for bonded ellagic acid[7] with N/10 sulphuric acid and sodium nitrite which gives a rose → violet → blue colour change is negative; the reaction for free reducing sugars with aniline phthalate is also negative. Brevilagin-I is dextro-rotatory, $[\alpha]_D^{20} +159.5°$ (ethanol), and elementary analysis indicates the molecular formula $C_{34}H_{24-28}O_{24}$. The uncertainty in the hydrogen content is a well known difficulty in gallotannin chemistry, as gallotannins are usually very hygroscopic substances. The molecular weight of brevilagin-I was determined as 820 by the ebullioscopic method in acetone and the formula $C_{34}H_{24-28}O_{24}$ requires a molecular weight of 816.5–820.6.

The tannin gave, on hydrolysis with 5% sulphuric acid for 36 hr at 100°, 17–18% of glucose which was estimated both gravimetrically and polari-metrically and was identified by the formation of D-glucose phenylosazone. The calculated yield for 1 mole of D-glucose is 22%. The tannin does not contain the residues of either gallic acid or brevifolin carboxylic acid, and at this point we must correct our earlier opinion that acid hydrolysis gave brevifolin carboxylic acid. This view was based on preliminary experiments with very small amounts of material and on paper chromatographic examination of the hydrolysis products. Brevilagin-I is, however, hydrolysed with dilute sulphuric acid yielding ellagic acid (3), which was identified by its conversion to racemic hexamethoxydiphenic acid, m.p. 240°.[8] This crude product (approximately 55% yield) is surprisingly impure and consists only partly of ellagic acid. If it were derived from a molecule containing one glucose and two hexahydroxydiphenic acid residues, the yield of ellagic acid should have been about 80%.

The hydrolysis of brevilagin-I with boiling concentrated hydrochloric acid gave an unexpected result. It was completed in 10 minutes and during the reaction an almost colourless, crystalline compound separated in a yield approaching 65%. This compound was identified as the chloroellagic acid (5), by the degradations shown below.

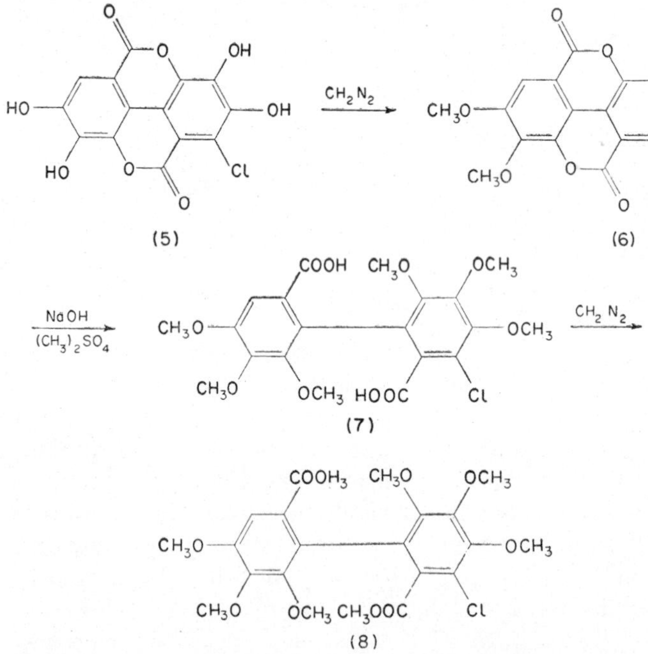

(5)   (6)

(7)

(8)

The chloroellagic acid which was previously unknown was converted into its tetramethyl ether (6) with diazomethane, methylated further with dimethyl sulphate and aqueous sodium hydroxide, and then esterified. This yielded a hexamethyl derivative of a dimethyl ester (8) and these transformations proved its constitution as monochloroellagic acid (5).

The brevilagin-I molecule contains 34 carbon atoms of which 6 are accounted for in the glucose residue; the remaining 28 carbon atoms could exist as two C_{14} residues. The 65% yield of chloroellagic acid shows that two C_{14} residues are indeed present and that they can both be transformed into chloroellagic acid. The yield corresponding to the production of one mole of chloroellagic acid is 41% and this is almost obtained when brevilagin-I is kept in concentrated hydrochloric acid for 2 hours at 4°.

Neither chebulagic acid nor corilagin, whose constitutions as esters of hexahydroxydiphenic acid have been established, affords chloroellagic acid on treatment with concentrated hydrochloric acid. We conclude from this that hexahydroxydiphenic acid residues are not present in brevilagin-I and this is supported by a negative result in the test for bonded ellagic acid.

The two C_{14} residues in brevilagin-I must be so constituted that it is possible to account for the formation of chloroellagic or ellagic acid by addition or disproportionation processes. The addition of hydrochloric acid recalls the similar reaction of quinone giving chlorohydroquinone. We assumed therefore the existence of a structural unit derivable from hexahydroxydiphenic acid by a dehydrogenation process and this unit had to contain carbonyl groups which were probably responsible for its yellow colour. This was supported by the reaction of brevilagin-I with phenylhydrazine in the cold to give a beautifully crystalline red tetrakisphenylhydrazone.

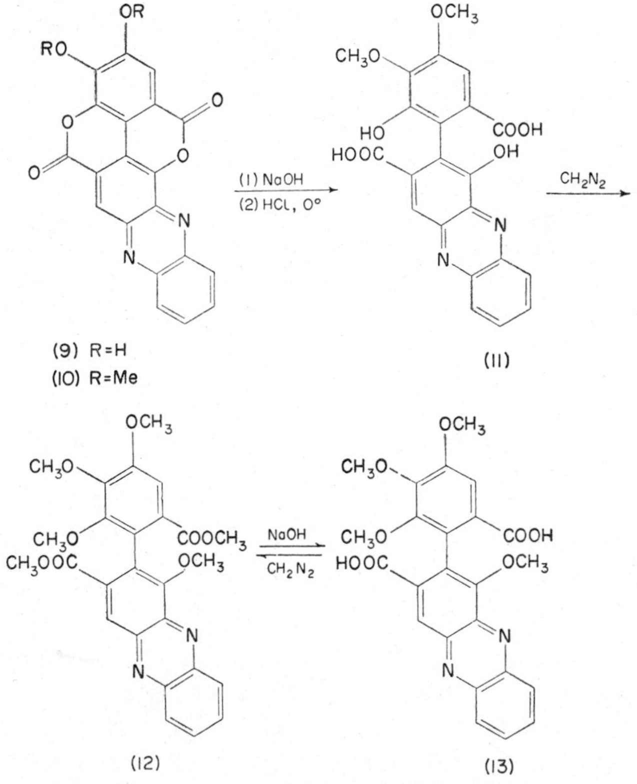

(9) R = H
(10) R = Me

(11)

(12)

(13)

Reactions of Phenazine-I

When we treated brevilagin-I with *o*-phenylenediamine in cold acetic acid, precipitation occurred almost immediately and was completed in 15–20 minutes. The amorphous, orange-yellow product is optically active, $[\alpha]_D^{25}$ +228° (tetrahydrofuran), and still shows the same blue-green ferric chloride reaction as brevilagin-I. Analysis shows that two moles of *o*-phenylenediamine have reacted with one mole of brevilagin-I and therefore the latter must contain two α-diketonic groupings or their tautomeric equivalents.

If this condensation product of brevilagin-I and *o*-phenylenediamine is boiled for 3 hours with 50% acetic acid, it is cleaved giving a beautifully crystalline salmon-red compound, subsequently referred to as phenazine-I (9). We were able to isolate from the filtrate a second compound, phenazine-II containing a glucose residue as well as a C_{14} unit which had similarly condensed with *o*-phenylenediamine. The reactions of phenazine-I are illustrated on page 143.

Phenazine-I dimethylether, $C_{22}H_{12}N_2O_6$, was obtained by reaction with diazomethane, and both phenazine-I (9) and its dimethyl ether (10) are dilactones. The dimethyl ether (10) was dissolved in aqueous sodium hydroxide and acidification at 0° gave a dimethyl ether dicarboxylic acid (11). This acid gave a tetramethyl ether dimethyl ester (12) on treatment with diazomethane.

Definitive information regarding the hydrogen content of phenazine-I was provided by analysis of its dimethyl ether which had the formula $C_{22}H_{12}N_2O_6$, and therefore phenazine-I contained only 8 hydrogen atoms. Since this number of hydrogen atoms was crucial, phenazine-I was characterized further as the dibenzoate (14) and the diphenylmethylene acetal (15).

(14)   (15)

Neither the dibenzoate (14) nor the diphenylmethylene acetal (15) showed absorption at 3.35–3.45 μ in their infrared spectra which would be characteristic of aliphatic C—H bonds. Consequently there must be present in brevilagin-I a residue derived from dehydrohexahydroxydiphenic acid (16). The carbon skeleton of this residue and the positions of the oxygen atoms are established by the formation of chloroellagic acid (17). The blue-green ferric chloride reaction and the methylation with diazomethane of both phenolic hydroxyl groups in phenazine-I (9) proves that one nucleus is benzenoid. The other nucleus is dehydrogenated and is actually *o*-quinonoid so explaining its ready condensation with *o*-phenylenediamine. This condensation must involve positions 3 and 4 (see 16) because the oxygen atom in position 2 forms part of a lactone ring. We assume that one carbonyl

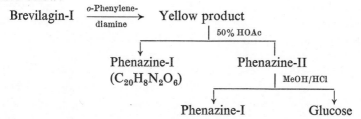

group in the *o*-quinonoid nucleus is hydrated which fits the elementary analysis of brevilagin-I and is in accord with its yellow colour. Furthermore, this hydration is analogous to the behaviour of the triketocyclohexane carboxylic acid (18) which is also hydrated,[9] although in neither case have the positions of hydration been established.

The relationship between brevilagin-I, phenazine-I, and phenazine-II is indicated below:

Brevilagin-I $\xrightarrow[\text{diamine}]{o\text{-Phenylene-}}$ Yellow product

| | 50% HOAc |
| | |
Phenazine-I   Phenazine-II
($C_{20}H_8N_2O_6$) | MeOH/HCl
                                   |
          Phenazine-I   Glucose

The hydrolysis of phenazine-II required rather more vigorous conditions, but when boiled for 5 hr with saturated methanolic hydrogen chloride it gave a crystalline compound identical with phenazine-I (9). This was confirmed by comparison of the infrared spectra of their dibenzoates (14). We may therefore summarize our present knowledge regarding the constitution of brevilagin-I by the part structure (19).

(19) Brevilagin-I ($C_{34}H_{24}O_{24}$)

Brevilagin-I does not have any free carboxyl groups as it is isolated from the phenolic portion of the *Algarobilla* tannin. The pH of its 1% aqueous solution is 4 and on electrophoresis it does not move towards the anode. Diazomethane methylation indicates that brevilagin-I contains at least six acidic groups, but the possibility that it forms a heptamethyl derivative cannot be excluded on the analytical evidence. We have not yet succeeded in obtaining the compounds formed initially on sulphuric acid hydrolysis of brevilagin-I for they are apparently too unstable and are partly transformed into ellagic acid by disproportionation processes. We have attempted its hydrolysis with tannase but even under these milder conditions no direct hydrolysis products could be isolated and this enzymic hydrolysis yielded only 32.4% of impure ellagic acid.

BREVILAGIN-II

This tannin has also been isolated from *Algarobilla* but whereas the yield of brevilagin-I is about 1–2% that of brevilagin-II is only about 0.5%. Brevilagin-II is also yellow, but it has no characteristic melting point. It is optically active, $[\alpha]_D$ +81° (ethanol), the ferric chloride coloration is blue in methanol, the reaction for bonded ellagic acid[7] is positive, and the reaction for free sugar reducing groups with aniline phthalate is negative. Elementary analysis indicates the molecular formula $C_{34}H_{24}O_{23}$, but again the hydrogen values are rather high. Its 1% aqueous solution has a pH of 4 and, like brevilagin-I, it does not migrate towards the anode on electrophoresis.

The brevilagin-II molecule contains residues derived from glucose, (-)-hexahydroxydiphenic acid, and the same quinonoid dehydrohexahydroxy-diphenic acid as occurs in brevilagin-I (see 19). Concentrated hydrochloric acid hydrolysis of brevilagin-II gave a mixture of ellagic acid and chloro-ellagic acid.

Methylation of brevilagin-II with diazomethane gave a nonamethyl derivative which on alkaline hydrolysis yielded (-)-hexamethoxydiphenic acid

(21).[10] On treatment of brevilagin-II with *o*-phenylenediamine, phenazine-I (9) can be obtained in 80% yield thus demonstrating that cleavage from the sugar residue occurs very easily with this tannin. The part structure (20) may be proposed for brevilagin-II and its reactions are summarized in Fig. 1.

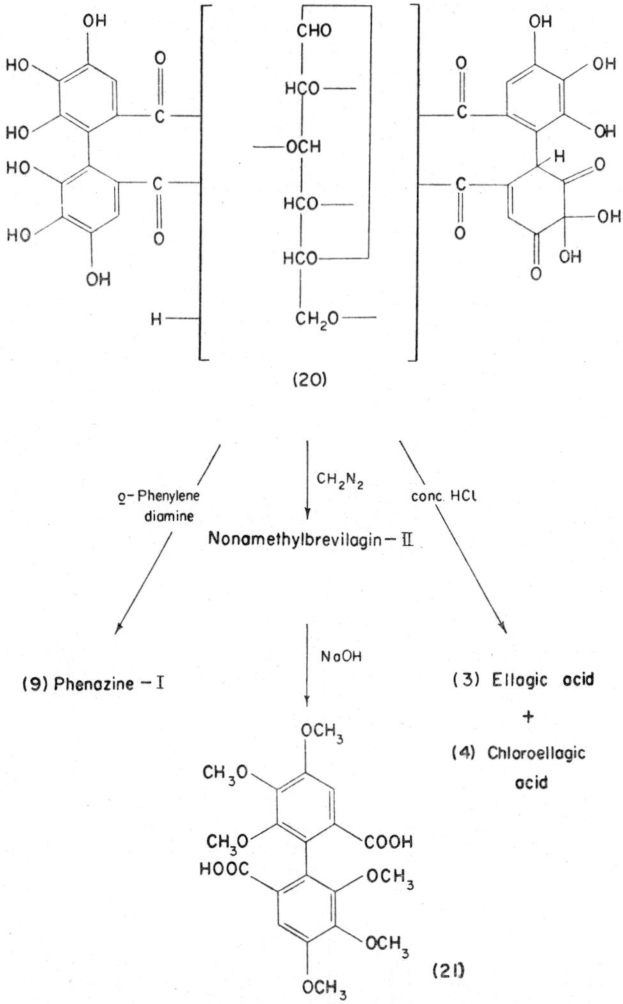

FIG. 1. Structure and reactions of Brevilagin-II ($C_{34}H_{24}O_{23}$).

The part structures (19) and (20) for brevilagin-I and brevilagin-II summarize the progress which we have so far made in the determination of the constitutions of these two tannins. There remains to be settled the positions of the ester groups on the glucose core and the detailed structure and stereochemistry of the dehydrohexahydroxydiphenic acid residues. It

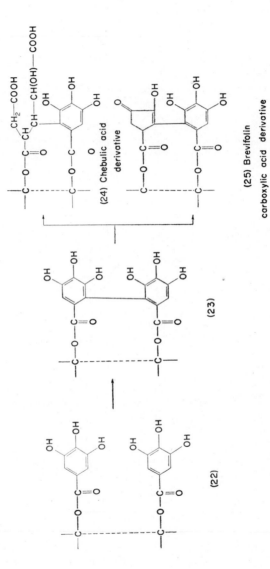

Fig. 2. Biogenetic Relationships.

would appear that substances with related structures also occur naturally and we have recently isolated from *Myrobolams* three new tannins, of which one is yellow and contains glucose, gallic acid, and dehydrohexahydroxy-diphenic acid residues.

BIOGENETIC RELATIONSHIPS

The discovery of derivatives of dehydrohexahydroxydiphenic acid seems to us to be especially interesting. We have developed a hypothesis to account for the origin of these compounds and for the results which we obtained in our earlier studies of ellagitannins.[11] This hypothesis relates the structures of hexahydroxydiphenic acid, chebulic acid, and brevifolin carboxylic acid. Thus oxidative coupling of the two galloyl residues in a digalloylglucose (22) could lead to the diester of hexahydroxydiphenic acid (23) which could be transformed to derivatives of chebulic acid (24) or brevifolin carboxylic acid (25) possibly by processes involving oxidation, benzylic acid type rearrangement, and either hydrolytic cleavage (to chebulic acid derivative) or decarboxylation (to brevifolin carboxylic acid derivative).

The inter-relationships indicated in Fig. 2 have received excellent support from the studies by Mayer, Bachmann and Kraus[9] on the reactions of the triketocyclohexanecarboxylic acid obtained by the reduction of gallic acid. Raney nickel reduction of gallic acid (26) gives a dihydrogallic acid (27) when the reduction is carried out in alkaline solution. This dihydrogallic acid is a cyclic reductone and is easily oxidized to the triketocyclohexanecarboxylic acid (28); this acid is an isomer of gallic acid, to which it is readily converted. This triketocyclohexanecarboxylic acid (28) reacts with cold dilute sodium

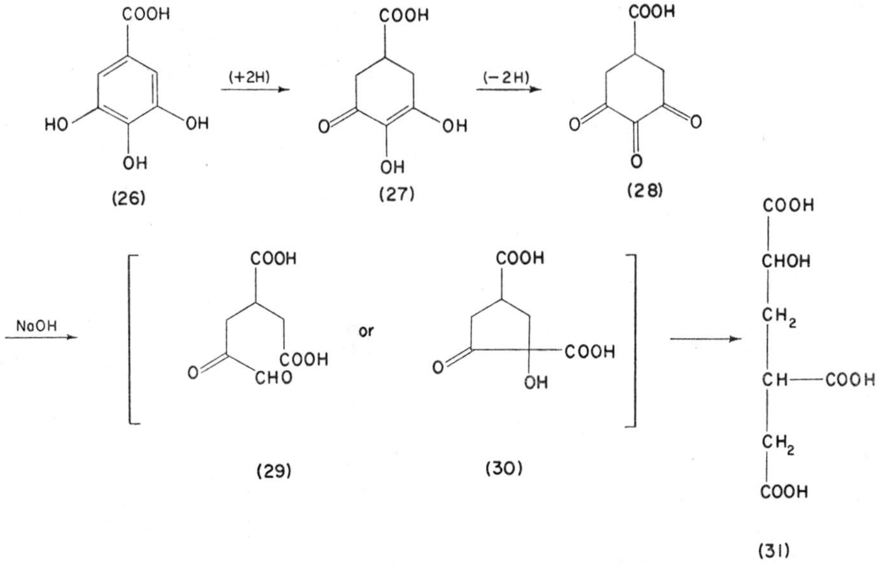

hydroxide solution giving 2-hydroxy-4-carboxyadipic acid (31) *via* the ketoalde-
hyde (29) or the five-membered β-ketoacid (30) neither of which was isolated.

The transformation of gallic acid (26) into 2-hydroxy-4-carboxyadipic acid
(31) is clearly related to the proposed route for the conversion of the hexahydroxydiphenic acid derivative (23) to the chebulic acid derivative (24).
The formation of chebulic acid (32) and brevifolin carboxylic acid (33) could
involve an analogous route (see Fig. 3) and the structures of brevilagins I
and II provide strong evidence in support of these biogenetic proposals.

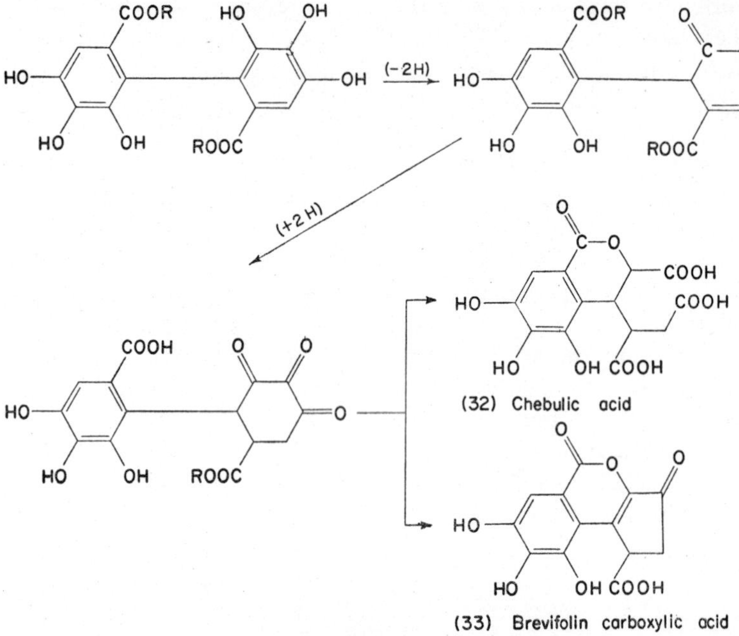

Fig. 3

It is probable that gallic acid is formed from carbohydrates *via* dehydroshikimic acid as indicated by Dr. Haslam (Chapter 7). The formation of
hexahydroxydiphenic acid could involve gallic acid as a precursor either as
the free acid or in a combined state. The alternative postulate has been
made by Wenkert[12] that hexahydroxydiphenic acid is formed from gallic
acid and dehydroshikimic acid. In our view the balance of evidence appears
to favour the derivation of hexahydroxydiphenic acid and its derivatives by
oxidative coupling process from two molecules of bonded gallic acid.

REFERENCES

1. O. Th. SCHMIDT and K. BERNAUER, *Annalen.* 1954, **588**, 211.
2. O. Th. SCHMIDT, unpublished results.
3. O. Th. SCHMIDT and R. ECKERT, *Z. Naturforsch.* 1956, **11b**, 757; *Annalen*, 1958, **618**, 71.

4. O. TH. SCHMIDT, F. BLINN, and R. LADEMANN, *Annalen.* 1952, **576**, 75.
5. O. TH. SCHMIDT and H. GRÜNEWALD, *Annalen.* 1957, **603**, 183.
6. L. REICHEL and A. SCHWAB, *Annalen.* 1942, **550**, 152.
7. O. TH. SCHMIDT, *Moderne Methoden der Pflanzenanalyse* Ed. Paech and M. V. Tracey),
   Springer Verlag 1955, Band III, 526.
8. J. HERZIG and J. POLLAK, *Monatsh.* 1908, **29**, 263.
9. W. MAYER, R. BACHMANN and F. KRAUS, *Chem. Ber.* 1955, **88**, 316.
10. O. TH. SCHMIDT and K. DEMMLER, *Annalen.* 1952, **576**, 85.
11. O. TH. SCHMIDT and W. MAYER, *Angew. Chem.* 1956, **68**, 103.
12. E. WENKERT, *Experientia*, 1959, **15**, 165; *Chem. and Ind.*, 1959, 609.

CHAPTER 9

BIFLAVONYLS

W. Baker and W. D. Ollis

The University, Bristol

THE examination of the flavanoid constituents of plants has been in progress for very many years. These investigations have led to the recognition of the almost universal occurrence of flavanoids and to the great variety of structure shown by them. The recent discovery of a new class of natural product related to the flavonoids was, therefore, rather unexpected, particularly as they are widely distributed among the Gymnosperms. They have been designated *biflavonyls*[1] to indicate that their structures contain two flavonoid units.

The biflavonyls whose structures have been determined are listed in Fig. 1 and there is evidence that other members of the biflavonyl group occur naturally.[2,3,4]

Biflavonyl	Molecular formula
Sciadopitysin[1,4–13]	$C_{30}H_{15}O_7(OMe)_3$
Kayaflavone[14,16,17]	$C_{30}H_{15}O_7(OMe)_3$
Ginkgetin[1,20–22]	$C_{30}H_{16}O_8(OMe)_2$
Isoginkgetin[1]	$C_{30}H_{16}O_8(OMe)_2$
Sotetsuflavone[15,17,23]	$C_{30}H_{17}O_9(OMe)$
Hinokiflavone[24,25]	$C_{30}H_{18}O_{10}$

FIG. 1.

1. EARLY HISTORY OF GINKGETIN

The story of the study of biflavonyls begins with the work of Furukawa[20] who isolated from the autumnal leaves of the ginkgo or maidenhair tree a yellow phenolic compound which he called compound B. He suggested that compound B had the molecular formula $C_{16}H_{12}O_5$ and the 5,8-dihydroxy-4'-methoxy-flavone structure (1) was proposed for it. However, the synthesis[26] of this compound (1), its isomer (2), and certain derivatives showed that this structural proposal for compound B was not correct. Examination of Furukawa's evidence led Baker and his co-workers to suggest that compound B, which they named ginkgetin, probably had a higher molecular weight[26] than that corresponding to a normal flavonoid structure. They suggested that formulae such as $C_{19}H_{14}O_6$ might be possible and this speculation

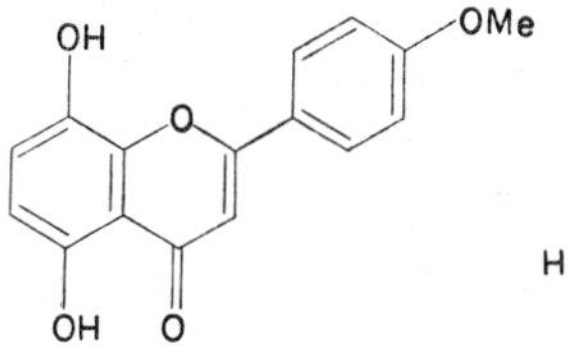

(1) 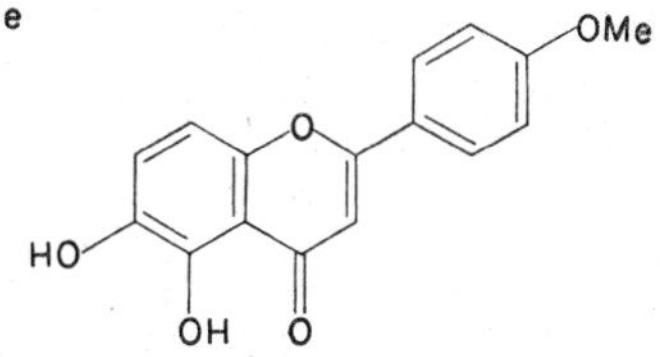   (2)

resulted in the synthesis of quite a large number of compounds.[27] These included substances such as the furano-flavone (3), but they were all different from ginkgetin.

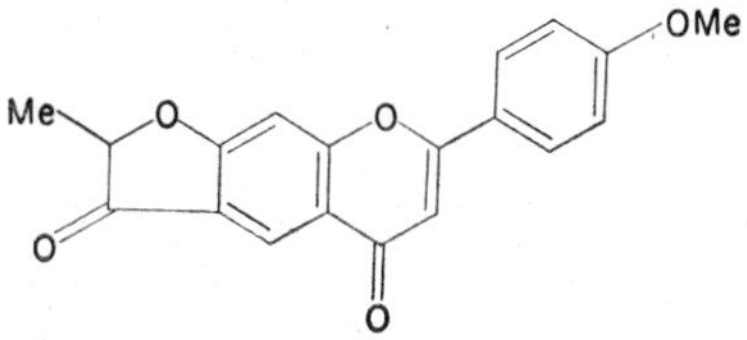

(3)

In retrospect this early work is seen to possess little more than historical interest, but it served to establish the fact that ginkgetin, although behaving in many respects as a flavone, was more complex than the simpler members of this series. It is, moreover, very probable that Furukawa's ginkgetin was a mixture and that the products obtained by hydrolysis were not derived from a single substance.

The source of ginkgetin is the leaves of *Ginkgo biloba* L., a tree of considerable botanical and taxonomic interest. It is the only surviving species of the order Ginkgoales of the gymnosperms and probably first made its appearance some 250 million years ago.[28] It has apparently remained unchanged since the Cretaceous or even the Jurassic period, and Darwin has referred to this tree as a "living fossil". Fossil records show that in the Mesozoic era some 60–180 million years ago, members of the Ginkgoales order were quite widespread, indeed in a petrified forest in Washington State, U.S.A., about 200 species have been recognized from their fossilized remains.[29] In view of the special botanical interest in the ginkgo tree, it is rather surprising that further work on the characterization of ginkgetin was not reported until 1941, when Nakazawa published two important papers[21,22] establishing for the first time the size of the ginkgetin molecule.

2. GINKGETIN

The Work of Nakazawa (1941–1956)

Our knowledge of the chemistry of ginkgetin was considerably extended by Nakazawa.[21,22] This work was first published in 1941, but we in Bristol

11

were not familiar with it for some years because, owing to war-time conditions, this paper was not abstracted until 1950.

Nakazawa showed that ginkgetin could not be obtained in a pure state by routine methods. He did, however, find that the following method gave ginkgetin in a yield of 0.02–0.03%. When the ether extract of the yellow, autumnal ginkgo leaves was shaken with aqueous potassium carbonate, a potassium salt of ginkgetin separated and this could be recrystallized from warm potassium carbonate solution. This potassium salt yielded pure ginkgetin, m.p. 297°, for which the molecular formula $C_{30}H_{16}O_8(OMe)_2$ was proposed. This suggestion was also in accord with the complexity of the products of the alkaline hydrolysis of ginkgetin and with the molecular weight of ginkgetin tetraethyl ether determined by the Rast method.

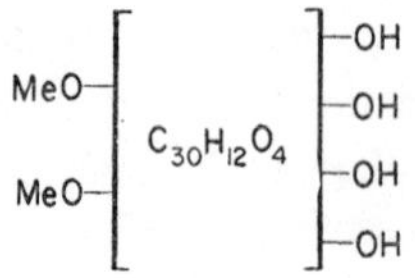

(4)

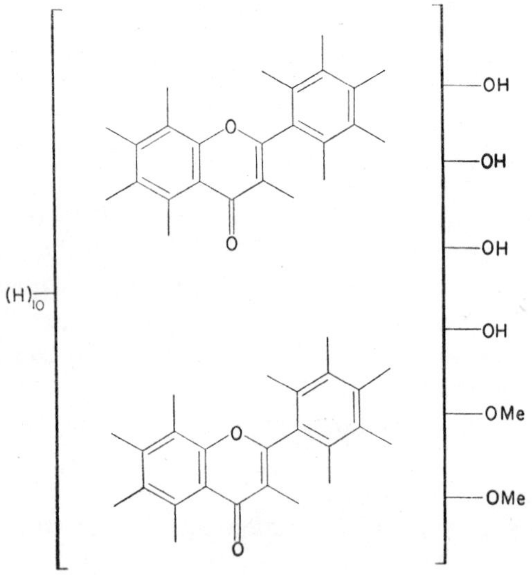

(5)

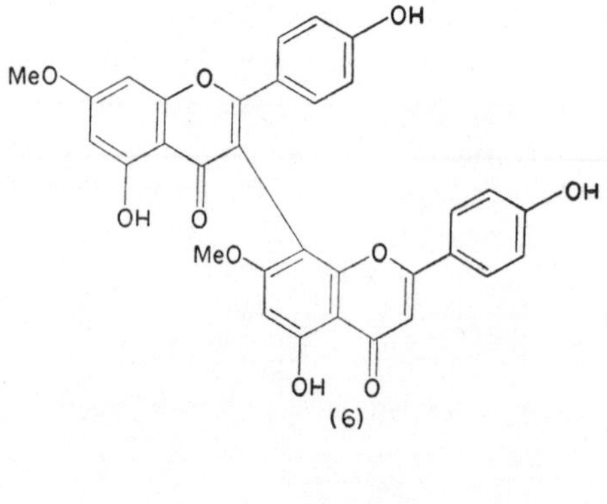

(6)

Ginkgetin contained two methoxyl groups and four phenolic or enolic hydroxyl groups, forming a tetra-acetate, a tetramethyl ether, and a tetra-ethyl ether. Demethylation gave a compound, $C_{30}H_{12}O_4(OH)_6$, characterized as its hexa-acetate. It could therefore be represented by the part structure (4) and since in many of its reactions it behaved as a flavonoid it was suggested that the C_{30} residue (see 4) contained two flavonoid (C_{15}) units (see 5).

Two of the phenolic hydroxyl groups of ginkgetin were resistant to methylation which suggested that they were in the 5-positions. Alkali fusion of ginkgetin gave acetic acid, phloroglucinol, p-hydroxybenzoic acid and an acid formulated as $C_9H_{10}O_5$. Permanganate oxidation of ginkgetin yielded no isolable products, but under similar conditions the dimethyl ether gave anisic acid. Hydrolysis of ginkgetin with 20% potassium hydroxide afforded

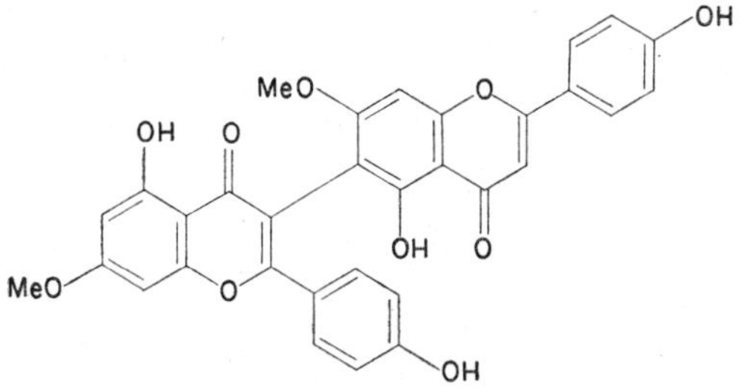

(7)

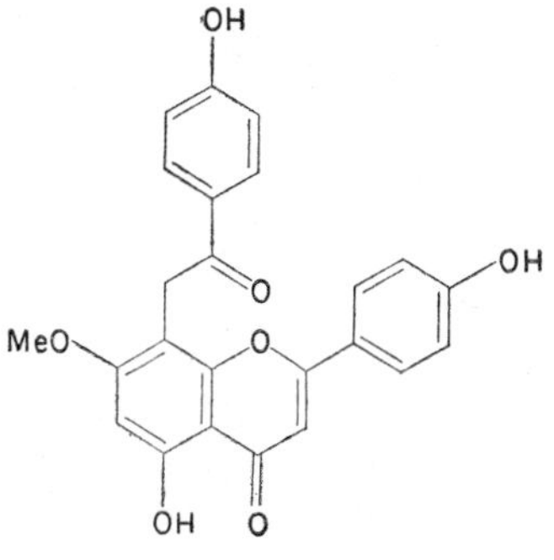

(8)

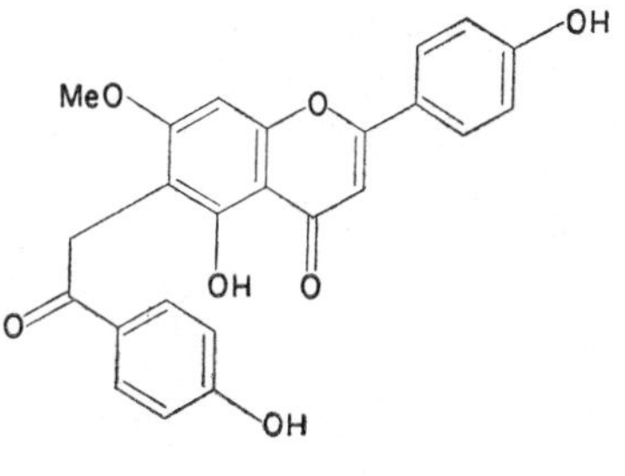

(9)

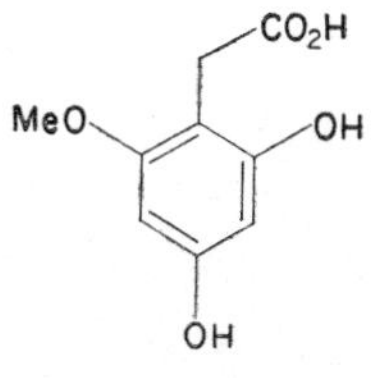

(10)

p-hydroxyacetophenone, phloroglucinol monomethyl ether, and a keto-flavone, $C_{24}H_{18}O_7$. Nakazawa regarded these degradation products as being characteristic of genkwanin (5,4′-dihydroxy-7-methoxyflavone) and he made the tentative proposal that ginkgetin contained two genkwanin type units. The acid, $C_9H_{10}O_5$, was considered by Nakazawa to be a derivative of phenylacetic acid, so that ginkgetin probably contained an isoflavone residue. He was thus led to advance two possible structures (6) and (7) for ginkgetin. The structures proposed for the ketoflavone, $C_{24}H_{18}O_7$, were the deoxybenzoins (8) or (9) which were also consistent with the presence of an isoflavone residue in ginkgetin. Structure (10) followed for the acid, $C_9H_{10}O_5$.

Nakazawa's subsequent work with Matsuura[30] was mainly concerned with the synthesis of the ketoflavones (8) and (9) and their di- and tri-methyl ethers, but these synthetic compounds differed from the ketoflavone and its derivatives obtained from ginkgetin. This work showed that, although satisfactory in a number of respects, the formulae (6) or (7) could not represent ginkgetin correctly.

3. SCIADOPITYSIN
The Work of Kariyone and Kawano (1956)

Kariyone and Kawano[4,5,6,7] carried out a major investigation of scia-dopitysin isolated from the leaves of the Umbrella Pine, *Sciadopitys verticellata* Sieb. and Zucc. This Japanese tree is seldom grown in Britain; it takes its common name from the fact that the long, thin leaves are arranged in whorls around the stems rather like the ribs of a folded umbrella. *Sciadopitys* is a monotypic genus of the *Sciadopityaceae* family in the *Coniferales* order.

Extraction of the dried leaves with trichlorethylene gave sciadopitysin in yields as high as 0.5%. It is therefore a much more readily accessible substance than ginkgetin and extensive degradative investigations of its structure were possible. Sciadopitysin, $C_{30}H_{15}O_7(OMe)_3$ gave a trimethyl ether identical with ginkgetin tetramethyl ether and methylation under milder conditions gave a monomethyl ether identical with ginkgetin dimethyl ether. Demethylation of sciadopitysin and gingketin gave the same product, $C_{30}H_{12}O_4(OH)_6$, characterized as its hexa-acetate. These reactions proved that ginkgetin, $C_{30}H_{12}O_4(OH)_4(OMe)_2$, and sciadopitysin, $C_{30}H_{12}O_4(OH)_3(OMe)_3$, had the same skeletal structure.

An extensive investigation of the alkaline degradation of sciadopitysin and its trimethyl ether was carried out using aqueous potassium hydroxide of concentration between 20% and 50%; the various products which were isolated are listed in Fig. 2. Products (16) and (17) were isolated after fusion with potassium hydroxide. The names given in Fig. 2 are those used in the original publications.

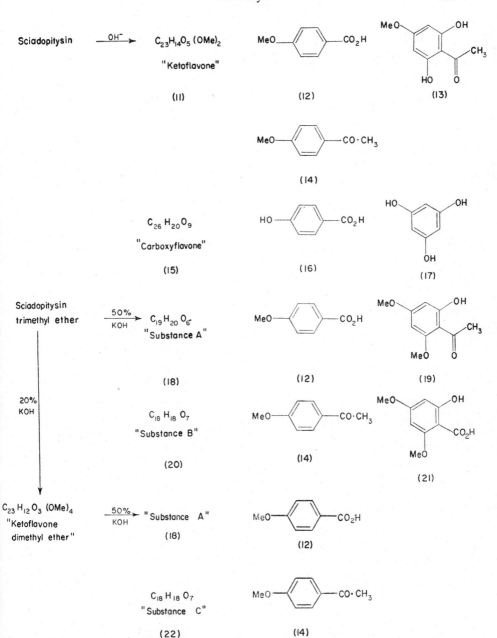

FIG. 2. Hydrolysis products of sciadopitysin and its trimethyl ether (Kariyone and Kawano).

The attempted rationalization of these results (Fig. 2) led Kariyone and Kawano[7] to propose for sciadopitysin the structure (23), in which position 8 of a flavone unit is directly linked to position 2 of an isoflavone unit.

(23)

Kariyone and Kawano recognized that this flavone-isoflavone structure (23) for sciadopitysin differed from the biflavonyl structure (6) for ginkgetin which had been proposed earlier by Nakazawa. On the basis of their structure for sciadopitysin, the five unidentified products from the hydrolysis of sciadopitysin and sciadopitysin trimethyl ether (see Fig. 2) which included the "ketoflavone" (11), the "carboxyflavone" (15), and substances A (18), B (20), and C (22) were given the structures (24–28) indicated below.

In Bristol we considered that these structural proposals were unsatisfactory on three counts. (a) If sciadopitysin were represented by structure (23) then the "carboxyflavone" and "substance B" had to be formulated as the β-keto-acids (25) and (27). It was inconceivable that these *stable* compounds produced by vigorous alkaline hydrolysis could have such structures. (b) In terms of structures (24) and (25) thermal decarboxylation of "carboxyflavone" should have given the keto-flavone. Thermal decarboxylation of the "carboxyflavone" gave a product, $C_{25}H_{20}O_7$, which was different from the ketoflavone.[6] (c) The trimethyl ether of the ketoflavone obtained from ginkgetin was shown[6] to be identical with the dimethyl ether of the keto-flavone derived from sciadopitysin. On the basis of either the structure proposed for ginkgetin (6) or that for sciadopitysin (23), the fully methylated ketoflavones would have to be formulated as in the structure (29). Comparison of these fully methylated ketoflavones with an authentic synthetic specimen of the compound (29) showed that they were different[30].

These facts convinced us that sciadopitysin did not have the structure (23) and that the corresponding structure for ginkgetin was also not acceptable.

4. GINKGETIN, ISOGINKGETIN, AND SCIADOPITYSIN

The Work of Baker, Finch, Ollis, and Robinson

Some work on ginkgetin had been proceeding at Bristol for a number of years,[31] but no effective progress was made until 1956 because until that time

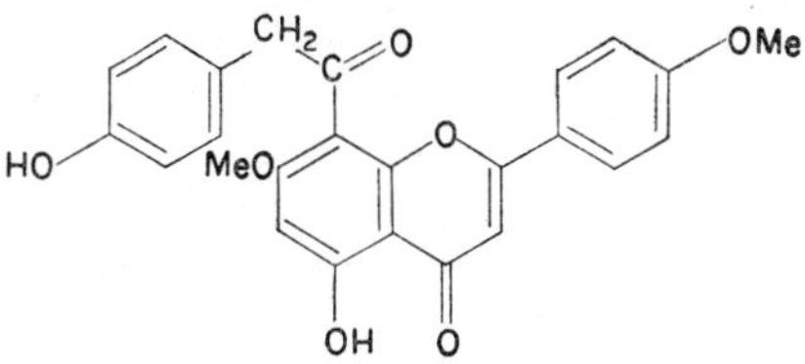

(24) "Ketoflavone"

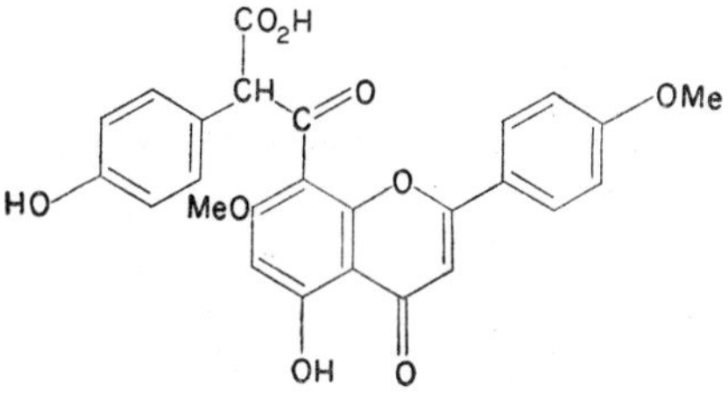

(25) "Carboxyflavone"

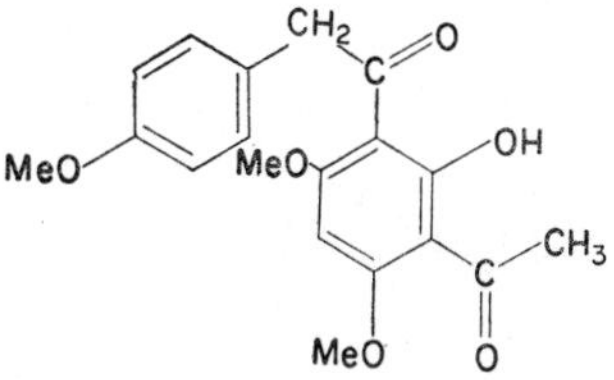

(26) "Substance A"

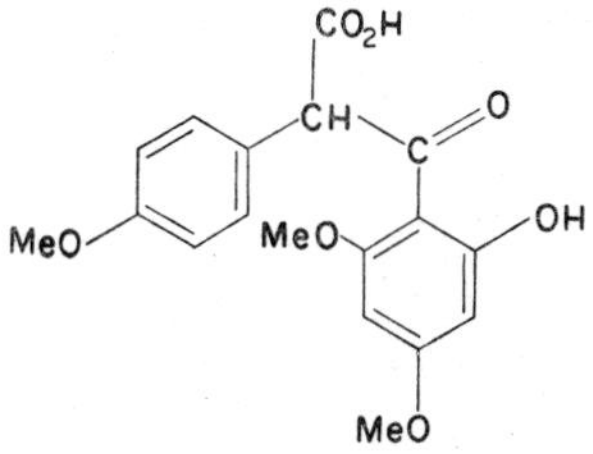

(27) "Substance B"

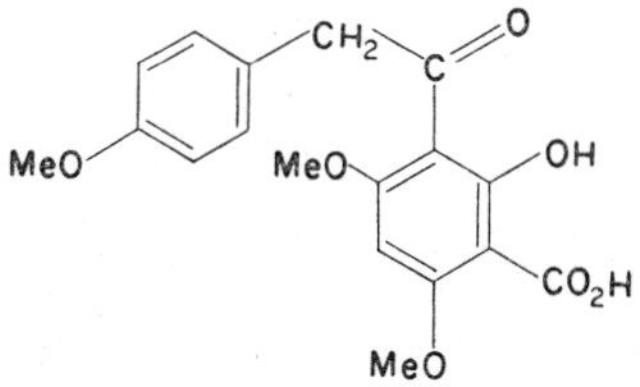

(28) "Substance C"

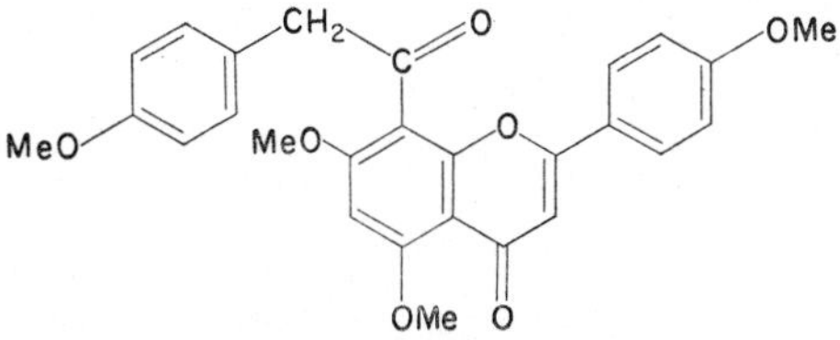

(29)

pure products were not obtainable. The material isolated from the ethereal extracts of the autumnal leaves of the ginkgo tree was undoubtedly a mixture but nearly all the attempts which were made to effect a separation of this mixture were unsuccessful. These attempts included fractional crystallization of the crude mixture and its acetylation product. Many different methods of adsorption and partition chromatography and countercurrent distribution were also investigated. The last method was very tedious, but the experiments of Dr. A. Pelter and Dr. A. C. M. Finch showed that the crude material contained at least three related natural products of which two were later named ginkgetin and isoginkgetin. Eventually it was shown that two of these compounds could be comparatively easily isolated by taking advantage of Nakazawa's observation[21] that ginkgetin formed a rather insoluble crystalline potassium salt. Crystallization of the mixture from aqueous potassium carbonate gave the potassium salt of ginkgetin, and acidification of the mother liquors gave isoginkgetin. Later, we made the observation, which was surprising in view of our earlier efforts, that the mixture could be separated into the less soluble isoginkgetin and ginkgetin by fractional crystallization from acetone. This success as compared with the failure of modern methods is worthy of note.

The melting points of ginkgetin and isoginkgetin were markedly dependent upon the rate of heating, and the melting of isoginkgetin was preceded by a preliminary softening and rehardening. Our ginkgetin showed m.p. 342–344° (with decomposition) and it is probable that the lower melting point of 297° recorded by Nakazawa is that of a hydrate. Professor Nakazawa kindly supplied us with specimens of ginkgetin and its potassium salt and direct comparison with our material showed that they were identical. Isoginkgetin had melting point 347–351° (with decomposition) after preliminary softening and resolidification.

Ginkgetin and isoginkgetin have the same molecular formula, $C_{30}H_{12}O_4(OH)_4(OMe)_2$, and yield isomeric tetra-acetates and tetra-ethyl ethers. Both, however, yield the same tetramethyl ether and demethylation gives the same hexahydroxy compound, $C_{30}H_{12}O_4(OH)_6$ characterized as its hexa-acetate. Clearly ginkgetin and isoginkgetin contain the same skeletal structure and oxygenation pattern.

Previously the only molecular weight determinations in this group of compounds had been made by Nakazawa[21] on ginkgetin and its tetraethyl ether using Rast's method. Our experiences with this method on ginkgetin and its derivatives were not satisfactory and we therefore used the modified Menzies-Wright ebullioscopic method[32] and established the formula of the acetylated ginkgetin as $C_{30}H_{12}O_4(OAc)_4(OMe)_2$.

Comparison of the ultraviolet spectra (see Fig. 3) of ginkgetin, isoginkgetin, their tetra-acetates, and tetramethyl ether with those of apigenin (30), acacetin (31), genkwanin (32), and their derivatives was particularly informative.

The similarity of the spectra of the parent compounds and corresponding derivatives indicated very strongly that ginkgetin and isoginkgetin were derivatives of 5,7,4'-trihydroxyflavone. Moreover, the intensities of absorption for corresponding bands of ginkgetin and isoginkgetin were approximately double those of the model compounds. This demonstrated the

Compounds	λ_{max} mμ (ε_{max}) in EtOH		
Ginkgetin	212 (76,000)	271.5 (42,200)	335 (40,000)
Isoginkgetin	213 (90,000)	271.5 (42,000)	330 (36,500)
Apigenin		269 (18,800)	340 (20,900)
Acacetin	~210	269 (20,300)	330 (20,800)
Genkwanin		269 (17,000)	337 (19,600)
Ginkgetin tetra-acetate	211 (63,500)	248–258* (34,500)	317 (47,000)
Isoginkgetin tetra-acetate	220 (74,000)	250* (47,000)	324 (50,500)
Acacetin diacetate	222* (21,200)	258 (13,300)	325 (26,300)
Ginkgetin tetramethyl ether	212 (63,000)	267 (48,000)	328.5 (45,500)
Apigenin trimethyl ether	212 (37,000)	265 (21,200)	325 (24,000)
	* = points of inflexion		

Fig. 3. Ultraviolet spectra.

presence of two isolated flavonoid chromophores per molecule in ginkgetin and isoginkgetin. This proposal received strong support from the infrared spectral characteristics of ginkgetin and isoginkgetin which both showed a

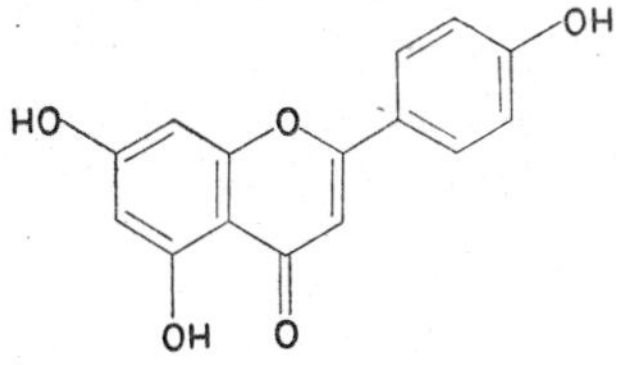

(30)

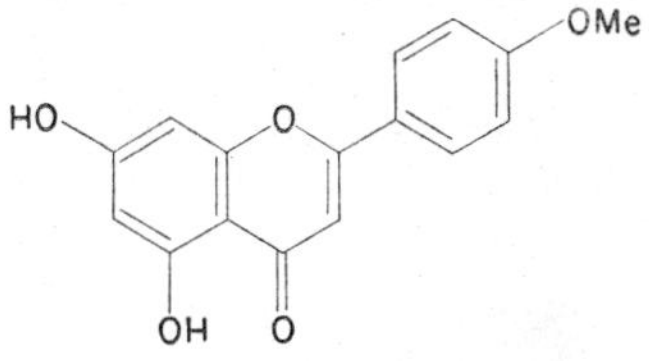

(31)

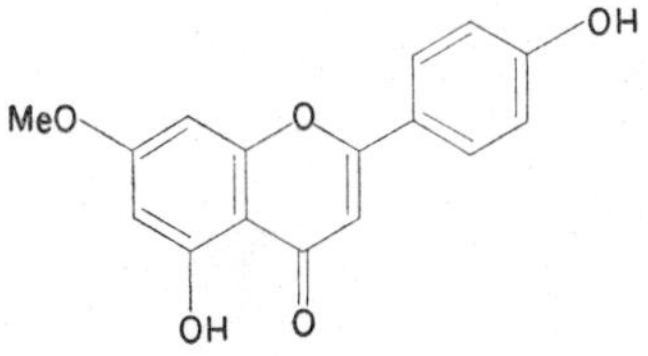

(32)

strong, sharp absorption band at 1660 cm^{-1} as do apigenin (30), acacetin (31), and apigenin-7,4'-di-O-methyl ether. This band is characteristic of 5-hydroxy-flavones. Alkylation of the 5-OH group produced a shift to *lower* frequencies as in ginkgetin tetramethyl ether (ν_{max} 1644 cm^{-1}), ginkgetin tetra-ethyl ether (ν_{max} 1643 cm^{-1}), and isoginkgetin tetra-ethyl ether (ν_{max} 1640 cm^{-1}). These figures match those of apigenin trimethyl ether (ν_{max} 1645 cm^{-1}), acacetin diethyl ether (ν_{max} 1645 cm^{-1}), and 5-O-ethyl-7,4'-di-O-methyl-apigenin (ν_{max} 1641 cm^{-1}). An exactly analogous shift to *lower* frequencies has also been observed on acylation of the 5-OH group. Thus isoginkgetin tetra-acetate absorbs at 1650 cm^{-1}, which is to be compared with apigenin triacetate (ν_{max} 1650 cm^{-1}) and acacetin diacetate (ν_{max} 1645 cm^{-1}).

Thus the ultraviolet and infrared evidence strongly favoured the presence in the ginkgetin structure of two flavonoid units (33) bearing oxygen atoms in the 4', 5, and 7 positions, and it seemed highly probably on spectroscopic and chemical evidence that each flavonoid unit had a 5-OH group.

(33)

Biogenetic considerations led us to consider it probable that the biflavonyl structure could arise by oxidative coupling of flavonoid precursors. The biosynthetic importance of this type of reaction (see Chapter 5) has recently been emphasized by Barton and Cohen,[33] and by Erdtman and Wacht-meister.[34]* The oxygenation pattern of the precursor (33) restricts the interflavonyl linkage to positions 6, 8, and 3'. This leads to six possible biflavonyl structures containing 8–8, 8–6, 8–3', 6–6, 6–3', and 3'–3' linkages. A decision between them was made possible by studying the oxidation of ginkgetin tetramethyl ether with alkaline hydrogen peroxide. The products, which were obtained in high yield, were anisic acid (39), 2-hydroxy-4,6-dimethoxybenzoic acid (36), and a compound, $C_{17}H_{16}O_8$.

The compound, $C_{17}H_{16}O_8$, was a dicarboxylic acid (equivalent found, 172; required, 174) which had two pK_a values of 5.3 and 6.8 in 50% aqueous ethanol. Its infrared spectrum showed two bands in the carbonyl region (ν_{max} 1685 and 1640 cm^{-1}) and it gave a very strong colour with ferric chloride so that clearly it contains an isolated carboxyl group and was in addition a salicylic acid. The compound also contained three methoxyl groups so that it could be formulated as $C_{12}H_4(OMe)_3OH(CO_2H)_2$ and must therefore be a derivative of biphenyl. The ultraviolet absorption spectrum of this dicarboxylic acid [λ_{max} mμ (ε_{max}) 222 (26,700), 247 (27,100), 256 (26,800), 299 (3,900)] was in very satisfactory agreement with the composite curve

* We should like to thank Professor D. H. R. Barton for interesting discussions on this and other aspects of the importance of phenol dehydrogenation reactions in biosynthesis.

[λ_{max} mμ (ε_{max}) 218 (35,000), 257 (27,100), 264 (22,400), 294 (4,300)] obtained by addition of the spectra of anisic acid (39) and of 2-hydroxy-4,6-dimethoxy-benzoic acid (36). The structures (37) or (38) were therefore proposed for the dicarboxylic acid, $C_{17}H_{16}O_8$.[1]

These facts prove that a biphenyl residue must exist in the ginkgetin molecule and that the interflavonyl linkage must involve position 3' of one flavonoid residue and position 6 or 8 of the other. Two structures (34) and (35) may therefore be considered for ginkgetin tetramethyl ether; their relationship to the three degradation products is illustrated below.

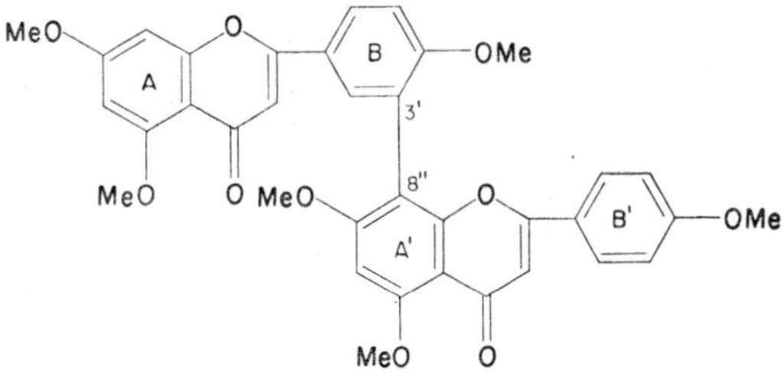

(34) [3'–8" linkage]

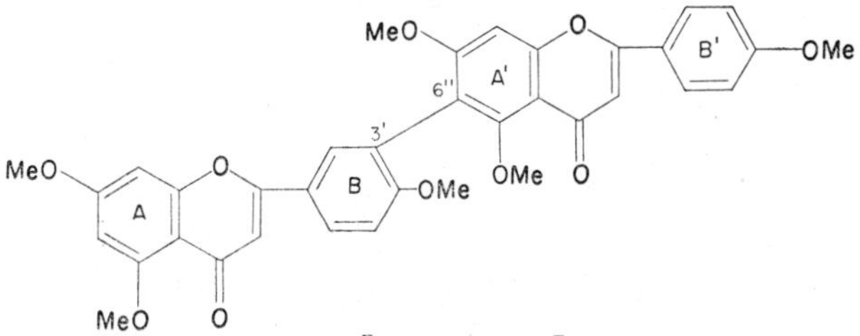

(35) [3'–6" linkage]

Of the two structures (34) and (35) for ginkgetin tetramethyl ether, the one (34) involving the 3'–8" linkage was preferred. The other structure (35) was considered unlikely since the 5"-OH in a compound with this structure would be very sterically hindered and there was no evidence that this hydroxyl group in ginkgetin was exceptionally difficult to alkylate. Therefore structure (34) was proposed for ginkgetin tetramethyl ether and structure (37) for the derived dicarboxylic acid.

The isolation of the biphenyl derivative (37) immediately proved that ginkgetin could not have the structure (6) or the structure (7) proposed by Nakazawa and that sciadopitysin could not have structure (23). At this stage in our investigations the important papers by Kariyone and Kawano[4,5,6,7] on sciadopitysin appeared. They showed that sciadopitysin trimethyl ether and ginkgetin tetramethyl ether were identical. We have already given our reasons (Section 3) for believing that the structure (23) proposed for scia-dopitysin was not correct, but it was reassuring to discover that Kariyone

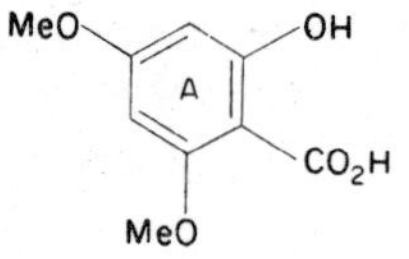

(36)

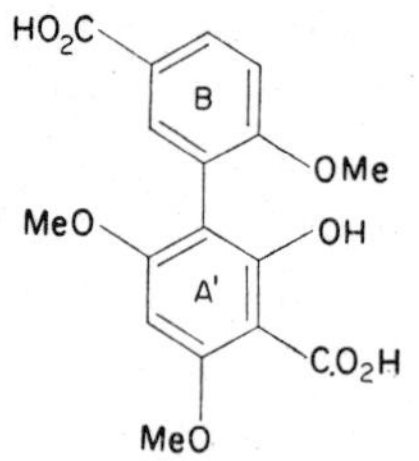

(37)

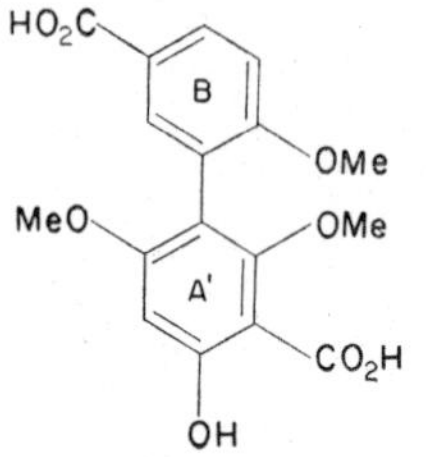

(38)

(39)

and Kawano's very extensive degradative evidence was compatible with our structure (34) for sciadopitysin trimethyl ether (ginkgetin tetramethyl ether). The degradation products of sciadopitysin trimethyl ether have been summarized in Fig. 2 and structure (34) leads to the revised structures given in Fig. 4 for these hydrolysis products.

Our proposals for the structures of the hydrolysis products (see Fig. 4) of sciadopitysin and its trimethyl ether fitted all the published evidence[5,6,7] with the exception of the properties of the "carboxyflavone". This discrepancy is discussed in more detail later. Thus substance A gave a strong colour with ferric chloride whereas its mono-acetate did not. Substance A also gave a monoxime, but its mono-acetate gave a dioxime. Clearly substance A was a diketone in which one of its carbonyl groups was *ortho* to a phenolic group as in structure (42). Substance B was a carboxylic acid which easily formed a monomethyl ester. Substance B did not form an oxime whereas monoxime derivatives were easily formed from its mono-acetate and monomethyl ether. Substance B therefore contained an unhindered carboxyl group and an *o*-hydroxy-ketone grouping as in structure (43). This structure for substance B restricted the choice for substance C to structure (44) produced by an exchange of acetyl and carboxyl groupings.

Since alkaline hydrolysis of the "ketoflavone dimethyl ether" gives substance A (42), substance C (44), anisic acid, and *p*-methoxyacetophenone, only one structure (cf. 40a and 40b) is possible for the "ketoflavone dimethyl ether." The molecular formula, $C_{26}H_{20}O_9$, originally proposed[5] for the "carboxyflavone", is incompatible with the structural proposals given above and we have suggested[1] that it probably has the molecular formula $C_{24}H_{18}O_8$,

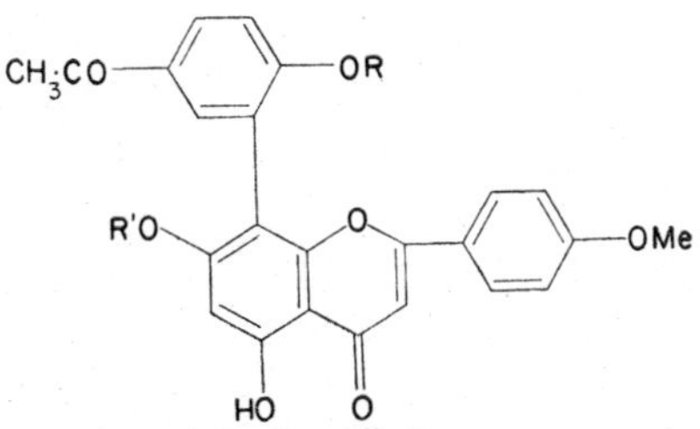

(40a) R = Me; R' = H
(40b) R = H ; R' = Me
["Ketoflavone" (24)*]

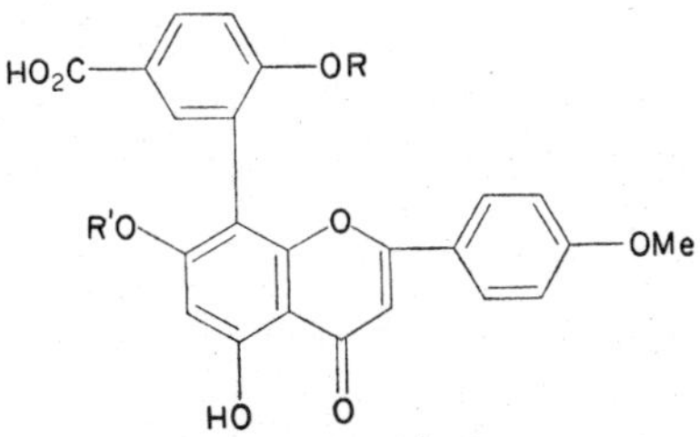

(41a) R = Me; R' = H
(41b) R = H ; R' = Me
["Carboxyflavone" (25)*]

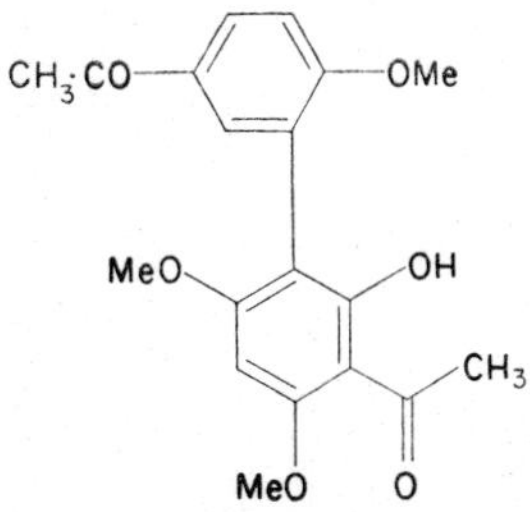

(42)
["Substance A" (26)*]

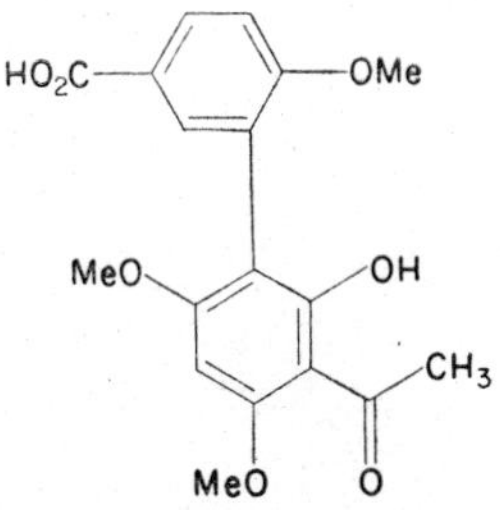

(43)
["Substance B" (27)*]

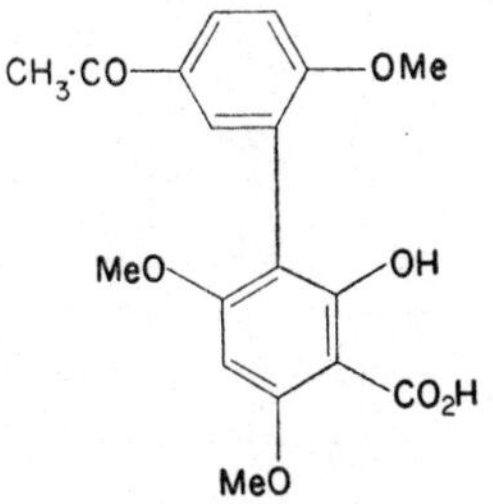

(44)
["Substance C" (28)*]

FIG. 4. Hydrolysis products of sciadopitysin and its trimethyl ether.

* These numbers refer to the structures originally proposed by Kariyone and Kawano, given on pages 157 and 159.

which is compatible with the published analytical data. This leads to two possible structures for the "carboxyflavone" (41a or 41b) corresponding to the two possible structures (40a or 40b) for the "ketoflavone".

Thus our proof that ginkgetin contained a biphenyl residue (see page 20), coupled with a different interpretation of Kariyone and Kawano's very extensive degradation studies on sciadopitysin, encouraged us to propose partial structures for ginkgetin and isoginkgetin (45), and for sciadopitysin (46), with the reservation that the alternative 3′–6″ linkage had not been rigidly excluded though it was unlikely.

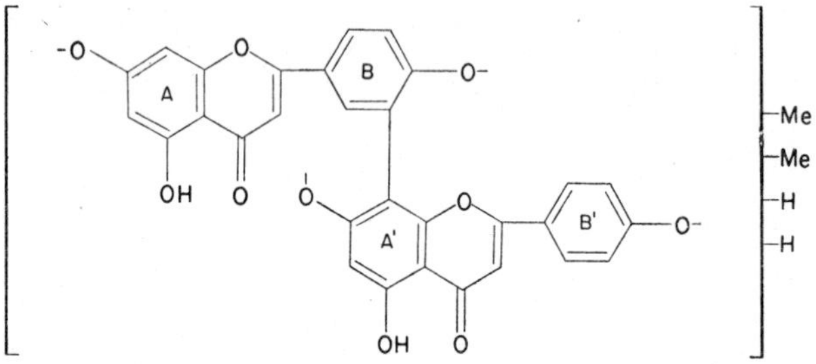

(45)

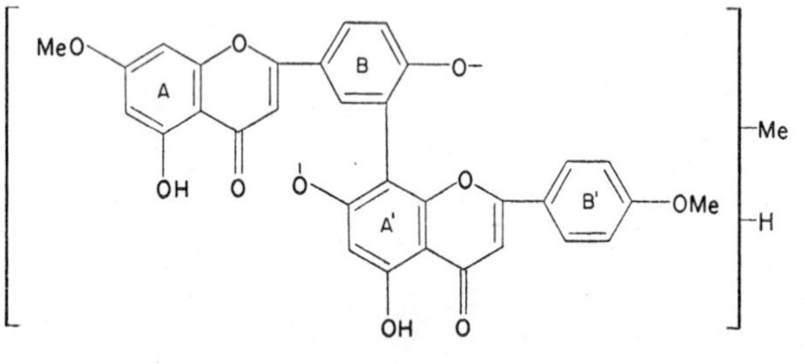

(46)

At this stage in the investigation of the structure of the biflavonyls (45) and (46) there were two outstanding problems. The first was a rigid proof of the positions of the four oxygen atoms attached to rings B and A′ which had so far been placed on ultraviolet and infrared evidence, biogenetic arguments, and the structures proposed for the hydrolysis products (see Fig. 4) and the oxidation product (37). These proposed structures were almost certainly correct but they could not be regarded as rigorously established. The second problem concerned the placing of the O-methyl groups in structures (45) and (46). Contributions to the solution of both these problems were made by studying the oxidation of ginkgetin, isoginkgetin, and sciadopitysin with alkaline hydrogen peroxide. The products are shown in Fig. 5.[1]

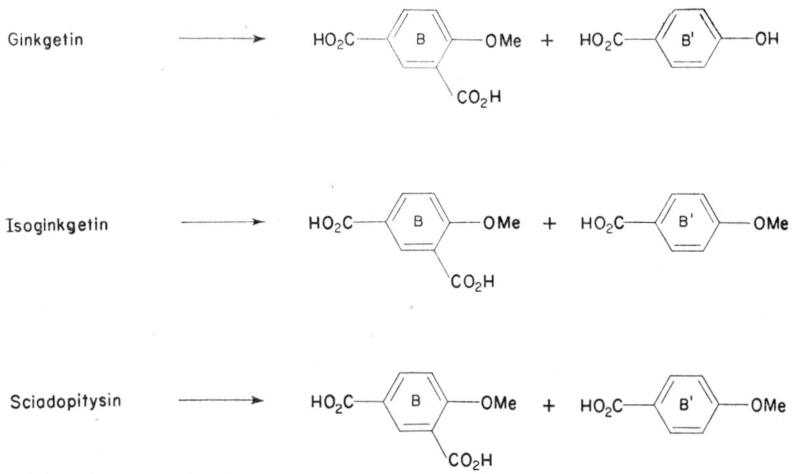

FIG. 5. Oxidation of biflavonyls with alkaline hydrogen peroxide.[1]

The results given in Fig. 5 permitted the assignment of structures to isoginkgetin (47) and sciadopitysin (48) and of two possible structures (49a) or (49b) to ginkgetin.*

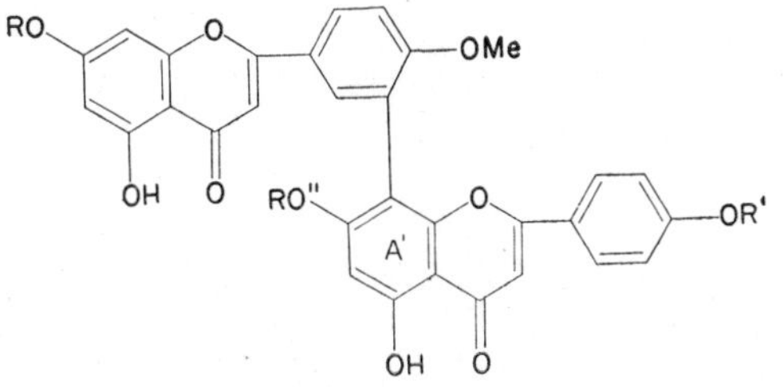

(47) R = R''= H; R' = Me Isoginkgetin
(48) R = R'= Me; R''= H Sciadopitysin
(49a) R = Me; R'=R''=H ⎫
                        ⎬ Ginkgetin
(49b) R''= Me; R=R'=H ⎭

The only structural feature apart from the interflavonoid linkage in these biflavonyl formulae (47–49) about which there could be any doubt was the position of the R''O-group on ring A'. It was proved to be in the indicated position by Kawano (see Section 7).

The decision between the two possible structures (49a) or (49b) for ginkgetin was made possible by a detailed study of the effect of base upon the ultraviolet spectra of biflavonyls (see Section 5) and by determining the structures of the "ketoflavones" obtained from the biflavonyls by alkaline hydrolysis (see Section 6).

* These structures were first proposed by us in a Lecture at the University of Cambridge in February 1958 and later at a Plant Phenolics Group Meeting in Cambridge in September 1958.

Compound	Neutral Ethanol λ_{max} mμ (ε_{max})		N/50 (NaOEt–EtOH)		N/500 (NaOEt–EtOH)		N/5000 (NaOEt–EtOH)	
	Band I	Band II	Band I	Band II	Band I	Band II	Band I	Band II
Apigenin (30)	269 (18,800) 300* (13,500)	340 (20,900)			277 (21,900) 330 (13,000)	400 (31,700)		
Acacetin (31)	269 (20,300) 298* (16,400)	330 (20,800)	279 (31,300)	371 (13,300)	278 (32,600) 295* (21,000)	376 (14,200)	278 (26,600)	347 (14,500)
Genkwanin (32)	269 (17,000) 300* (12,000)	337 (17,000)			269 (13,600) 292* (10,500)	397 (23,800)		
Isoginkgetin (47)	271.5 (42,000)	330 (36,500)	280 (53,000)	376.5 (24,300)	279.5 (54,500) 295* (42,500)	378 (25,700)	274 (45,000)	345 (29,000)
Sciadopitysin (48)	271.5 (37,600)	330 (35,000)	287 (50,800)	378 (16,000)	273* (34,000) 286 (36,800)	348 (26,200)	272 (35,000) 282* (33,100)	317 (30,000) 337 (29,500)
Ginkgetin (49a or 49b)	271.5 (42,200)	335 (40,000)	284 (46,500)	397 (30,800)	271 (38,500) 281 (40,400)	340 (30,000) 400 (29,800)	270 (38,800) 280 (37,000)	343 (32,000) 397 (24,800)

Fig. 6. Effect of base on ultraviolet spectra of flavones and biflavonyls.

* = point of inflexion.

5. ULTRAVIOLET SPECTRA OF BIFLAVONYLS

During our structural investigations described in Section 4, we were greatly assisted by ultraviolet spectroscopic studies of these compounds which indicated that they had biflavonyl structures and that the two flavonyl units were oxygenated in the 5-, 7-, and 4'-positions. In order to locate the positions of the O-methyl groups when the part structures (45) and (46) had been proposed, it was decided to investigate the influence of base upon their ultraviolet spectra. This had been shown by Swain and his colleagues[35] to be a very valuable method for the study of the simple flavonoids. The results are recorded in Fig. 6.

All the spectra in Fig. 6 show two maxima in neutral ethanol which will be referred to as Band I ($\sim$270 mμ) and Band II ($\sim$330–340 mμ). The effect of sodium ethoxide on the positions and the intensities of these bands is of diagnostic value and these effects based upon the results of Swain *et al.*[35] and our own experiences with other flavones are summarized in Fig. 7.

(*a*) When a 7-OH group is present:
  Band I. Shift ($\sim$270$\rightarrow$280 mμ) with *greatly increased* intensity.
  Band II. Shift ($\sim$330$\rightarrow$370 mμ) with *reduced* intensity.
(*b*) When a 4'-OH group is present:
  Band I. Shift ($\sim$270$\rightarrow$280 mμ) with *reduced* intensity.
  Band II. *Large* shift ($\sim$330$\rightarrow$400 mμ) with *increased* intensity.

FIG. 7. Effect of base upon the positions and intensities of Bands I and II.

The effects of base given in Fig. 7 are due to the formation of the mesomeric anions (50) and (51). When a flavone contains both 7- and 4'-hydroxyl groups, then it may be presumed that effects due to the removal of a proton from the 7-hydroxyl group will predominate because this is the more acidic of the two hydroxyls. Nevertheless, some effect due to ionization of the 4'-hydroxy group should be apparent because in base an equilibrium will be established involving both types (50) and (51) of anion. A 5-hydroxyl group will be much less acidic because it is internally hydrogen bonded and under these conditions of measurement its presence will not contribute towards the effect of base on the ultra-violet spectra.

The influence of base upon the ultra-violet spectra of the three biflavonyls given in Fig. 6 may be summarized as follows:

Isoginkgetin:

Band I. Shift (271.5$\rightarrow$280 mμ) with substantial intensity increase.
Band II. Shift (330$\rightarrow$376.5 mμ) with considerable intensity decrease.

Sciadopitysin:

Band I. Shift (271.52$\rightarrow$87 mμ) with substantial intensity increase.
Band II. Shift (330$\rightarrow$378 mμ) with considerable intensity decrease.

12

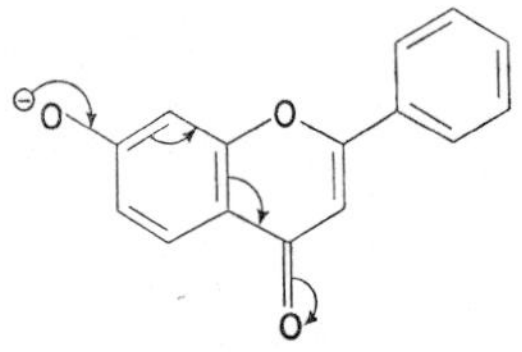

(50) 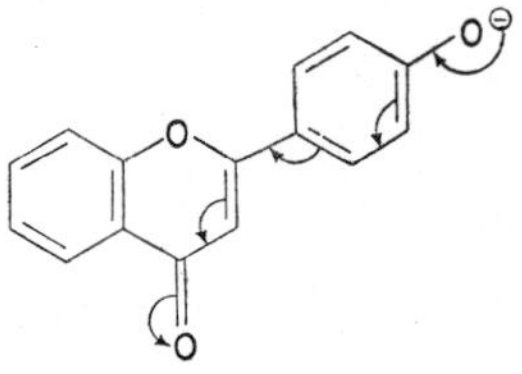   (51)

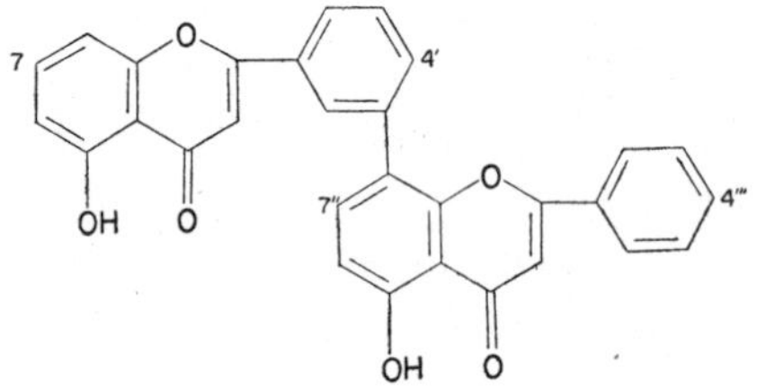

(52)

Ginkgetin:

Band I.   Shift ($271.5 \rightarrow 284$ mμ) with slight intensity increase.

Band II.   Shift ($335 \rightarrow 397$ mμ) with an intensity decrease but of comparatively smaller magnitude.

For isoginkgetin it is clear that it is of the case (*a*) type (see Fig. 7) and as there is no shift of Band II beyond 376.5 mμ it follows that a phenolic group cannot be located at positions 4′ or 4‴ in structure (52). Therefore, the hydroxyl groups must be located at positions 7 and 7″ so confirming the structure (47) for isoginkgetin already proposed on chemical grounds.

The spectral changes shown by sciadopitysin are also of the case (*a*) type (see Fig. 7). However, it will be noticed that the spectra taken in the presence of N/500 and N/5000 sodium ethoxide still exhibit features indicating the presence of the undissociated sciadopitysin molecule, and that these features do not disappear until the base strength is raised to N/50. Therefore, in sciadopitysin there is a 7-hydroxyl group present, but it must be in a special environment to account for this reduced acidity. Of the two positions, 7 and 7″, which are available (see 52), the position 7 would not produce a reduction in acidity. However, the position 7″ is very sterically hindered and as in the case of other ortho-substituted phenols,[36] it would be expected to be much less acidic. Therefore, sciadopitysin has its hydroxyl group located at position 7″ and its three methoxyl groups must therefore be at positions 7, 4′ and 4‴ as in formula (48).

Ginkgetin shows spectral changes (cf. case (*b*) in Fig. 7) showing the presence of at least one 4′-hydroxyl group. However, it is clear that both phenolic hydroxyls cannot be located in positions of this type because even in the presence of N/50 base the shift of Band I is associated with a slight intensity increase, and Band II with an intensity decrease. These changes are not of the type or magnitude associated with the presence of *two* hydroxyl groups of the 4'-type. Therefore ginkgetin contains only one phenolic group of this type which on chemical grounds [see formulae (49a) or (49b)] has been placed in the 4'''-position and hence a methoxyl group must be in position 4'. It follows that the other hydroxyl group must be either in the 7- or 7''-positions [see (52)] and the decision between these two possibilities can be made by noticing that the spectral characteristics of ginkgetin itself disappear only when the base strength has been increased to N/50. It follows therefore that ginkgetin must contain a 7-type hydroxyl group which is sterically protected. This hydroxyl group must be located in the 7''-position [see (52)].

Therefore by a close examination of the effect of base upon its ultraviolet spectrum, it was possible to select one of the two possible structures (49a) or (49b) for ginkgetin and it therefore has the structure (53)[1] (i.e. 49a).

(53)

6. THE "KETOFLAVONES"

The so-called "ketoflavones" are characteristic degradation products of the biflavonyls. Nakazawa first obtained a ketoflavone, $C_{23}H_{15}O_6$.OMe, from ginkgetin by alkaline hydrolysis and he formulated it as (9).[21,22] Similarly, Kariyone and Kawano obtained a keto-flavone, $C_{23}H_{14}O_5(OMe)_2$, from sciadopitysin and gave it the structure (24).[5,6,7] They also showed[6] that these "ketoflavones" were simply related, the compound from sciadopitysin being a monomethyl ether of that derived from ginkgetin.

The structure (53) which was first proposed for ginkgetin on ultraviolet and other evidence[1] was confirmed by a further study of the "ketoflavones" derived from ginkgetin, isoginkgetin, and sciadopitysin.[17] Hydrolysis of ginkgetin by Kariyone and Kawano's procedure[5] gave a ketoflavone, $C_{24}H_{18}O_7$, containing one methoxyl group, p-hydroxyacetophenone, and 2,6-dihydroxy-4-methoxyacetophenone. The infrared spectrum of the compound $C_{24}H_{18}O_7$ showed two carbonyl bands (ν_{max} 1658 and 1645 cm^{-1}) and hydroxyl absorption. Clearly this ketoflavone must have structure (54) because the location of the 4'-methoxy group in ginkgetin was already settled (see Fig. 5). This placed the structure (53) for ginkgetin beyond dispute.

Alkaline hydrolysis of both isoginkgetin and sciadopitysin gave the same "ketoflavone" (55), thus confirming completely the structures proposed for

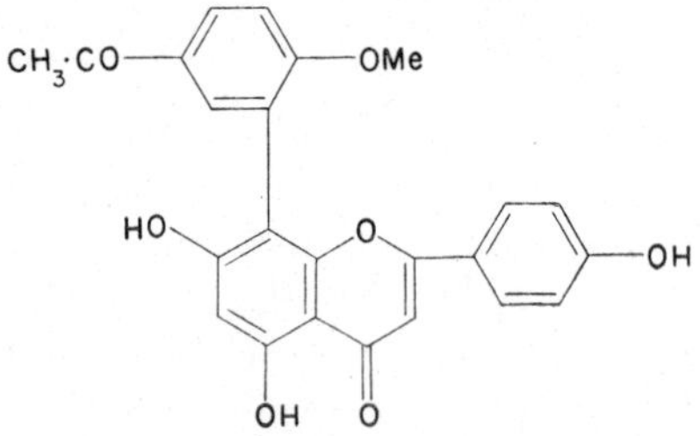

(54)

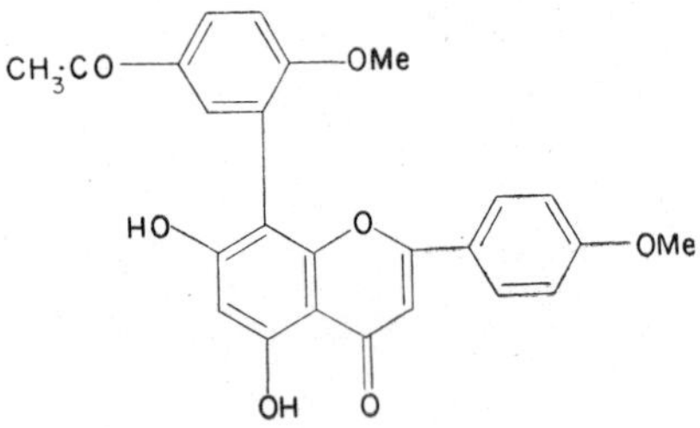

(55)

these two biflavonyls. Of the structures (40a) or (40b) considered for the ketoflavone derived from sciadopitysin, the former (40a = 55) is correct.

7. SCIADOPITYSIN.

Further Work by Kariyone and Kawano (1959)

While our work (see Sections 4, 5, and 6) on ginkgetin, isoginkgetin, and sciadopitysin was proceeding, simultaneous studies on sciadopitysin were being pursued by Kariyone, Kawano, and their collaborators. Their independent work was published when most of our studies were completed and they have now withdrawn their earlier structural proposals and have reached the same conclusions as we have regarding the structure of the biflavonyls. In many cases their work is complementary to ours.

During these investigations the compound has been synthesized with the structure (26) originally allocated to substance A (18); they were not identical.[8] Hydrolysis of sciadopitysin trimethyl ether with methanolic barium hydroxide gave substance B (see Fig. 2) in better yields than were obtained previously. It was suggested that substance B was a biphenyl derivative[9] and not a deoxybenzoin (27) as suggested previously.[7] The biphenyl structure (56) for substance B was proved in the following way.[10]

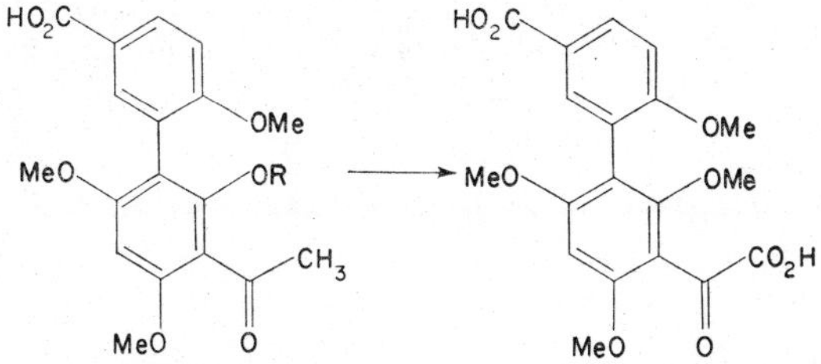

(56) R = H
(57) R = Me

(58)

Permanganate oxidation of substance B gave the α-keto-acid (58) which on heating at 215–220° gave the acid (59). Decarboxylation of this acid (59) in boiling quinoline with copper powder gave a tetramethoxybiphenyl, which

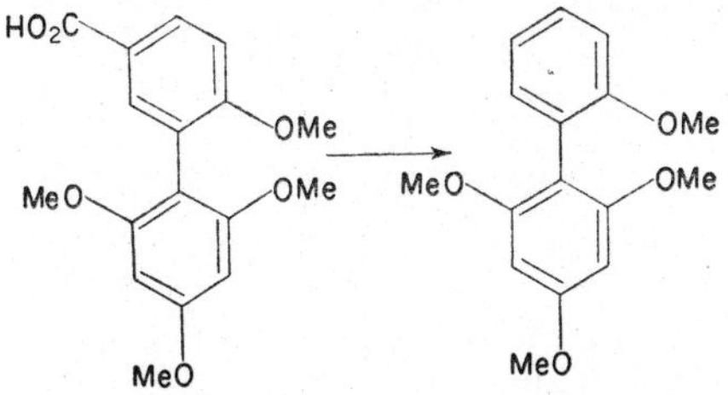

(59)   (60)

was proved to be 2,4,6,2'-tetramethoxybiphenyl by synthesis from 2-iodo-anisole and bromophloroglucinol trimethyl ether. This important result obtained by Kawano[10,12] proved the relative positions of the four oxygen atoms attached to rings B and A' in sciadopitysin trimethyl ether (61).

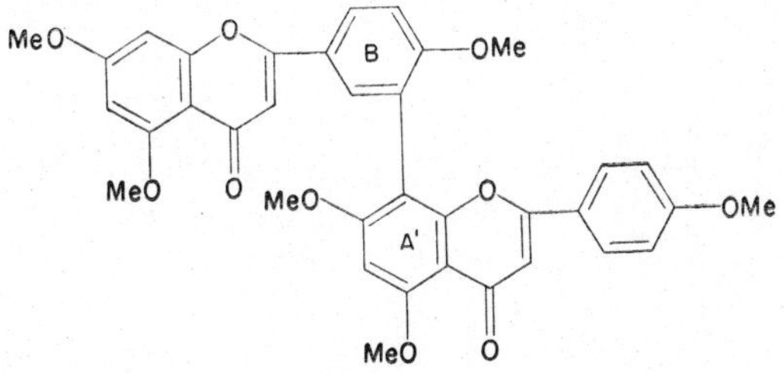

(61)

Kawano recognized that these results, coupled with the formation of 2,6-dihydroxy-4-methoxyacetophenone and anisic acid by alkaline hydrolysis, were compatible with two possible structures (62) or (63) for sciadopitysin.[10] A decision between these structures was made possible by the following degradation.[11] Hydrolysis of sciadopitysin triethyl ether with methanolic barium hydroxide gave a phenolic acid, $C_{20}H_{22}O_7$, with a structure corresponding to that of substance B (56). Permanganate oxidation of this phenolic acid gave 4-methoxy-isophthalic acid proving that sciadopitysin had the structure (62).[13] This structure for sciadopitysin is identical with the structure (48) proposed earlier on largely different evidence.[1]

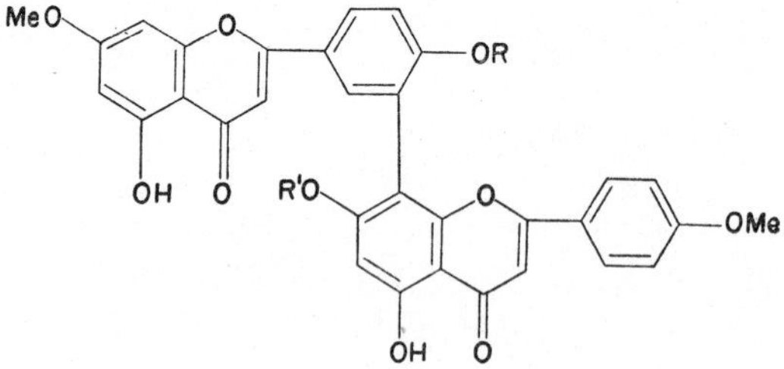

(62) R = Me, R' = H
(63) R = H , R' = Me

8. THE STRUCTURE OF KAYAFLAVONE

Kayaflavone was isolated from the leaves of the gymnosperm, *Torreya nucifera* Sieb. et Zucc. by Kariyone and Sawada.[14,16] It possessed the properties of a biflavonyl and had the formula, $C_{30}H_{12}O_4(OH)_3(OMe)_3$; it

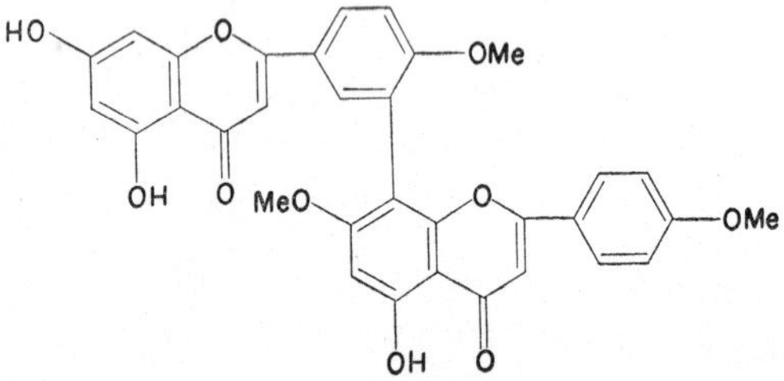

(64)

was isomeric with sciadopitysin. Moreover, it yielded the same trimethyl ether as sciadopitysin and a monomethyl ether identical with ginkgetin dimethyl ether so it must possess free hydroxyl groups in the 5- and 5"-positions.

The structure originally proposed for kayaflavone[19] was based upon an incorrect structure (23) for sciadopitysin. Its structure was established as follows.[17] Oxidation of kayaflavone with alkaline hydrogen peroxide yielded 4-methoxyisophthalic acid and anisic acid and since it is an isomer of sciadopitysin (48) it must have the structure (64).

Kariyone and Sawada[16] obtained a "ketoflavone", $C_{23}H_{13}O_4(OMe)_3$, and a diketone, $C_{18}H_{18}O_6$, by alkaline hydrolysis of kayaflavone. These must be formulated as (65) and (66) respectively.[17] The structure (64)

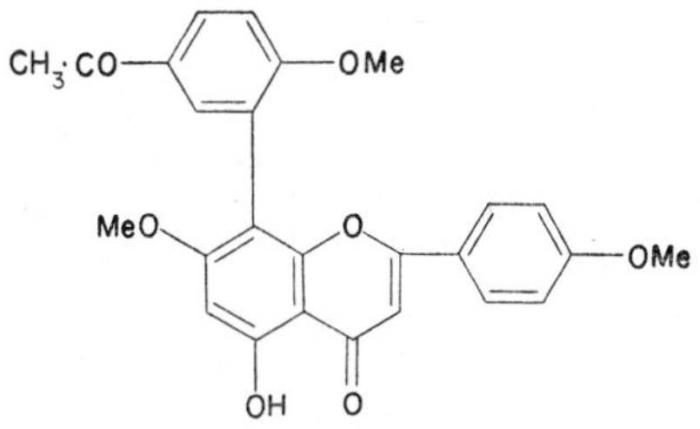

(65)

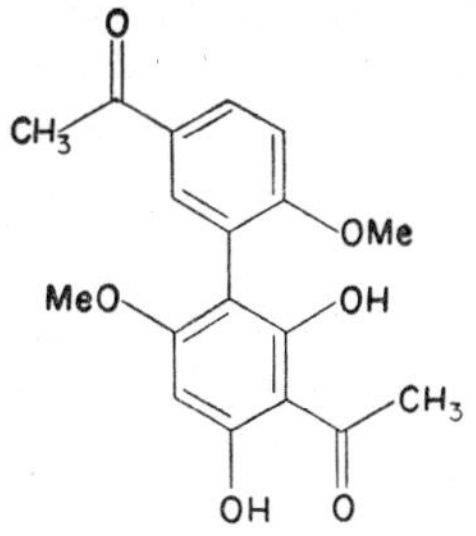

(66)

received strong support from the study of the effect of base on its ultraviolet spectrum which demonstrated the presence of a hydroxyl group in the 7-position.[17]

9. THE STRUCTURE OF SOTETSUFLAVONE

Sotetsuflavone, $C_{30}H_{12}O_4(OH)_5OMe$, was isolated from the leaves of the cycad, *Cycas revoluta* Thunb., as well as from other gymnosperms.[15] Its pentamethyl ether was identical with ginkgetin tetramethyl ether and its trimethyl ether was identical with ginkgetin dimethyl ether. Alkaline hydrolysis of sotetsuflavone gave *p*-hydroxybenzoic acid, *p*-hydroxyacetophenone, and a "ketoflavone", $C_{23}H_{15}O_6.OMe$.[16] It was claimed that this "ketoflavone" was identical with the "ketoflavone" similarly obtained from ginkgetin, so having determined the structure of ginkgetin,[17] Baker *et al.* proposed a structure for sotetsuflavone assuming this claim to be correct. Further work by

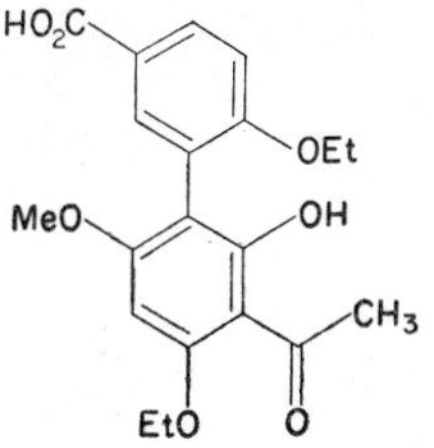

(67)

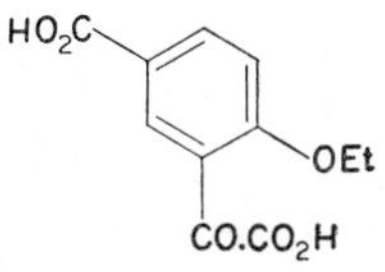

(68)

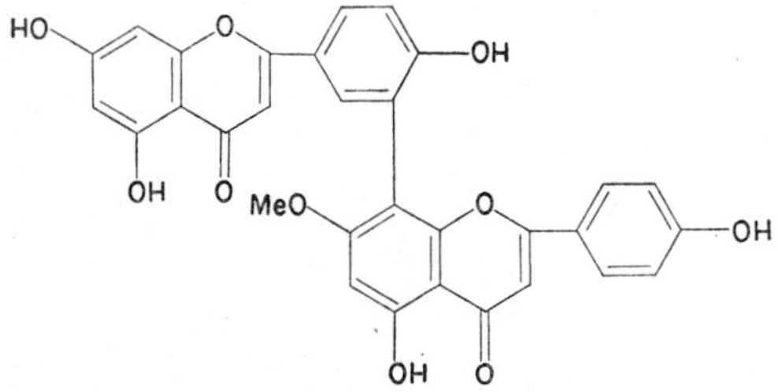

(69)

Kawano and Yamada[23] has shown that the ketoflavones from ginkgetin and sotetsuflavone are in, fact, different. They deduced the structure of sotetsuflavone as follows. Treatment of sotetsuflavone pentaethyl ether with methanolic barium hydroxide gave 2,4-diethoxy-6-hydroxyacetophenone, p-ethoxybenzoic acid, and a phenolic acid, $C_{20}H_{22}O_7$, different from the isomeric acid similarly obtained from sciadopitysin triethyl ether (see Section 7). The phenolic acid, $C_{20}H_{22}O_7$, from sotetsuflavone pentaethyl ether was shown to have the structure (67) since oxidation with alkaline permanganate gave the keto-acid (68) which was also prepared by an unambiguous synthesis. Sotetsuflavone, therefore, has the structure (69).

10. THE SYNTHESIS OF GINKGETIN TETRAMETHYL ETHER AND THE STRUCTURE OF THE BIFLAVONYLS

Nakazawa[37] has recently effected a synthesis of ginkgetin tetramethyl ether by a mixed Ullman reaction between 3'-iodo-5,7,4'-trimethoxyflavone (70) and 8-iodo-5,7,4'-trimethoxyflavone (71); Ullman reactions leading to other simpler biflavonyls have been reported.[45]

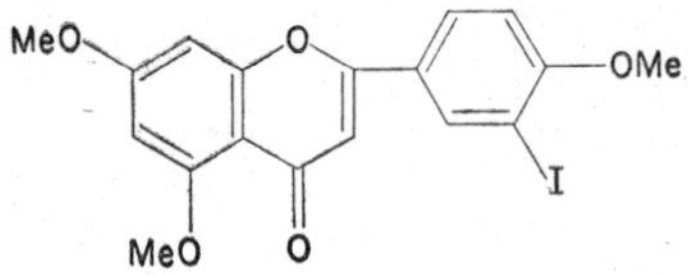

(70)

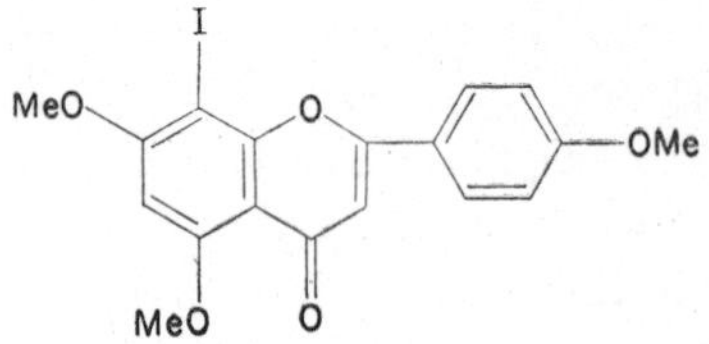

(71)

This synthesis demonstrated for the first time with absolute certainty that ginkgetin contained a 3'-8″ interflavonyl linkage (see 34) and clinched the structures of the biflavonyls, sotetsuflavone (72), ginkgetin (73), isoginkgetin (74), sciadopitysin (75), and kayaflavone (76).* It is indeed appropriate that the first chapter of the story of the investigation of the biflavonyls which was initiated by Nakazawa in 1941 (Section 2) should have been concluded by him in 1959.

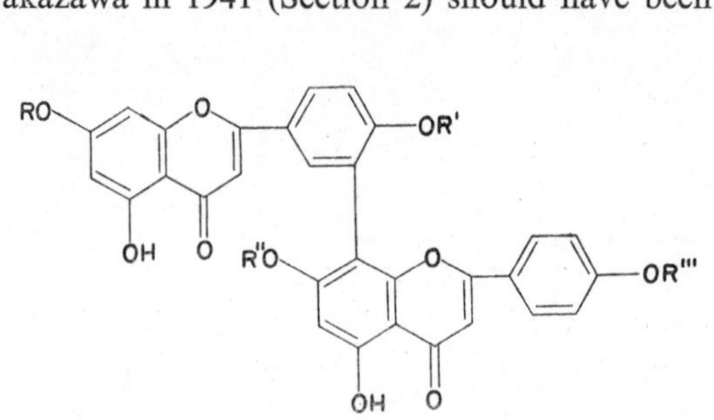

* Recently the structure of armentoflavone has been quoted[46] as a further member of this family [(72)–(76); R = R' = R″ = R‴ = H].

	R	R′	R″	R‴
Sotetsuflavone (72)	H	H	Me	H
Ginkgetin (73)	Me	Me	H	H
Isoginkgetin (74)	H	Me	H	Me
Sciadopitysin (75)	Me	Me	H	Me
Kayaflavone (76)	H	Me	Me	Me

Finally, the optical properties of the biflavonyls were investigated as there was the possibility that these natural products might conceivably exist in optically active forms owing to restricted rotation about the interflavonyl linkage, but comparison with similarly substituted biphenyls showed that this was unlikely.[44] Professor Carl Djerassi very kindly examined the rotatory dispersion characteristics of isoginkgetin and sciadopitysin in the range 390–700 mμ, but found no optical activity.

Recently Kogure[38] has published a series of papers on the degradation of ginkgetin and its structure. Although it is clear that he is probably working with ginkgetin, the molecular formula, $C_{26}H_{20}O_8$, which he proposes for it is incorrect, and the structural formulae of ginkgetin and its derivatives which are given are clearly erroneous.

11. THE STRUCTURE OF HINOKIFLAVONE

Kariyone and Sawada[24] isolated from the leaves of *Chamaecyparis obtusa* Endl. a compound of the biflavonyl type with the molecular formula, $C_{30}H_{18}O_{10}$. Originally they believed it contained six hydroxyl groups and that it formed corresponding derivatives such as a hexa-acetate and hexamethyl ether. The fully methylated derivative was different from ginkgetin tetramethyl ether thus showing that hinokiflavone had a biflavonyl structure different from the known type. Its ultraviolet spectrum [λ_{max} (log ε_{max}), 271 (4.57) and 348 mμ (4.71)] was also different from that of the biflavonyls (see Fig. 3), but the spectrum of its "hexamethyl ether" [λ_{max} (log ε_{max}), 265 (4.52) and 325 mμ (4.71)] was not unlike that of ginkgetin tetramethyl ether.

These results suggested that hinokiflavone was a biflavonyl with an inter-flavonyl linkage other than 3′-8″. Further work[25] proved that hinokiflavone contained only five hydroxyl groups and that it forms a penta-acetate and pentamethyl ether. Its partial structure, $C_{30}H_{13}O_5(OH)_5$, suggested that it could be a biflavonyl ether and this was shown to be true by the following degradation.[25]

Alkaline hydrolysis of hinokiflavone (77) gave *p*-hydroxyacetophenone, a phenolic ketone (78) and a "ketoflavone" (82). This "ketoflavone" gave *p*-hydroxyacetophenone and the ketone (78) on further degradation. The phenolic ketone (78) gave a trimethyl ether (79) which was oxidised to the acid (80). This acid was decarboxylated giving 2,4,6-trimethoxydiphenyl ether (81).

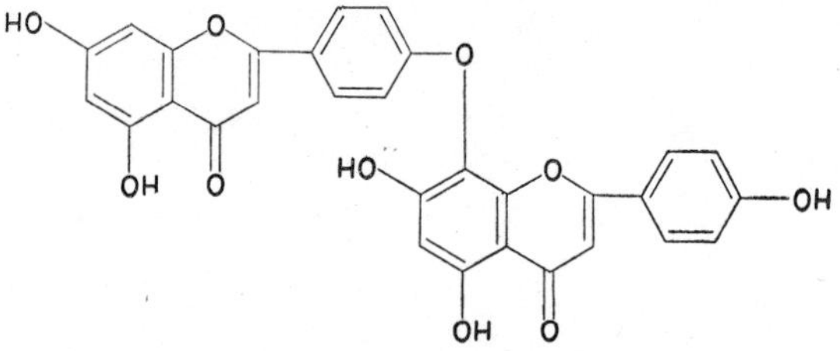

(77)

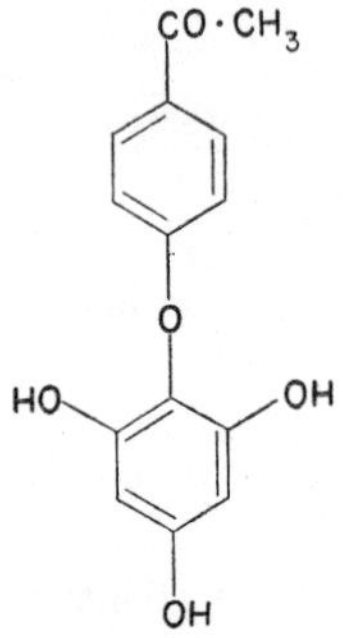

(78)

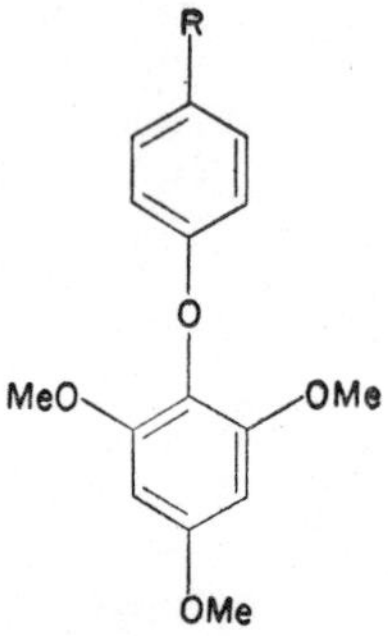

(79)　R = CO.CH₃
(80)　R = CO₂H
(81)　R = H

Alkaline hydrolysis of hinokiflavone pentamethyl ether gave anisic acid, p-methoxyacetophenone, 2,4-dimethoxy-6-hydroxyacetophenone, a phenolic acid, $C_{15}H_{10}O_5(OMe)_2$, and a phenolic diketone, $C_{16}H_{12}O_4(OMe)_2$. The acid

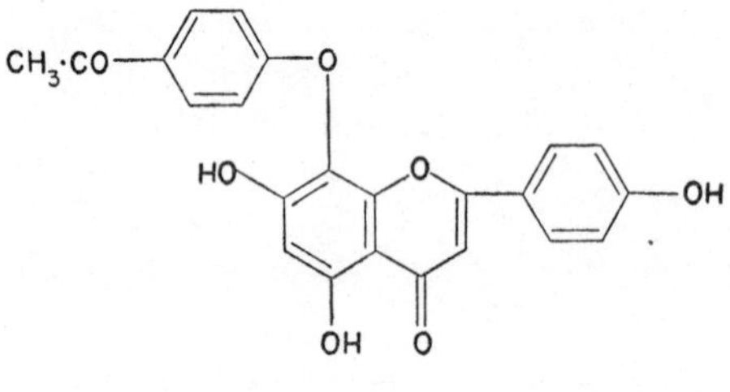

(82)

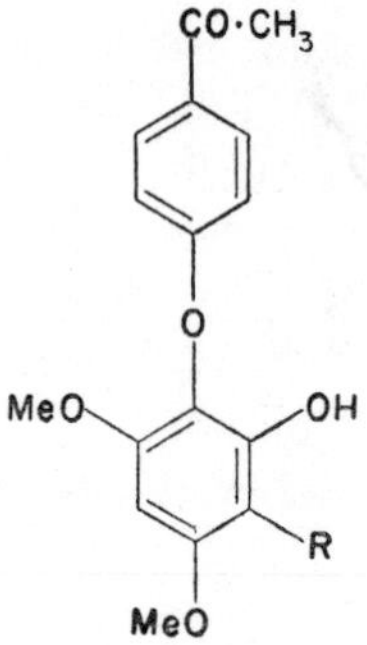

(83)　R = CO₂H
(84)　R = CO·CH₃

and the diketone have been represented by the formulae (83) and (84) respectively and were each transformed into the diphenyl ether (81) by methylation, oxidation, and decarboxylation. These facts led to two possible formulae for hinokiflavone, and of these structure (77) was preferred.[25] The other structure containing a 4′–6″ ether linkage was excluded on colour tests (Gibbs) given by certain degradation products and by its ultra-violet and infra-red spectra.

12. BIOSYNTHESIS OF THE BIFLAVONYLS

It has already been suggested (see p. 19) that the biflavonyls are probably produced in the plant by oxidative coupling (see Chapter 5) of a flavonoid precursor such as apigenin or a closely related compound. This could be followed by methylation of the di-apigeninyl in various positions, and this is in agreement with the simultaneous occurrence of different biflavonyls (72–75) in the same plant. It is also supported by the biflavonyl ether structure of hinokiflavone since it is recognized that oxidative coupling of phenols can lead to either diaryls or diaryl ethers.[33,34] It could be argued using the postulate due to Wenkert[39] that the interflavonyl linkage in the biflavonyls is formed by interaction of a flavone with dehydroshikimic acid and that the second flavonyl residue is built on to the shikimic acid residue by the usual flavonoid biosynthetic processes. We, however, prefer the first hypothesis and it would be of interest to determine whether generally labelled apigenin is converted into generally labelled biflavonyls by feeding it to a suitable plant.

The pigment ergoflavin, $C_{30}H_{26}O_{14}$, produced by the fungus *Claviceps purpurea*, has structural features which suggest that it may have been derived from a C_{15}-precursor possibly of the flavonoid type.[40]

13. THE TAXONOMIC DISTRIBUTION OF THE BIFLAVONYLS

A large number of plants have been examined for biflavonyls and with one exception they are restricted to the leaves of Gymnosperms. The taxonomic classification of the seed-bearing plants separates them into Gymnosperms and Angiosperms as indicated in Fig. 8. The Gymnosperms include about 700 plants which are accommodated in four orders: Cycadales (~85 plants), Ginkgoales (1 plant—*Ginkgo biloba*), Coniferales (~540 plants) and Gnetales (~70 plants).

The distribution of the biflavonyls has been studied by Kariyone,[19] Sawada,[41] and Hasegawa *et al.*,[42] and their results are summarized in Table 1. Hasegawa detected biflavonyls in plant extracts by paper chromatography, but Sawada made a very extensive investigation of a large number of plants and isolated the biflavonyls as pure compounds. The data in Table 1 are almost entirely due to Sawada.[41]

From an examination of Table 1 it is clear that the biflavonyls are very widely distributed among the gymnosperms. There is therefore a striking phytochemical relationship between the gymnosperms which occupy a special position on taxonomic grounds and the production by them of a particular type of natural product—the biflavonyls. Erdtman,[43] who has

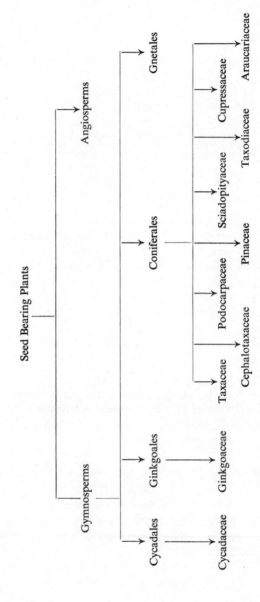

Fig. 8. A taxonomic classification of seed bearing plants.

TABLE 1. DISTRIBUTION OF BIFLAVONYLS

Orders	Families, Genera and Species	G.	I.	Sc.	K.	So.	H.
CYCADALES	Cycadaceae *Cycas revoluta* Thunb.	–	–	–	–	●	–
GINKGOALES	Ginkgoaceae *Ginkgo biloba* L.	●	●	–	–	–	–
CONIFERALES	Taxaceae *Taxus cuspidata* Sieb. and Zucc.	–	–	●	–	–	–
	T. cuspidata var. *nana* Hort.	–	–	●	–	–	–
	T. floriana Chap.	–	–	●	–	–	–
	Torreya nucifera Sieb. and Zucc.	–	–	–	●	–	–
	Cephalotaxaceae *Cephalotaxus drupacea* Sieb. and Zucc.	–	–	–	●	–	–
	C. nana Nakai	–	–	–	●	–	–
	Podocarpaceae *Podocarpus macrophylla* D. Don	–	–	–	●	–	–
	P. chinensis Sweet	–	–	–	●	–	–
	P. nagi Zoll. and Moritz	–	–	–	●	–	–
	Pinaceae *Abies firma* Sieb. and Zucc.	–	–	–	–	–	–
	A. homolepsis Sieb. and Zucc.	–	–	–	–	–	–
	A. mariessii Mast.	–	–	–	–	–	–
	A. veitchii Lindley	–	–	–	–	–	–
	A. sachalinensis var. *Schmidtii* Tatewaki	–	–	–	–	–	–
	Keteleeria davidiana Beissner	–	–	–	–	–	–
	Pseudotsuga japonica Carriere	–	–	–	–	–	–
	Tsuga sieboldii Carriere	–	–	–	–	–	–
	T. diversifolia Mast.	–	–	–	–	–	–
	Picea polita Carriere	–	–	–	–	–	–
	P. glehnii Mast.	–	–	–	–	–	–
	P. maximowiczii Regel	–	–	–	–	–	–
	P. koyamai Shirasawa	–	–	–	–	–	–
	P. bicolor Mayer	–	–	–	–	–	–
	P. jezoensis var. *hondoensis* Rehder	–	–	–	–	–	–
	Pseudolarix kaempferi Gordon.	–	–	–	–	–	–
	Larix kaempferi Sargent	–	–	–	–	–	–
	Cedrus deodara Loud.	–	–	–	–	–	–
	Pinus densiflora Sieb. and Zucc.	–	–	–	–	–	–
	P. koraiensis (and 22 other spp. of *Pinus* not named)	–	–	–	–	–	–
	Sciadopityaceae *Sciadopitys verticillata* Sieb. and Zucc.	–	–	●	–	–	–
	Taxodiaceae *Taxodium distichum* Rich.	–	–	–	–	–	●
	Sequoia sempervirens E.	–	–	–	●	–	●
	Metasequoia glyptostroboides Hu and Cheng	–	–	–	–	–	●
	Glyptostrobus pensilis K. Koch	–	–	–	–	–	●
	Cunninghamia lanceolata Hooker	–	–	●	●	●	●
	C. lanceolata var. *konishii* Fujita	–	–	–	●	–	●
	Taiwania cryptomerioides Hayata	–	–	–	–	–	●
	Cryptomeria japonica D. Don	–	–	●	●	●	–
	C. japonica var. *araucarioides* Hort.	–	–	●	●	●	–

GYMNOSPERMAE

[continued overleaf]

182 W. Baker and W. D. Ollis

Table 1 (Continued)

Orders	Families, Genera and Species	G.	I.	Sc.	K.	So.	H.
CONIFERALES	Cupressaceae						
	Callitris glauca R. Brown	–	–	–	–	–	●
	Thujopsis dolobrata Sieb. and Zucc.	–	–	●	–	●	●
	Thuja standishii C.	–	–	–	–	–	●
	T. occidentalis L.	–	–	–	–	–	●
	Biota orientalis Endl.	–	–	–	–	–	●
	Libocedrus formosana Frolin	–	–	–	–	–	●
	L. decurrens Torrey	–	–	–	–	–	●
	Cupressus funebris Endl.	–	–	–	–	–	●
	C. arizonica	–	–	–	–	–	●
	Chamaecyparis obtusa Endl.	–	–	–	–	–	●
	C. obtusa var. *breviana* Mast.	–	–	–	–	●	●
	C. pisifera Mast.	–	–	–	–	–	●
	C. pisifera var. *filifera* Mast.	–	–	–	–	–	●
	C. pisifera var. *squarrosa* Mast.	–	–	–	–	–	●
	Sabina chinensis Antoine	–	–	–	●	–	●
	S. virginiana Antoine	–	–	–	●	–	●
	S. procumbens Sieb. and Zucc.	–	–	–	●	–	●
	S. sargentii Nakai	–	–	–	●	–	●
	S. sargentii var. *kaizuka* Hort.	–	–	–	●	–	●
	Juniperis utilis Koidz.	–	–	–	●	–	●
	J. conferta Parl.	–	–	–	●	–	●
GNETALES	Ephedraceae						
	Ephedra gerardiana Wall.	–	–	–	–	–	–
CASUARINALES	Casuarinaceae						
	Casuarina stricta Ait.	–	–	–	–	–	●

(left margin, top section: GYMNOSPERMAE; lower section: ANGIOSPERMAE)

G. = ginkgetin; I. = isoginkgetin; Sc. = sciadopitysin; K. = kayaflavone; So. = sotetsuflavone; H. = hinokiflavone.

made a most important contribution to chemical taxonomy, has commented upon the interest of this distinctive production of biflavonyls by gymnosperms.

Plants belonging to the *Araucariaceae* family have not been examined but with the notable exception of the Pinaceae all the other families in the Coniferales order contain species from which biflavonyls have been isolated. The fact that biflavonyls are absent from the leaves of all the plants in the Pinaceae family which have been examined is of considerable interest, and is in accord with the suggestion that *Pinus* and related genera should be separated from the other plants in the Coniferales. Some taxonomists prefer to accommodate them in a separate Pinales order.

All the Cupressaceae which have been examined contain hinokiflavone and in connection with the suggestion that *Sabina* and *Juniperus* belong to an independent family, the Juniperaceae, it may be noted that *Sabina* and *Juniperus* both contain kayaflavone as well as hinokiflavone whereas the other members of the Cupressaceae do not.

The separation of *Sciadopitys verticillata* from the Taxodiaceae would appear to be justified from a comparison of the biflavonyls associated with it and with those associated with the other plants in the family. Similarly, the Taxaceae are characterized by the presence of sciadopitysin whereas the Cephalotaxaceae yield kayaflavone.

The presence of biflavonyls in plants of the Gnetales order has not been established, but only one plant has been examined. The only plant which is not a gymnosperm which has been shown to contain a biflavonyl, namely, hinokiflavone, is the angiosperm, *Casuarina stricta*. This is particularly interesting because of all the angiosperms, *Casuarina* is the most closely related to the gymnosperms.

REFERENCES

1. W. BAKER, A. C. M. FINCH, W. D. OLLIS and K. W. ROBINSON, *Proc. Chem. Soc.* 1959, 91.
2. K. W. ROBINSON, *Dissertation* (Bristol), 1959.
3. T. SAWADA, Private communication quoted by N. KAWANO, ref. 12.
4. T. KARIYONE and N. KAWANO, *J. Pharm. Soc. Japan* 1956, **76**, 448.
5. T. KARIYONE and N. KAWANO, *J. Pharm. Soc. Japan* 1956, **76**, 451.
6. T. KARIYONE and N. KAWANO, *J. Pharm. Soc. Japan* 1956, **76**, 453.
7. N. KAWANO, *J. Pharm. Soc. Japan* 1956, **76**, 457.
8. T. KARIYONE, N. KAWANO and M. MAEYAMA, *J. Pharm. Soc. Japan* 1959, **79**, 382.
9. T. KARIYONE, N. KAWANO and H. MIURA, *J. Pharm. Soc. Japan* 1959, **79**, 1182.
10. N. KAWANO, *Chem. Pharm. Bull. Japan* 1959, **7**, 698.
11. N. KAWANO, *Chem. Pharm. Bull. Japan* 1959, **7**, 821.
12. N. KAWANO, *Chem. and Ind.* 1959, 368.
13. N. KAWANO, *Chem. and Ind.* 1959, 852.
14. T. KARIYONE and T. SAWADA, *J. Pharm. Soc. Japan* 1958, **78**, 1010.
15. T. KARIYONE and T. SAWADA, *J. Pharm. Soc. Japan* 1958, **78**, 1013.
16. T. KARIYONE and T. SAWADA, *J. Pharm. Soc. Japan* 1958, **78**, 1016.
17. W. BAKER, W. D. OLLIS and K. W. ROBINSON, *Proc. Chem. Soc.* 1959, 269.
18. T. KARIYONE and T. SAWADA, *Complete Publication in Memory of Professor T. Kariyone*, 1956, p. 16. Quoted by H. Erdtman, ref. 43.
19. T. KARIYONE, *Proceedings of the Phytochemical Symposium, Kuala Lumpur*, 1957, p. 160.
20. S. FURUKAWA, Abstract from The Bulletin of the Institute of Physical and Chemical Research, Tokyo, 1929, **2**, 5; *Sci. Papers Inst. Phys. Chem. Res. Tokyo* 1932, **19**, 27; 1933, **21**, 278.
21. K. NAKAZAWA, *J. Pharm. Soc. Japan* 1941, **61**, 174. (*Chem. Abs.* 1950, **44**, 9441).
22. K. NAKAZAWA, *J. Pharm. Soc. Japan* 1941, **61**, 90, 228.
23. N. KAWANO and M. YAMADA, *J. Amer. Chem. Soc.* 1960, **82**, 1505.
24. T. KARIYONE and T. SAWADA, *J. Pharm. Soc. Japan* 1958, **78**, 1020.
25. Y. FUKUI and N. KAWANO, *J. Amer. Chem. Soc.* 1959, **81**, 6331.
26. W. BAKER and W. H. C. SIMMONDS, *J. Chem. Soc.* 1940, 1370; W. BAKER and G. F. FLEMONS, *J. Chem. Soc.* 1948, 2138; W. BAKER, G. F. FLEMONS and R. WINTER, *J. Chem. Soc.* 1949, 1560.

184   W. Baker and W. D. Ollis

27. Z. Horii, *J. Pharm. Soc. Japan* 1940, **60**, 222; M. Ikawa, *J. Chem. Soc. Japan* 1941, **62**, 1052; A. Kogure, *J. Chem. Soc. Japan* 1952, **73**, 271 (*Chem. Abs.* 1954, **48**, 2055); A. Kogure, *J. Chem. Soc. Japan* 1952, **73**, 308 (*Chem. Abs.* 1953, **47**, 10527); A. Kogure and T. Kubota, *J. Inst. Poly. Osaka City Univ.* 1952, **2**, 70 (*Chem. Abs.* 1953, **47**, 10525); A. Kogure and T. Kubota, *J. Inst. Poly. Osaka City Univ.* 1952, **2**, 76 (*Chem. Abs.* 1953, **47**, 10526).
28. A. C. Seward, *Science Progress* 1937, **32**, 420.
29. V. D. Martin, *Proc. Indiana Acad. Sci.* 1935, **44**, 166 (*Biol. Abs.* 1936, **10**, 19505).
30. K. Nakazawa and S. Matsuura, *J. Pharm. Soc. Japan* 1953, **73**, 481, 484, 751; 1954, **74**, 40; 1955, **75**, 68, 467, 716.
31. V. S. Butt, *Dissertation* (Bristol), 1948; P. J. L. Binns, *Dissertation* (Bristol), 1951; A. Pelter, *Dissertation* (Bristol), 1956.
32. W. Baker, W. D. Ollis and T. S. Zealley, *J. Chem. Soc.* 1951, 208.
33. D. H. R. Barton and T. Cohen, *Festschrift Arthur Stoll*, Birkhäuser, Basel, 1957, p. 117.
34. H. Erdtman and C. A. Wachtmeister, *Festschrift Arthur Stoll*, Birkhäuser, Basel, 1957, p. 144.
35. G. H. Mansfield, T. Swain, and C. G. Nordström, *Nature, London* 1953, **172**, 23; C. G. Nordström and T. Swain, *J. Chem. Soc.* 1953, 2764.
36. N. D. Goggeshall and A. S. Glessner, *J. Amer. Chem. Soc.* 1949, **71**, 3150.
37. K. Nakazawa, *Chem. Pharm. Bull.* (*Japan*) 1959, **7**, 748.
38. A. Kogure, *J. Chem. Soc. Japan* 1959, **80**, 1352, 1355, 1462, 1467.
39. E. Wenkert, *Experientia* 1959, **15**, 165; *Chem. and Ind.* 1959, 906.
40. G. Eglington, F. E. King, G. Lloyd, J. W. Loder, J. R. Marshall, A. Robertson and W. B. Whalley, *J. Chem. Soc.* 1958, 1833.
41. T. Sawada, *J. Pharm. Soc. Japan* 1958, **78**, 1023.
42. M. Hasagawa, H. Nakamura and S. Tsurono, *J. Jap. Forestry Soc.* 1955, **37**, 488.
43. H. Erdtman, *Fourth International Congress of Biochemistry*, Vol. 2, p. 1, Pergamon Press, London 1959.
44. R. L. Shriner, R. Adams and C. S. Marvel, *Organic Chemistry* (ed. by H. Gilman), Vol. 1, p. 361, John Wiley, 1943.
45. F. C. Chen, C. T. Chang, M. Hung, Y. C. Lin and S. T. Choong, *Proc. Chem. Soc.* 1959, 232, and references there cited.
46. C. T. Chang, T. S. Chen, T. Ueng, S. T. Choong and F. C. Chen, *J. Formosan Sci.* 1960, **14**, 1.

Adonis vernalis L.

Spartium junceum L.

Sources of C-glycosides (see Tables 1 and 4)

Polygonum orientale L.

CHAPTER 10

NEW PHENOLIC C-GLYCOSIDES IN PLANTS

L. Hörhammer and H. Wagner

University of Munich

ALTHOUGH O-glycosides of flavonoids and related compounds have been known for a very considerable time, it was not until 1957 that the existence of a C-glycosyl grouping in vitexin was fully established, although vitexin had been recognized as a natural product some 57 years earlier. Recently, considerable progress has been made in the recognition and proof of structure of quite a large number of other natural products related to vitexin, and this chapter reviews the studies which have been made. It is suggested that these substances should be called C-glycosides and their relationship to O-glycosides is indicated below.

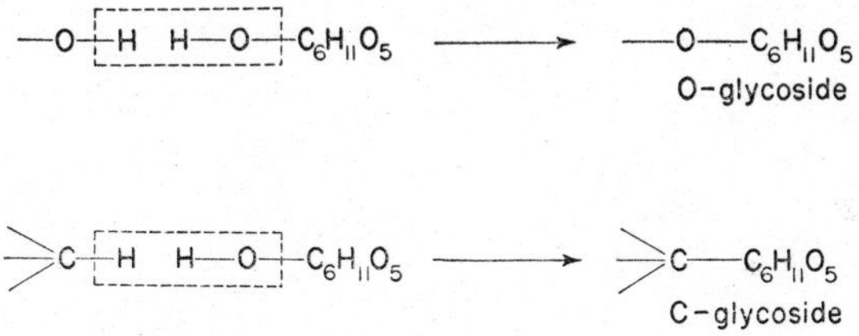

VITEXIN AND SAPONARETIN

In 1900, Perkin[1] isolated a flavone derivative from the wood of *Vitex littoralis* (puriri-wood) which he called vitexin and during the following years several structures were proposed for this compound. Barger[2] found that it was also formed, along with a second compound, in the hydrolysis of saponarin, while Nakaoki[3] was the first to show that an apigenin residue was present in vitexin and suggested that it possessed a pentahydroxy-n-hexyl group in the C_6 or C_8 position. The definitive proof of a C-glycosyl structure was achieved by Evans and co-workers[4] and on the basis of the degradative reactions shown in Fig. 1, these workers proposed the structure (1) for vitexin.

Vitexin possessed the formula $C_{21}H_{20}O_{10}$ and formed a hepta-acetate. It was exceptionally stable towards acidic and enzymic hydrolysis but was smoothly cleaved to apigenin, either by catalytic hydrogenation or reduction with hydriodic acid; no sugar could be detected. Sodium hydroxide titration

of the formic acid formed by periodic acid oxidation revealed that 4.6 moles
of acid were formed per mole of vitexin.

The periodate oxidation of vitexin (1) caused ring cleavage and the formation of dehydrosecovitexin (2), which on treatment with sulphuric acid led
to D-glyceraldehyde in the form of its dimethyl acetal and an apigenin
derivative (3) with a glyceraldehyde residue located at position 8 of its
skeleton. By acid treatment of vitexin, saponaretin (1a) was produced, from
which it may be deduced that the C-glycosyl residue in saponaretin is present
in an open-chain form.

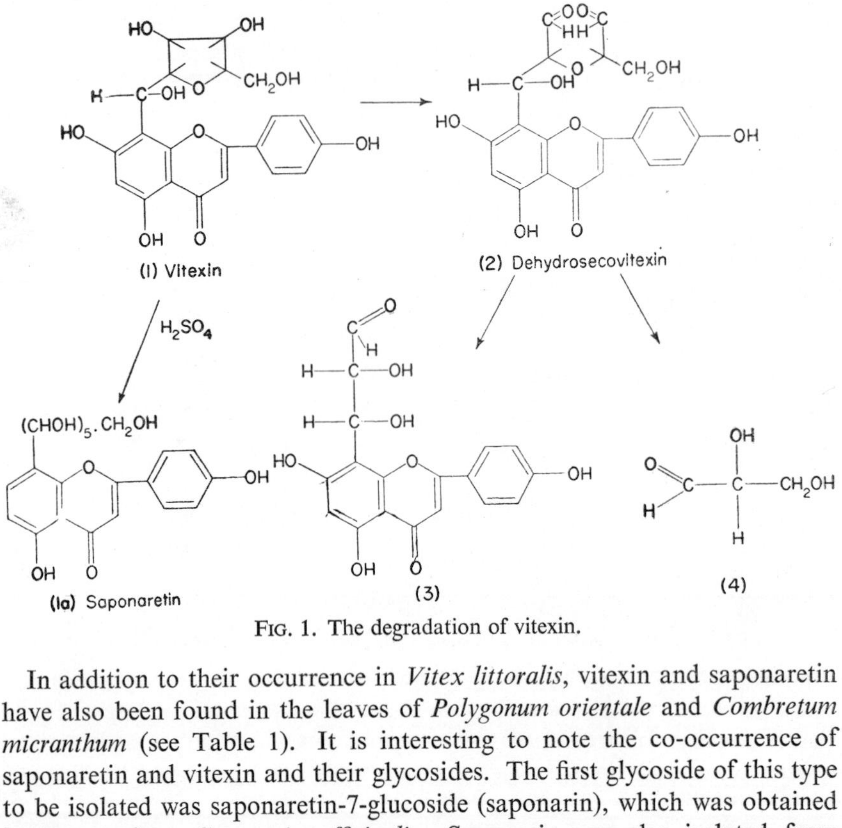

Fig. 1. The degradation of vitexin.

In addition to their occurrence in *Vitex littoralis*, vitexin and saponaretin
have also been found in the leaves of *Polygonum orientale* and *Combretum
micranthum* (see Table 1). It is interesting to note the co-occurrence of
saponaretin and vitexin and their glycosides. The first glycoside of this type
to be isolated was saponaretin-7-glucoside (saponarin), which was obtained
by Barger from *Saponaria officinalis*. Saponarin was also isolated from
Hordeum vulgare by Seikel and Geissman and it occurs in *Spirodella oligor-
rhiza* together with the isomeric saponaretin-4'-glucoside (isosaponarin).
Including vitexin-4'-rhamnoside obtained from *Crataegus oxyacantha*, five
vitexin or saponaretin derivatives are known at present (see Table 1).

The ultraviolet maxima for these C-glycosides and for apigenin in ethanol
and in ethanol containing sodium acetate are shown to be remarkably
similar (see Table 2). Table 3 contains the R_f values of the same compounds

(*a*) in ethyl acetate–formic acid–water (10:2:3) and (*b*) in isopropanol–formic acid–water (2:5:5).

On unsprayed paper chromatograms, vitexin, saponaretin, and apigenin show a brown fluorescence in ultraviolet light, but after treatment with aluminium chloride or basic lead acetate solution the colour of the fluorescence changes to a yellow-green.

TABLE 1. DISTRIBUTION OF SUBSTANCES OF THE VITEXIN TYPE

Species	Family	Compound	Isolation
Vitex littoralis A.	Verbenaceae	Vitexin	A. G. Perkin[1]
Polygonum orientale L.	Polygonaceae	Vitexin Saponaretin	L. Hörhammer and H. Wagner[5]
Combretum micranthum G. Don	Combretaceae	Vitexin Saponarin	L. Fuchs and J. Jentzsch[6]
Saponaria officinalis L.	Caryophyllaceae	Saponarin	K. Barger[2]
Hordeum vulgare L.	Gramineae	Saponarin	M. K. Seikel and T. A. Geissman[7]
Spirodella oligorrhiza Hegel	Lemnaceae	Saponarin Isosaponarin	L. Jurd, T. A. Geissman and M. K. Seikel[8]
Crataegus oxyacantha L.	Rosaceae	Vitexin-4′-rhamnoside	U. Kranen-Fielder[9]

TABLE 2.

Substance	Ethanol		Ethanol–sodium acetate	
	λ_{max}(I) mμ	λ_{max}(II) mμ	λ_{max}(I) mμ	λ_{max}(II) mμ
Vitexin	334	270	370	278
Saponaretin	336	272	378	280
Saponarin	335	272	336 (400)	271
Vitexin-4′-rhamnoside	335	272	380	280
Apigenin	336	269	379	277

TABLE 3.

Substance	R_f (a)	R_f (b)
Vitexin	0.37	0.55
Saponaretin	0.51	0.75
Saponarin	0.25	—
Vitexin-4′-rhamnoside	0.30	—
Apigenin	0.86	0.33

ORIENTIN AND HOMO-ORIENTIN

Since apigenin and luteolin frequently occur together in the same plants, it was not surprising that new *C*-glycosyl compounds of the luteolin type were also found. The luteolin analogue of vitexin, orientin, was first discovered by Hörhammer and co-workers in the leaves of *Polygonum orientale* in association with vitexin and saponaretin. Orientin, m.p. 255–257°, has the formula $C_{21}H_{20}O_{11}$.[5] It forms an octa-acetate and on alkaline degradation gives phloroglucinol and protocatechuic acid, products typical of a luteolin derivative. Like vitexin, orientin is stable to vigorous acid hydrolysis and enzymic hydrolysis (emulsin, tannase, anthocyaninase), but it is transformed quantitatively into luteolin by means of catalytic hydrogenation or hydriodic acid reduction. Titration of the formic acid from periodate oxidation shows that, as with vitexin, 4.5 moles of acid are produced per mole of orientin thus indicating the presence of one glucosyl residue in the orientin molecule (5).

(5) Orientin   (6) Homo-orientin

The infrared spectrum of orientin (Fig. 2) very closely resembles the spectrum of vitexin with the exception of bands in the 750 to 880 cm⁻¹ region. The infrared spectrum of vitexin (Fig. 3) shows a strong band at 835 cm⁻¹, which is typical of flavones containing a p-substituted phenyl group, while in the infrared spectrum of orientin this band lies at a somewhat shorter wavelength, namely 850 cm⁻¹, and there are two other bands of lower intensity at 790 cm⁻¹ and 820 cm⁻¹. These bands are found in flavones with an o-disubstituted phenyl group. For comparison the infrared spectrum of luteolin-7-glucoside (Fig. 4) is given. The infrared spectrum of luteolin-7-glucoside is clearly distinguished from that of vitexin or orientin in the OH-stretching region, and this distinction is undoubtedly due to the different arrangements of the hydroxyl groups in the C-glycosyl and O-glycosyl moieties.

It is interesting to note that the saponaretin analogue of orientin also exists and has been designated homo-orientin (6). Crystallization of homo-orientin has not yet been accomplished, but on the basis of paper chromatographic behaviour and its ultra-violet spectrum there is little doubt that it is in fact the luteolin analogue (6) of saponaretin (1a).

Orientin has also been isolated from the blossoms of *Spartium junceum* and from the leaves of *Oxalis acetosella* and *Hordeum vulgare*. The search for glycosides corresponding to orientin and homo-orientin has also been successful. From the leaves of *Adonis vernalis* a compound has been isolated which yielded xylose, orientin, and homo-orientin on acid hydrolysis. The

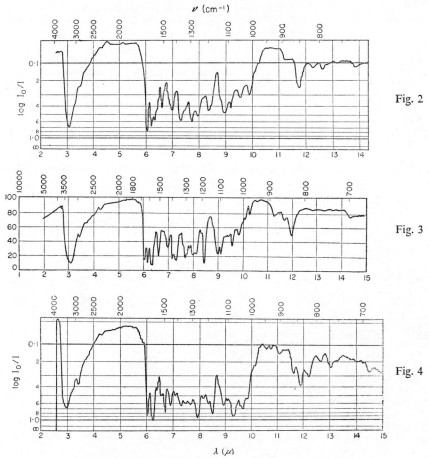

Infrared spectra (KBr disks) of orientin (Fig. 2), vitexin (Fig. 3) and luteolin-7-monoglucoside (Fig. 4).

CH-analysis of this compound clearly indicated a homo-orientin-xyloside type structure. Since, on the basis of ultraviolet spectrophotometric measurements, it was clear that the hydroxyl groups at C_3, $C_{4'}$, and C_7 were free, it followed that the xylose residue must be bound directly to the glycosyl residue. Similarly, the compound scoparoside, isolated first by Paris[10] from the leaves of *Sarothamnus scoparius*, proved to be a luteolin *C*-glycosyl compound. Alkaline degradation of scoparoside gave among other products vanillic acid, demonstrating that a methoxyl group must be present in the 3'-position. Treatment with hydrogen iodide led to an almost quantitative yield of luteolin, (5). Scoparoside possesses the molecular formula $C_{22}H_{22}O_{11}$ and separates with 5 molecules of water of crystallization, three of which are lost by drying in high vacuum at 120°. Periodic acid oxidation gives a

TABLE 4. Distribution of Substances of the Orientin Type

Species	Family	Compound	Isolation
Polygonum orientale L.	Polygonaceae	Orientin Homo-orientin	L. Hörhammer and H. Wagner[5]
Spartium junceum L.	Papilionaceae	Orientin	L. Hörhammer and H. Wagner[11]
Oxalis acetosella	Oxalidaceae	Orientin	T. A. Geissman[12]
Hordeum vulgare L.	Gramineae	Orientin	M. K. Seikel[7]
Sarothamnus scoparius Koch	Papilionaceae	Orientin-3'-mono- methyl ether (scoparoside)	L. Hörhammer and H. Wagner[13]
Adonis vernalis L.	Ranunculaceae	Adonivernoside (homo-orientin monoxyloside)	L. Hörhammer and H. Wagner[14]

TABLE 5

Substance	Ethanol		Ethanol + sodium acetate		Ethanol + sodium acetate + boric acid	
	$\lambda_{max}(I)$ mμ	$\lambda_{max}(II)$ mμ	$\lambda_{max}(I)$ mμ	$\lambda_{max}(II)$ mμ	$\lambda_{max}(I)$ mμ	$\lambda_{max}(II)$ mμ
Orientin	351	257	381	275	377	265
Homo-orientin	350	258	384	274	380	267
Adonivernoside	350	260	382	275	377	265
Scoparoside	345	270	395	280	345	275
Luteolin	350	247	382	264	375	261
Luteolin-4'-glucoside	335	270	382	275	338	269
Luteolin-7-glucoside	355	256	367	270	368	253

TABLE 6

Substance	$R_f(a)$
Orientin	0.29
Homo-orientin	0.46
Adonivernoside	0.37
Scoparoside	0.40
Luteolin	0.80

result similar to that obtained with vitexin and orientin. As indicated in Table 4 the number of known luteolin *C*-glycosyl compounds is four.

For comparison with the data in Tables 2 and 3, the more important ultra-violet spectrophotometric and paper chromatographic data for orientin, homo-orientin, adonivernoside, scoparoside, luteolin, luteolin-4'-glucoside, and luteolin-7-glucoside are presented in Tables 5 and 6.

Orientin and homo-orientin produce brown fluorescent spots on paper chromatograms and after spraying with aluminium chloride or treatment with lead tetra-acetate an orange fluorescence appears. Scoparoside gives a yellow fluorescence which is attributable to its 3′-methoxyl group.

PUERARIN

Shibata[14] has recently isolated a *C*-glycosyl compound which belongs to the isoflavone series. Puerarin is present in the roots of *Pueraria Thunbergiana* Benth., an important medicament in old Chinese medicine. It has the

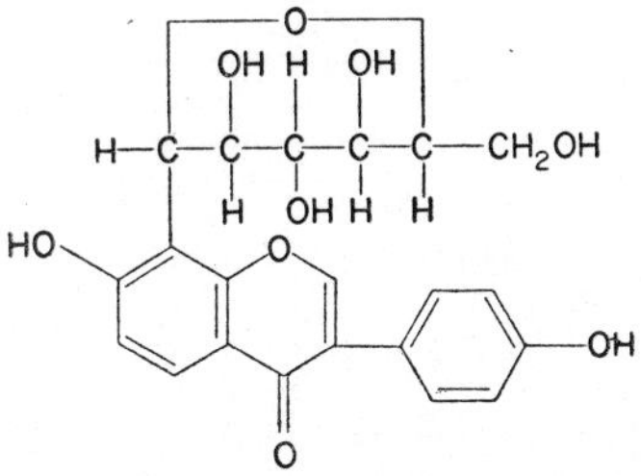

(7) Puerarin

molecular formula $C_{21}H_{20}O_9$, yields resorcinol and *p*-hydroxybenzoic acid on potash fusion, and forms a hepta-acetate. On treatment with mineral acid puerarin does not yield a sugar, but on ozonolysis it gives D-glucose and D-arabinose suggesting that the D-glucopyranosyl grouping is attached with a C—C linkage. Oxidation of *O*-dimethylpuerarin with excess periodate produces an aldehydic compound which is identical with synthetic 8-formyl-daidzein, and the structure of puerarin is therefore established as a 8-D-glucopyranosyl daidzein (7). In addition to puerarin, *Pueraria* root also contains a monoxyloside of puerarin which forms an octa-acetate.

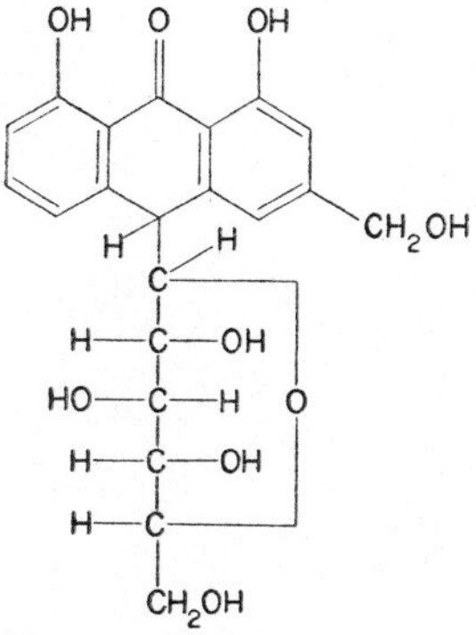

(8) Aloin

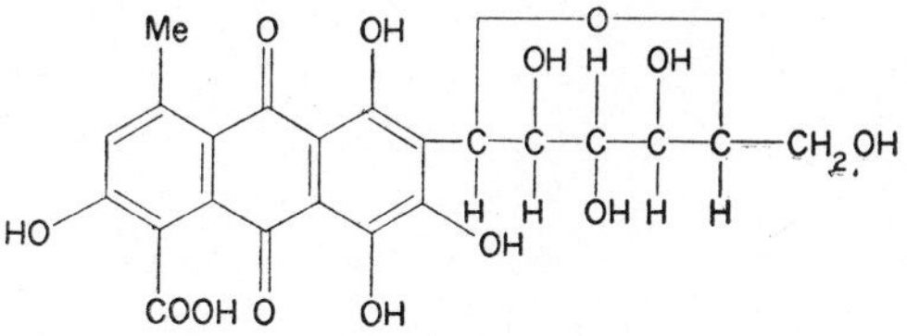

(9) Carminic acid

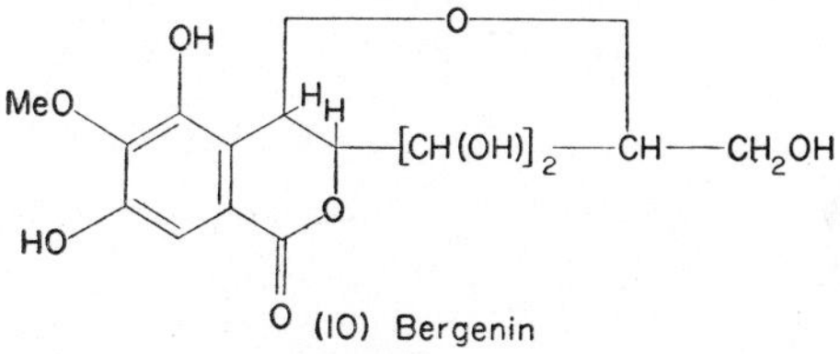

(10) Bergenin

ALOIN, CARMINIC ACID AND BERGENIN

C-Glycosyl compounds are not limited to the flavanoid series but are also found among the anthraquinone derivatives, aloin (8) and carminic acid (9). Mühlemann has proved the C-glycosyl structure for aloin,[16] and a similar structural feature has recently been established by Ali and Haynes[17] in carminic acid (9). The isocoumarin structure of bergenin (10) elucidated by Hay and Haynes[18] is of particular interest.

MANGIFERIN (HEDYSARIDE)

Our systematic study of the Papilionaceae family has led to the discovery of a C-glycosyl compound in the xanthone series. From *Hedysarum obscurum*, an alpine plant, a compound, hedysaride,[19] has been isolated which gives a strong green fluorescence in ultraviolet light. It has the formula $C_{19}H_{18}O_{11}$, m.p. 258–260°, and forms an octa-acetate. Reaction with hydriodic acid results in the quantitative formation of 1,3,6,7-tetrahydroxyxanthone whose ultra-violet spectrum shows maxima corresponding with those of hedysaride (λ_{max} 240, 257, 315, and 365 mμ). These experiments demonstrate that hedysaride is a derivative of 1,3,6,7-tetrahydroxyxanthone. Attempted acidic hydrolysis or enzymic hydrolysis does not affect the compound, but periodic acid oxidation produces an acid fraction which yields 4.5 moles of formic acid per mole of hedysaride. Alkaline hydrogen peroxide oxidation of hedysaride gives malonic acid, arising from the xanthone residue, but no sugar is isolated. In earlier work, Iseda[20] isolated the same compound as hedysaride from *Mangifera indica*. He called it mangiferin and assigned to it the 1,3,6,7-tetrahydroxy-7-glucoside structure (11). We do not agree with this structure so far as the postulated O-glycosidic linkage is concerned. Since hedysaride behaves like vitexin and orientin towards acidic and enzymic hydrolysis and is not cleaved even under forcing conditions, a

(II) Mangiferin

(12) Hedysaride

C-glycosyl linkage seems to be extremely probable and experiments are now in progress to determine the exact position of this C—C linkage in hedysaride (12).*

BIOSYNTHESIS OF *C*-GLYCOSIDES

The formation of these *C*-glycosyl compounds in plants may take place by two routes involving a *C*-glycosidylation process which occurs either *before* or *after* the synthesis of the aglycone. The former route would involve alkylation of a poly-β-ketonic precursor (see Chapter 1) and although no strong argument in favour of one or other route is possible at this stage, *C*-alkylation of the aglycone may be more probable (see Chapter 2, p. 42). By analogy with other C—C bond-forming reactions in organic synthesis, it is certainly conceivable that the alkylation might, under certain physiological conditions, be directed towards an anionoid carbon atom rather than towards an oxygen atom. In this connection it is of biogenetic interest to note the co-occurrence in plants of many of the *C*-glycosyl derivatives which have been described with the corresponding *O*-glycosides.

REFERENCES

1. A. G. PERKIN, *J. Chem. Soc.* 1898, **73**, 1019.
2. G. BARGER, *J. Chem. Soc.* 1906, **89**, 1210.
3. T. NAKAOKI, *J. Pharm. Soc. Japan* 1944, **64**, IIa; *Chem. Abs.* 1952, **46**, 108.
4. H. W. EVANS, A. McGOOKIN, L. JURD, A. ROBERTSON and W. R. N. WILLIAMSON, *J. Chem. Soc.* 1957, 3510.
5. L. HÖRHAMMER, H. WAGNER and F. GLOGGENGIESSER, *Arch. Pharm. Ber. dtsch. pharmaz. Ges.* 1958, **291/63**, 126.
6. L. FUCHS and K. JENTZSCH, private communication.
7. M. K. SEIKEL and T. A. GEISSMAN, *Arch. Biochem. Biophys.* 1957, **71**, 17.
8. L. JURD, T. A. GEISSMAN and M. K. SEIKEL, *Arch. Biochem. Biophys.* 1957, **67**, 284.
9. U. KRANEN-FIEDLER, *Arzneimittel-Forsch.* 1955, **5**, 609.
10. M. MASCRÉ and R. PARIS, *Bull. Sci. pharmacol.* 1937, **44**, 401.
11. L. HÖRHAMMER, H. WAGNER and H. S. DHINGRA, *Arch. Pharmaz. Ber. dtsch. pharmaz. Ges.* 1959, **292/64**, 83.
12. T. A. GEISSMAN, private communication.
13. L. HÖRHAMMER, H. WAGNER and P. BEYERSDORFF, in the press.
14. L. HÖRHAMMER, H. WAGNER and W. LEEB, *Arch. Pharmaz. Ber. dtsch. pharmaz. Ges* 1960, **293/65**, 264.
15. S. SHIBATA, private communication to W. D. OLLIS.
16. H. MÜHLEMANN, *Pharmac. Acta Helv.* 1952, **27**, 17.
17. A. ALI and L. J. HAYNES, *J. Chem. Soc.* 1959, 1133.
18. J. E. HAY and L. J. HAYNES, *J. Chem. Soc.* 1958, 2231.
19. L. HÖRHAMMER, H. WAGNER and W. DENECKE, in press.
20. S. ISEDA, *Bull. Chem. Soc. Japan* 1957, **30**, (6), 625.

* Since this chapter was written a short note has been published by J. D. Ramanathan and T. R. Seshadri (Current Science, 1960, 29, 131) in which they also postulate a C—C linked glucose residue in mangiferin. It is also suggested that the carbon atom which is bonded to the glucose residue is most likely to be in the 2-position of the xanthone nucleus.

CHAPTER 11

THE BETACYANINS, A CLASS OF RED PIGMENTS IN THE *CENTROSPERMAE*

ANDRE S. DREIDING

University of Zurich

THE attention of chemists interested in natural products has always been drawn to those parts of plants which exhibited some conspicuous character-istics and their aim was the isolation and examination of the substances responsible for these features. Since one of the most obvious and readily appreciated properties is colour, the common pigments belong to the earliest and most thoroughly investigated classes of natural products.

It is, therefore, rather surprising that there exist two groups of incompletely characterized pigments which occur in such well known vegetables, fruits and decorative plants as the beetroot, the flowers of cacti, and the bougainvillea bush.

One group of pigments is red-violet and the other yellow in colour. When they occur alone, the pigmented part of the plant is either red-violet (as in the red beet, the pokeberry or the bougainvillea leaf) or yellow (as in the yellow beet or most cactus flowers). They are also often found together and then the colour of the pigmented part of the plant may vary from violet-red, red, fire-red, orange-red and orange to yellow, depending on the relative amounts of the two types of pigments. For reasons mentioned in the course of this article the red-violet pigments will be called *betacyanins* and the yellow pigments, *betaxanthins*.

The betacyanins and the betaxanthins occur in the cell sap (vacuoles) and thus belong to the chymochromes.[1] In this they are similar to the antho-cyanins* and to the flavones.[6,7] In fact, there are so many other similarities to the anthocyanins that they have often been classified with them. It will be seen that some of these similarities are real but others are superficial and have obscured the picture in this field for some time.

The betacyanins have so far received much more attention than the

---

* The expression "anthocyanin" was originally proposed (1835)[2] and subsequently used for many decades to signify all the blue and red pigments of flowers. After the identification of the great majority of them as flavylium salts[3] this expression became associated specifically with the flavylium salt structure.[4,5] It will be used here in this sense.

betaxanthins. Very little is known about the betaxanthins beyond their distribution and that they usually accompany the betacyanins. This review is therefore limited to the betacyanins.

1. *Early interest in betacyanins:* Obviously such conspicuous colours as that of the beet or the pokeberry were examined at an early stage in pigment investigation. However, much of the older information has not been mentioned in the modern literature and will thus be reviewed here. In the 19th century the practical interest in these water- and alcohol-soluble red colours stemmed mostly from the wine industry and from government institutions concerned with the specifications for wine. The price paid for red wine depended at that time on the richness of its colour. The beverage was, therefore, often adulterated with (among others) the coloured juices of the red beet[8] and of the pokeberry.[9] The hardy and richly coloured Virginian pokeweed (*Phytolacca americana*) is said to have been planted as a safeguard on a small corner of many a vineyard in southern countries of Europe.[11] While the beet juice is harmless, the pokeberry extract apparently also contains an emetic and purgatory substance.[11] It was thus prohibited* by law as a food colouring in 1892.[10]

2. *Spectroscopic examination* (1869): Chemical attention to the beet- and pokeberry-juices was directed towards tests for their recognition in wine. For that purpose the pigment was obviously the most convenient component. In the first attempts at detection, Sorby[9] proposed a spectroscopic examination which relied upon two absorption bands: one between the Fraunhofer lines E and D (538 mμ) and the other (weaker) at line F (486 mμ). The wine pigment did not have the second band. These observations were confirmed by Macagno and by Vogel[12]. It is now known[10] that only the 538 mμ absorption is due to the red betacyanin, and that the band at 486 mμ belongs to the betaxanthin which accompanies the betacyanin to a greater or lesser extent probably depending in some cases on the ripeness of the plants.

3. *Caryophyllinenroth* (1876): The same criterion was also used for the detection of other betacyanins by Bischoff[13] and Hilger.[14] They relied, however, more heavily on colour tests, which were at the time fashionable among botanists and chemists. They observed that the colours of most flowers and fruits changed successively from red to violet, to blue, to green, and finally to yellow when a potassium hydroxide solution was added. The pigments of a few plants, however, were exceptional as the colour changed immediately from red to yellow. (As is shown in Table 1 this is indeed a characteristic difference between anthocyanins and betacyanins.) Bischoff

---

* In Germany the pokeberry is called Kermesbeere. But the same name, Kermesbeere, is also used for the dried female Kermes louse (*Lecanium ilicis* L.), which contains an alizarin type red substance. It is not impossible that they were occasionally confused, which may have contributed to the legal resistance in Germany to the pokeberry "enrichment" of wine.

	Anthocyanins	Betacyanins	Reference
Old names	"Weinroth" "Verfärbungsroth"	"Caryophyllinenroth" "Rübenroth" "Nitrogenous anthocyanins" "Betanins"	13 21 27 7, 35
Addition of alkali: [KOH, NaOH, Ca(OH)$_2$, Ba(OH)$_2$]	Slow discoloration from violet, *via* blue and green to yellow Colour change at same point as litmus	Rapid discoloration to yellow (On cautious addition of alkali: violet, violet-brown, yellow) Colour change when litmus is already blue	13 19 21
Reacidification of alkaline solution after some minutes:	Red colour can be regenerated on acidification	Red colour cannot be regenerated on acidification (Only after immediate reacidification or dilution with distilled water is the red colour partly regenerated)	13 13, 21
Addition of ammonia:	Same behaviour as with alkali	Colour remains violet for some time in the cold	21
Addition of mineral acids:	Solution becomes lighter red Precipitation from concentrated acid solution on heating. The precipitate is alcohol soluble	Solution becomes darker violet Destruction of colour in a hot acid solution	21 21
At neutral point:	Solution slowly becomes decolorized	Solution remains violet-red	10
Addition of lead acetate:	Blue-green or blue-grey precipitation	Red-brown precipitation	13, 21
Addition of nitric acid:	Only slow destruction of red colour	Immediate destruction of red colour	21
Distribution between water and amyl-alcohol: (Erdmann-reaction).	Red colour enters the amyl-alcohol-phase at low pH. (When the amyl-alcohol solution is shaken with dilute aqueous ammonia it becomes colourless and the aqueous phase blue-green)	Red colour does not enter the amyl-alcohol-phase at high or low pH's	10, 21
Extraction from dried plant material (a) with absolute alcohol: (b) with distilled water:	Some red colour is extracted. The extract is, however, green-red Some colour is extracted, but the extract is green and becomes strongly red only upon acidification	No red colour is extracted, only chlorophyll. All the violet colour bleeds out very readily	21 21

and Hilger found this exceptional behaviour in the indicated representatives of the following families:

Chenopodiaceae
   Chenopodium Quinoa
   Beta vulgaris var. *rubra*
Amaranthaceae
   Amaranthus caudatus
   Amaranthus salicifolius
   Celosia
Phytolaccaceae
   (*Phytolacca americana*) *Phytolacca decandra*
Portulacaceae
   Portulaca
Polygonaceae
   Rumex acetosa
   Polygonum fagopyrum

Bischoff and Hilger recognized that they were detecting an unusual pigment whose occurrence was limited to a group of related plants. All their examples were at that time thought to belong to the *Centrospermae*, or, as they were then also called, the "Caryophyllinen", so Bischoff called the new pigment "Caryophyllinenroth". It is clear that Bischoff and Hilger must be considered the pioneers of betacyanin chemistry since their "Caryophyllinenroth" is practically synonymous with betacyanin. We cannot, however, still accept their expression since it was later shown that of the families in the *Centrospermae*, the *Caryophyllaceae* do not have betacyanins, but have anthocyanins instead.

Bischoff's tests required very careful observation and were not infallible when applied to the crude plant extracts. Thus it became known later[15] that his last two examples which belonged to the *Polygonaceae* contained only ordinary anthocyanins. This error may be partly explained by the fact that botanists[16] first placed the *Polygonaceae* in the *Centrospermae*, a classification which was changed later.[17]

Bischoff's observations were followed up and expanded in the following twenty years mostly by the Hilger school, who concentrated on the pigment of *Phytolacca decandra* and its detection; Hasterlick[18] described carefully the absorption spectra and water-insoluble red-violet lead salt of this pigment. Haverland[19] examined several substances present in *Phytolacca decandra* (pokeweed) and described in detail the isolation of its pigment. This is described in a later section of this review. Mai[20] studied the products of bromination and the zinc reduction. Heise[10] wrote a complete account on the methods of detection of wine pigments and those of *Phytolacca decandra* used for adulteration of the wine. In particular, he advised the recognition of *Phytolacca* pigment by observing that it cannot be extracted from acidic or alkaline aqueous solutions with amyl alcohol. This is a negative Erdmann-test, typical of the behaviour of betacyanins, whereas the wine pigment (anthocyanin) is extractable from acidic solutions (positive Erdmann-test).

 4. *Weinroth and Rübenroth* (1894): The next observation on the beta-cyanins as a separate group of red plant pigments was made by Weigert,[21] apparently in ignorance of Bischoff and Hilger's work. On the basis of carefully described colour reactions (see Table 1) he divided the red pigments of a number of plants into two groups, the "*Weinroth*" and the "*Rübenroth*". The behaviour of the members of the "Weinroth" group was similar to the pigment of the wine, while the members of the "Rübenroth" group resembled that of the red beet. Since the "Weinroth" pigments showed the same reactions as shown by the colouring matter of leaves that had turned red in the autumn, he also named this group "*Verfärbungsroth*".

 The "Weinroth" or "Verfärbungsroth" pigments gave a blue-grey or blue-green precipitate with lead acetate, showed a positive Erdmann-reaction, were precipitated by concentrated hydrochloric acid in the cold and exhibited slow colour change with alkali from red to violet, to blue, to green and to yellow. In addition, they could be extracted from the dried plants with alcohol, the extract being green-red and turning bright red on acidification.

 The members of the "Rübenroth" group, of which there were fewer, could not be extracted from the dried plant with absolute alcohol, but were readily extracted with cold water.* This group gave a red precipitate with lead acetate, reacted negatively in the Erdmann-test, were coloured darker violet by concentrated hydrochloric acid in the cold, but destroyed rapidly in the hot. They showed an immediate and irreversible colour change to yellow by alkali.

 It is evident from these tests that Weigert[21] had clearly defined the distinction between what we now call anthocyanins (Weinroth) and betacyanins (Rübenroth). In fact, the expression betacyanin† is an adaption of Weigert's name, which was, to our knowledge, first used by Willstätter and Schudel.[22] Weigert classified the following plants, which belong to three families, to the "Rübenroth" group (betacyanin group):

Chenopodiaceae
 Beta vulgaris var. *rubra*
 Atriplex hortensis var. *atrosanguinea*

---

 * The fact that aqueous extraction of the leaves of *Amaranthus melancholicus, Iresine Lindenii* and *Achyranthes Verschaffeltii* yielded intensively red solutions, whereas only insignificantly green extracts were obtained from most other bright red flowers had already been noticed by H. Molisch (*Bot. Ztg.*, 1889, **47**, 17). However, he attributed the exceptional behaviour of these three plants merely to a greater acidity of the cell sap.

 † Betacyanin from "*Beta*" = beet and "cyanin" to express a certain, not yet defined, relationship to the anthocyanins. This relationship probably does not lie in a similarity of chemical structure, as was often thought, but possibly involves their biogenetic derivation.

Amaranthaceae
  Amaranthus
  Achyranthes Verschaffeltii
  Iresine Lindenii
Phytolaccaceae
  Phytolacca decandra (*Phytolacca americana*)

These three families had already been shown to contain "Caryophyllinen-roth" (betacyanins) by Bischoff.[13] Weigert made no erroneous additions to this group but he did not seem to notice, or at least did not mention, the fact that the "Rübenroth" plants are closely related botanically.

In connection with a study on the autumnal colours of leaves, but without referring to any of the above mentioned previous work, Overton[23] expressed the opinion that the pigments of the *Amaranthaceae* and of the beet were the same but different from those of other flowers and fruits.

5. *Seven families with Rübenroth:* In 1906, Gertz[15] published a long dissertation in which he reviewed almost all the previous literature in this field and described the colours of a large number of plants. He named all the blue and red pigments "anthocyan" (according to Marquart) and divided them (according to Weigert) into "Rübenroth" and "Weinroth". He clearly stated that "Rübenroth" is characteristic of several plants in the *Centrospermae* order and fully confirmed the observations of Weigert[21] and Bischoff.[13]

He considerably increased the list of plants with known "Rübenroth" (betacyanin) content by applying the colour-tests to many other plants from the *Centrospermae* (see list at the end of the chapter) and he added examples from the following new families: *Nyctaginaceae*, *Aizoaceae*, and *Basellaceae*.

Gertz also showed that the *Polygonaceae* (contrary to Bischoff) and the *Caryophyllaceae* did not belong to the "Rübenroth" group, but instead contained the "Weinroth" pigment. (The *Polygonaceae* are now no longer included within the *Centrospermae*; the *Caryophyllaceae*, however, still are.)

6. *Betacyanins:* In the introduction to his dissertation on the isolation of the beet pigment (which he named betanin) Schudel,[22] a student of Willstätter, very briefly stated that it belonged to a group of substances called betacyanins which were present in the beet, the *Chenopodium* genus, the cockscomb (*Celosia cristata*) and erroneously the purple beech (*Fagus sylvatica*). It is unfortunate that the previous work on betacyanins was not cited in this dissertation, since it has been referred to frequently as the earliest chemical examination of this type of pigment. The work was not published by Willstätter in a journal.

A significant observation was made by Kryz[24] in 1920, when he found that the red pigment of the fruits and flowers of a representative of the *Cactaceae* (*Nopalxochia phyllanthoides*) gave the typical Rübenroth reactions. This brought the total of the betacyanin-containing families to the currently recognized number of eight. His claim that the colour of *Fuchsia discolor* (family: *Onagraceae*) also belongs to this group was later shown to be erroneous* by J. R. Price (mentioned in a publication by T. W. J. Taylor[25] and also in one by R. D. Gibbs[26]).

7. *Nitrogenous Anthocyanins:* In the years 1930 to 1938 the Robinsons studied the distribution and reactions of anthocyanins in flowers, fruits and leaves and discovered, as well as confirmed, the presence of betacyanins in many plants. Lawrence, Price, Robinson and Robinson summarized their observations in a large article,[27] at the end of which they listed the new group of pigments (betacyanins), which they called "nitrogenous anthocyanins". They used the term anthocyanins in the sense of Marquart and segregated the new group by the attribute "nitrogenous", since several authors (see section on isolation) had found nitrogen in two non-crystalline pigments isolated from *Beta* and *Bougainvillea* plants. Robinson's list of betacyanin-containing plants showed twenty-four examples in eight families† (see list at the end of the chapter).

In 1939, T. W. J. Taylor[25] participated in an expedition to Indefatigable Island of the Galapagos, where over 40% of the flora is indigenous. There he investigated the red pigments of many plants by the above mentioned colour tests and made the surprising observation that more than one third of the Dicotyledonous plants which were examined contained nitrogenous anthocyanins (betacyanins). All these plants belonged to six of the eight "betacyanin-families", which is a surprising confirmation of the specificity of betacyanin occurrence, particularly as the author[25] was unaware of this observation prior to the expedition.

8. *Chromatography* (1955): It was not until 15 years later that renewed attention was given to an analysis of the betacyanin pigments. The method of chromatography with a butanol:acetic acid:water solvent containing variable amounts of hydrochloric acid, which had been most successful in the field of anthocyanins,[28] was applied to a number of plants in the *Centrospermae* order by Reznik.[7,29] In butanol:acetic acid:water (4:1:5) the betacyanins (which he named betanins‡) migrated much more slowly than most of the anthocyanins and thus could be readily recognized.

By the chromatographic method it was possible to demonstrate clearly that there are several betacyanins, some of which can even co-occur in the same plant. Reznik[7] found, for instance, that most of the *Amaranthaceae* contain the same pigment (R_f 0·03), called *amarantin*,[35] which is clearly different from *betanin* (R_f 0·06). He also showed that the *Aizoaceae* and the *Cactaceae* each have their characteristic betacyanin. (Reznik's data suggest

* Dr. H. Wyler in this laboratory has also examined the berries of a *Fuchsia* variety and found them to contain an ordinary anthocyanin.

† In addition, the *Fuchsia* of the *Onagraceae* family, was erroneously included in this list due to Kryz's observations.

‡ We prefer the expression "betacyanins" because "betanin" has already been reserved for the pigment of the beet.[22]

to us that the *Aizoaceae* may contain betanidin, and the *Cactaceae*, betanin.) For an exact comparison of betacyanins, however, the solvent mixture butanol: acetic acid: water suffers from several disadvantages,[31] some of which are connected with the low R_f-values (0·02–0·20). Thus the results[7,31] show inconsistencies and are not reproduced here. For instance, the pigment of *Phytolacca* (*phytolaccanin*) and *betanin*, which have recently been shown to be identical,[30] were reported to have R_f-values of 0·03 and 0·06 respectively.[7] It is, however, not impossible that the plant has different betacyanins at different stages of its development.

More recently, aqueous solvents were used for the paper chromatographic comparison of betacyanins. The R_f-values in 0·05 M pyridine-formic acid and in 0·1 M formic acid were between 0·3 and 0·8. To avoid some other sources of inconsistency, the substances were placed on the start line only after the descending solvent had been allowed to run over the whole paper for some time. A pure sample of betanin was placed alongside as a marker in each run and the results were expressed in R_B-values, the ratio of the migrational distance of the sample to that of *betanin*. The slightly elongated spots sometimes made a reliable evaluation difficult. Some of these chromatographic results are summarized in columns 5 and 6 of Table 2.

9. *Electrophoretic studies* (1956): A major advance in betacyanin chemistry resulted from the application of paper-electrophoresis to *betanin* by O. Th. Schmidt and W. Schönleben[33] and by G. Linstead[34] at about the same time. The method brought to light a characteristic difference between anthocyanins and betacyanins, namely the presence of acidic groups in the latter compounds. Even at pH's down to 2·4 the betacyanins still migrate as anions, whereas the anthocyanins show practically no migration. The isoelectric point of most betacyanins is between pH 1 and 2. It now became extremely simple to recognize a betacyanin, so that the plant pigments could be classified very reliably.

Reznik[35] examined many plant extracts partly by low voltage- and partly by high voltage-electrophoresis. He confirmed with absolute certainty that betacyanins occur in the previously mentioned families of the *Centrospermae*. The new method also confirmed the chromatographic result, that there are several betacyanins. Reznik divided them in four groups as is shown in Table 3.

The high voltage (1200 V) electrophoresis gave even better separation and revealed a large number of betacyanins.[35] The expression of the results in ionic mobility requires rigorously controlled conditions if useful comparisons are to be made.

The necessity for such control is avoided when a pure sample of betanin is added to each electrophoresis paper strip and the results are expressed in migrational aptitude relative to betanin (E_B).[31,32] Some of the results of this method are summarized in columns 3 and 4 of Table 2. This Table also

TABLE 2. PAPER ELECTROPHORETIC AND PAPER CHROMATOGRAPHIC CHARACTERIZATION[a] IN 0·05 M PYRIDINE-FORMIC ACID AND 0·1 M FORMIC ACID[31,32]

Plant	1 Colour of purified pigment on paper	2 λ_{max} of eluted pigment mμ	3 E_B(PF 4·5) b	4 E_B(F 2·4) c	5 R_B(PF 4·5) d	6 R_B(F 2·4) e	7 Name given to pigment
Chenopodiaceae:							
Beta vulgaris var. rubra	red-violet	536–38	1·00	1·00	1·00	1·00	Betanin
Kochia scoparia	red-violet	536	1·00		1·00		Betanin
Atriplex hortensis	red-violet	534	1·20	1·05		1·16	Betanin
Amaranthaceae:							
Celosia cristata	red-violet	540	1·17			1·10	Amarantin
Celosia plumosa	red-violet		1·25				Amarantin
Amaranthus paniculatus	red-violet	535	1·20	1·05		1·16	Amarantin
Alternanthera Petsikiana	red-violet	536	1·23	1·10			Amarantin
Iresine Lindenii	red-violet	536–40	1·21		1·14		Amarantin
Iresine Herbstii	red-violet	536–40	1·21		1·14		Amarantin
Gomphrena globosa	red-violet	545	0·78	0·63		0·70	Gomphrenin
Phytolaccaceae:							
Phytolacca americana	red-violet	536–38	1·00	1·00	1·00	1·00	Betanin
Nyctaginaceae:							
Bougainvillea glabra	violet-red	544–46	0·45	0·39		0·30	Bougainvillein-v-0·45
	violet-red	542–46	0·56	0·47		0·55	Bougainvillein-v-0·56
	violet-red	538–40	0·80	0·77		0·87	Bougainvillein-v-0·80
Bougainvillea spectabilis	red-violet	532	0·55	0·45–0·54		0·27	Bougainvillein-r-0·55
	red-violet	532–34	0·88	0·83		0·8–0·9	Bougainvillein-r-0·88
Mirabilis Jalapa	red-violet	535	1·00	1·00		1·00	Betanin

	Colour	λ	E_B(PF 4·5)[b]	E_B(F 2·4)[c]	R_B(PF 4·5)[d]	R_B(F 2·4)[e]	Pigment[a]
Portulacaceae:							
Portulaca grandiflora	red-violet	535	0·96	0·97		0·95	Betanin
Basellaceae:							
Basella rubra	{red-violet	539	0·98	0·94		0·88	Basellain-r
	{violet	554	0·45	0·27		1·02	Basellain-v
Basella alba	violet	540	1·0		0·91		
Aizoaceae:							
Lampranthus roseus	violet	540–42	1·03	0·71		0·55	Betanidin
Conophytum minutum	violet	539	0·96		0·76		Betanidin?
Conophytum Pearsonii	violet	540	0·96			0·58	Betanidin?
Conophytum mirabile	violet	538	0·96	0·67		0·56	Betanidin?
Conophytum Poellnitzianum	violet		1·06				Betanidin?
Pleiospilos Bolusii	red-violet	537	0·96				
Cactaceae:							
Opuntia Bergeriana	red-violet	537	1·00	0·97		1·00	Betanin
Zygocactus truncatus	red-violet	536	1·38		1·04–1·07		
Thelocactus bicolor	red-violet		1·00		0·75		
Cereus peruvianus	red-violet	538	0·9		0·9		
Hylocereus undatus	red-violet	536	1·00		0·89		
Parodia Stuemeri var. *tilcarensis*	red-violet	537	1·45	0·96		1·18	Parodin
Monvillea Spegazzinii	{red-violet	534	1·34	1·00		0·91	Monvillein-1·34
Mammillaria hidalgensis	{red-violet	534	1·00	1·00		1·00	Betanin
	red-violet	534	1·00			0·99	
Gymnocalycium Mihanovichii	red-violet	536	1·15			1·08	Betanin?

a Only the major pigment is mentioned, even though it is usually accompanied by at least one minor satellite. When two pigments are present in approximately equal amounts, both are given. In the case of uncertainty due to spot elongation, the range is indicated.

b E_B(PF 4·5) = Paper electrophoretic migration relative to betanin in 0·05 M pyridine-formic acid, pH 4·5.

c E_B(F 2·4) = Paper electrophoretic migration relative to betanin in 0·1 M formic acid, pH 2·4.

d R_B(PF 4·5) = Paper chromatographic migration relative to betanin in 0·05 M pyridine-formic acid pH 4·5.

e R_B(F 2·4) = Paper chromatographic migration relative to betanin in 0·1 M formic acid, pH 2·4.

TABLE 3. PAPER ELECTROPHORESIS OF BETACYANINS AT pH 4·6 AND 120 VOLT.[35]

Group	Plant	Ionic mobility $(cm^2V^{-1}sec^{-1}\cdot 10^{-5})$	Possible name of pigment
1	Amaranthus Celosia	+7	Amarantin
2	Malephora Gymnocalycium Lobivia Conophytum	+5·5	
3	Beta Mirabilis	+4·5	Betanin
4	Beta	+3·8	Isobetanin?

includes the colour of the purified pigment on the paper (column 1) and its absorption maximum in the visible range of the spectrum (column 2) of the eluted purified pigments.

A study of Table 2 suggests a number of tentative deductions as to identities of pigments in different plants; they are mentioned in column 7 but in many cases they await rigorous confirmation.

10. *The mutually exclusive occurrence of the betacyanins and the anthocyanins:* The chromatographic and the electrophoretic methods of analysis have the great advantage that the different pigments in a plant extract can be separated. In the same operation, it is possible to draw conclusions on the presence of some type of substance and on the absence of another. This method of analysis clearly showed what had already been suspected that the presence of betacyanins in a plant precludes the presence of anthocyanins and vice versa. The two types of pigments were *never* found simultaneously in the same plant or even in the same family.[7,31,35] It appears that there are "betacyanin-families" and "anthocyanin-families". A number of results[7,31,35] confirmed that the *Caryophyllaceae* are an "anthocyanin-family" and that the other eight families of the *Centrospermae* with red-pigmented members* are all "betacyanin-families" (see list of plants at the end of this chapter). No exception to this rule is known at present.[35]

11. *Taxonomic significance of the betacyanins:* It is clear now that the "betacyanin-families" are closely related and that one of the characteristic aspects of this relationship is their inability to produce anthocyanins which is replaced by the ability to synthesize betacyanins. Thus this relation must be added to the other unifying features of the *Centrospermae*. All exceptions to this scheme including the *Polygonaceae*,[13] some *Chenopodiaceae*,[15] *Onagraceae*[24,27] and *Fagus sylvatica*,[22] were later shown to have been incorrect.

* Since no red-pigmented plant of the *Telygonaceae* seems to be known, it cannot be said to which type this family belongs.

The presence of betacyanins in the *Cactaceae* helped to secure their place in the order *Centrospermae*, a classification about which there had previously been some doubt. This problem has been discussed by Robinson,[27] Taylor,[25] Gibbs,[26] Reznik,[7,29,35] Friedrich[38] and particularly by Buxbaum.[39]

It is of interest that *Phytolacca americana* of the *Phytolaccaceae*, which is now considered the most primitive family of the *Centrospermae*[38,39] contains *betanin*,[30] the monoglucoside of *betanidin*.

One of the important problems posed by the observations reviewed here is the position of the *Caryophyllaceae* in the *Centrospermae*.[7,35,39] It would be interesting to know which of the biosynthetic mechanisms producing either anthocyanins or betacyanins is more primitive. A knowledge of the chemical structure of the betacyanins should be useful in this connection. Interesting information might also be obtained by an examination of the pigments in families bordering on the *Centrospermae*.

12. *Isolation of betacyanins:* The first attempt to isolate a betacyanin appears to have been described by Bischoff.[13] He precipitated the pigment from an aqueous alcoholic extract of the berries of *Phytolacca decandra* with lead acetate and regenerated it with alcoholic sulphuric acid. The alcohol soluble preparation which he obtained by repeating this procedure several times contained some nitrogen.

Sixteen years later, Haverland[19] again isolated the *Phytolacca* pigment (phytolaccanin) by precipitating it from an alcoholic extract with ether and he followed this with a further precipitation from concentrated aqueous solutions with alcohol. The pigment preparation obtained in this way was insoluble in alcohol and again contained nitrogen ($7 \cdot 02$–$7 \cdot 05 \%$). On acid hydrolysis Haverland obtained a sugar which was converted to an osazone, mp 192°.

Bischoff's sample must have been the sulphate and Haverland's the sodium salt of phytolaccanin.

The next attempt at isolation and purification of a betacyanin came from Willstätter's laboratory, where Schudel[22] worked with the beet pigment to which he gave the name *betanin*. The dried slices of the beet were extracted with methanolic hydrochloric acid and the pigment precipitated with ether. This material was then distributed as the chloropicrate between water and a mixture of acetophenone and amyl alcohol. Betanin was precipitated from the organic phase with ether and either (a) recrystallized from slightly acidified water or (b) precipitated again from a methanolic hydrochloric acid solution with ether.

A sample prepared by method (a) (partially crystalline) should have been the free betanin since we now know that the hydrochloride is hydrolysed in water but it still contained about $0 \cdot 8 \%$ chlorine. Sample (b) must have been betanin hydrochloride ($6 \cdot 74 \%$ Cl). The methoxyl content of 4% was probably due to contamination with the methyl ester, which was formed in an acid catalysed reaction with methanol during the isolation. Here again, nitrogen was found to be present to the extent of 8·6%.

Schudel hydrolysed his betanin sample and identified glucose, but could not isolate the aglucone. Alkali fusion did not yield phloroglucinol, a product obtained in this way from most anthocyanins. An ethanolysis procedure afforded the so-called "ethylated betanidin", which contained 3·76% Cl.

Since the betacyanins, such as *betanin*, were very difficult to isolate and purify, Robinson attempted to approach the structure by synthesis. He proposed the hypothesis that betanin is an aminoderivative of the flavylium salt series[40] and then proceeded to synthesize some compounds of this type. However, no deductions on the structure of betanin could be made.

In 1937, Ainley and Robinson[41] reinvestigated the isolation of the beet pigment, but directed their efforts mainly towards the aglucone, *betanidin*. The beet juice itself was allowed to hydrolyse its pigment and the aglucone was isolated by extraction with iso-amyl alcohol and precipitation with light petroleum. The analysis matched the formula $C_{20}H_{19-23}O_7N_2Cl.3H_2O$. With methanolic hydrochloric acid a product was obtained which contained chlorine and two methoxyl groups. Robinson proposed for consideration a cyanidin nucleus linked in some way with an ornithine residue. Again no phlorglucinol was found in an alkali degradation.

Robinson, together with Price,[42] also attempted to isolate a pigment from *Bougainvillea*. The aglycone, which they named *bougainvilleidin* was separated from the glycoside by butanol extraction. After recrystallization from 2% hydrochloric acid the *bougainvilleidin hydrochloride* showed an absorption maximum at 545 mμ and analysed approximately for $C_{22}H_{26-30}O_{10}NCl$.

In 1937, Pucher, Curtis and Vickery[43] also developed a good procedure for the isolation of *betanin*. The dried beet slices were extracted with alcoholic hydrochloric acid. Addition of LiOH to this acidic extract precipitated the pigment completely due to the conversion of the alcohol-soluble hydrochloride of *betanin* to the alcohol-insoluble lithium salt. The lithium salt was dissolved in water and the pigment again precipitated with lead acetate. Decomposition of the lead salt with methanolic hydrochloric acid, precipitation with ether and recrystallization from water gave an amorphous betanin sample with a specific absorption coefficient ($E_{1cm}^{1\%}$) of 798 (we now know that this represents about 70% purity). Elementary analysis suggested a $C_{21}H_{22}O_{10}N_2$ formula, but the chlorine figure (1·54%) and the ash-content (2·11%) indicated the presence of impurity. A quantitative hydrolysis gave 33·7% glucose.

Chromatographic purification of *betanin* was attempted by Chmielewska on alumina[44] and by Aronoff and Aronoff on a talc-Hyflo mixture.[45] The application of preparative electrophoresis to the betacyanin problem was described by G. Linstead[34] in 1956.

Schmidt and Schönleben's[33] purification over ion exchange resins seemed to result in removal of the nitrogen.

13. *Crystalline betanin:* The first authentically crystalline *betanin* was described in 1957.[46,47] It resulted from preparative electrophoretic purification procedures. The definite presence of nitrogen in these samples finally settled the question of whether the nitrogen belonged to the *betanin* molecule or whether it was due to an accompanying impurity.[40,33]

The free *betanin* had a tendency to crystallize together with its monobasic salt (potassium, ammonium, pyridinium and barium) in all proportions. The derivation of an empirical formula $C_{25}H_{26-30}O_{13}N_2$[48,49] for the free acid was, therefore, rather complicated and not completely reliable. *Betanin* also formed a monohydrochloride, which was readily hydrolysed in water. N-methyl, C-methyl and O-methyl groups could not be demonstrated by the usual methods.

Recently the pigment of *Phytolacca americana* (*phytolaccanin*) has also been isolated and crystallized as a "partial" pyridinium salt.[30] Its properties showed that it was identical with *betanin*. Both in *Beta vulgaris* and in *Phytolacca americana*, *betanin* accounts for about 95% of the betacyanin content and is accompanied by small amounts of *isobetanin*, *prebetanin* and *isoprebetanin*.[48,30]

14. *Betanidin and isobetanidin:* While it had been simple to obtain glucose from the acid hydrolysis of *betanin*[19,22,43] much difficulty was experienced in isolating the aglucone, due to its instability.[19,22,35,43] Ainley and Robinson used an enzymatic cleavage and were able to obtain crude *betanidin*.[41] Schudel's experiments yielded only an ethylated *betanidin*.[22]

Recently, crystalline *betanidin* was obtained as salts with bases and as a hydrochloride.[49,50] The analysis suggested the formula $C_{19}H_{16-20}O_8N_2$[49,50] for the free acid. *Betanidin* isomerized readily to *isobetanidin* either by the action of acid or more easily by base in the absence of oxygen. An equilibrium mixture, in which *isobetanidin* predominates in the ratio 7 : 3, was reached from either betanidin or isobetanidin.[50] *Betanidin* is optically active.[49]

Alkaline degradation of *betanidin* yielded 5,6-dihydroxy-indole-2-carboxylic acid, 4-methylpyridine-2,6-dicarboxylic acid and ammonia.[50] Upon heating, 3 moles of CO_2 were evolved.[49] The oxidation with peracetic acid has been reported to give *L*-aspartic acid.[49]

In spite of the fact that the problem of the structure of the betacyanins has been under investigation or consideration during the last 90 years, the structures of these unusual and yet so common pigments is not yet solved.

15. *Betanidin and isobetanidin as basic substances of all betacyanins:* Recently, a number of betacyanins from seventeen different plants were isolated in microquantities and subjected to acid hydrolysis. The products (aglycones) were analysed by paper electrophoresis and by paper chromatography[32]. It was surprising to find that all the products showed the same analytical properties, which are characteristic of a mixture of *betanidin* and *isobetanidin*. The seventeen plants examined were representative of all eight "betacyanin-families" of the *Centrospermae*.

It was also possible to crystallize the hydrolysis products from three different betacyanins (amarantin,[32] phytolaccanin[30] and bougainvillein-v-0·80[32]) and to demonstrate by comparison of X-ray diagrams and spectra that they consisted of *betanidin* and *isobetanidin*.[30,32]

The pigment of *Lampranthus roseus* was isolated and crystallized directly. The properties of the product identified it as 91 % *betanidin* and 9 % *isobetanidin*. Thus the aglycone itself can also be a native betacyanin. It is quite possible that all the red Mesembryanthemum plants contain *betanidin* and that all betacyanins are derived from *betanidin* and *isobetanidin*.

It is a pleasure to acknowledge the excellent assistance of my co-workers Dr. G. Vincenti, Dr. M. Mercier, Dr. G. Sassu, Mr. H. Dietrich and particularly Dr. H. Wyler.

LIST OF PLANTS IN WHICH BETACYANINS HAVE BEEN FOUND

FAMILY	PLANT	REFERENCES
Chenopodiaceae	*Beta vulgaris* var. *rubra* L.	7, 13, 21, 22, 27, 31, 32, 33, 35
	Beta vulgaris var. *rapacea* L.	31, 35
	Chenopodium virgatum Thunb.	15
	Chenopodium Quinoa	13
	Chenopodium amaranticolor	35
	Chenopodium album	36
	Atriplex hortensis L.	7, 22, 27, 31, 32
	Atriplex littoralis L.	15, 21, 27
	Atriplex hastata L.	15
	Corispermum canescens Kit.	15
	Kochia trichophylla Stapf., var. Childsii	27,31
	Suaeda maritima Dum.	27
Amaranthaceae	*Amaranthus caudatus* L.	7, 13, 21
	Amaranthus salicifolius	13, 21
	Amaranthus quitensis H. B. and K.	25
	Amaranthus gracilis Desf.	25
	Amaranthus paniculatus	31, 32, 35, 36
	Celosia sp.	13
	Celosia cristata	7, 22, 27, 31
	Celosia plumosa Hort.	27, 31
	Celosia argentea L.	25
	Celosia Thompsonii	35
	Alternanthera ficoidea (L.) R. Br.	25
	Alternanthera halimifolia (Lam.) Standley	25
	Alternanthera macrophylla Howell	25
	Alternanthera amoena, var. atropurpurea	35
	Alternanthera Petsikiana	31
	Achyranthes Verschaffeltii Lem.	15
	Mogiphanes brasiliensis	15
	Aerva sanguinolenta	7, 15, 35
	Iresine Herbstii Hook.	27, 31
	Iresine Lindenii var Houttei	7, 21, 31, 35
	Gomphrena globosa	31

Nyctaginaceae	*Oxybaphus nyctagineus* Sweet	15, 35
	Bougainvillea glabra Choisy	27, 31, 32
	Bougainvillea spectabilis	7, 31, 32
	Mirabilis Jalapa	7, 31, 32, 35
	Mirabilis himalaica (Edgew.)	36
	Boerhaavia coccinea Mill.	25
	Boerhaavia scandens L.	25
	Cryptocarpus pyriformis H. B. and K.	25
Phytolaccaceae	*Phytolacca americana*	7, 10, 13, 19, 21, 27, 30, 31, 15, 32, 35
	Phytolacca australis Phil.	25
	Rivina humilis	7
	Rivina aurantiaca	35
	Trichostigma peruvianum	7, 35
Ficoidaceae[37]	*Sesuvium Portulacastrum* L.	25
(Mesembryanthemaceae)	*Tetragonia crystallina* L'Herit.	15, 27
	Mesembryanthemum nodiflorum L.	15, 27
	Conophytum truncatum Thunb. var. *roseum*	27
	Conophytum marginatum	35
	Conophytum Taylorianum	35
	Conophytum Ernianum	35
	Conophytum Tischerii	7, 35
	Conophytum Marnierianum	35
	Conophytum Pearsonii	31, 35
	Conophytum minutum	31, 35
	Conophytum stellatum	35
	Conophytum Wettsteinii	35
	Conophytum tubatum	35
	Conophytum praegratum	35
	Conophytum maximum	35
	Conophytum turrigerum	35
	Conophytum limbatum	35
	Conophytum piluliforme	35
	Conophytum Poellnitzianum	31
	Lampranthus Zeyheri	35
	Lampranthus roseus	35
	Pleiospilos simulans	35
	Pleiospilos Bolusii	31
	Fenestraria aurantiaca	35
	Lithops kuibisensis	35
	Gibbaeum gibbosum	35
	Gibbaeum velutinum	35
	Trichodiadema bulbosum	35
	Trichodiadema densum	35
	Malephora mollis	35
	Dorotheanthus gramineus	35
Portulacaceae	*Portulaca* sp.	13
	Portulaca grandiflora Hook. (rose moss)	7, 13, 15, 27, 31, 32, 35
	Portulaca oleracea L.	25
	Calandrinia grandiflora Lindl.	35
	Anacampseros rufescens	7, 35

Basellaceae	*Basella rubra* L.	7, 15, 27, 31, 32
	Basella alba L.	7, 31
Cactaceae	*Pereskia aculeata*	7
	Mammillaria Zeilmanniana	35
	Mammillaria setigera	35
	Mammillaria Woodsii	35
	Mammillaria rhodantha	35
	Mammillaria surculosa	35
	Mammillaria pusilla	35
	Mammillaria hidalgensis	31
	Neoporteria ebenacantha	35
	Melocactus peruvianus	35
	Aylostera pseudodeminuta	35
	Hariota salicornioides	7
	Rebutia Krainziana	35
	Rebutia senilis	35
	Rebutia Marsoneri	35
	Rebutia minuscula	35
	Parodia mutabilis	35
	Parodia sanguiniflora	35
	Parodia Stuemeri var. *tilcarensis*	31, 32
	Lobivia famatimensis	35
	Lobivia chlorogona	35
	Cleistocactus jujuensis	35
	Notocactus Ottonis	35
	Notocactus mammulosus	35
	Gymnocalycium Andreaea	35
	Gymnocalycium Baldianum	35
	Gymnocalycium Mihanovichii	31
	Ariocarpus Kotschubeyanus	35
	Chamaecereus Silvestrii	35
	Cereus speciosus K. Schum.	27
	Selinocereus grandiflorus Mill.	27
	Cereus Thouarsii Weber	25
	Cereus peruvianus	31
	Hylocereus undatus	31
	Opuntia sp.	27
	Opuntia Bergeriana Weber	31
	Opuntia Soehrensii	35
	Zygocactus truncatus	7, 27, 31, 35
	Thelocactus bicolor, var. *bolansis*	31
	Monvillea Spegazzinii	32
	Nopalxochia phyllanthoides	24

REFERENCES

1. A. Seybold, *Ber. Dtsch. Bot. Ges.* 1942, **60**, 64; *S. B. Heidelberg Akad. Wiss.*, *Math.-Nat. Klasse*, 1953/54, 31.
2. L. C. Marquart, *Die Farben der Blüthen*, Bonn 1835.
3. R. Willstätter and co-workers, *Annalen*, 1914, **408**, 1; 1916, **412**, 113; *Chem. Ber.* 1914, **47**, 2865 and many later publications by P. Karrer, R. Robinson and others.
4. K. P. Link, Chapter No. 18, in Gilman's *Organic Chemistry*, 2nd edition (1943), John Wiley and Sons, Inc., New York, vol. II, p. 1316.
5. P. Karrer in Klein's *Handbuch der Pflanzenanalyse*, Springer, Vienna, 1932, vol. III, p. 941.
6. Ch. Sannie and H. Sauvain, *Les Couleurs des Fleurs et des Fruits*, edition du museum, Paris (1952).

7. H. REZNIK, *Z. Bot.* 1955, **43**, 499.
8. H. W. VOGEL, *Practische Spectralanalyse irdischer Stoffe.*
9. H. C. SORBY, *Quart. J. Micr. Sci.* New Series, 1869, **9**, 368.
10. R. HEISE, *Arb. kaiserl. Gesundh. Amte* 1895, **11**, 513.
11. L. EYMARD, *J. Pharm. Chim.* 1890, **21**, 243.
12. MACAGNO, *Atti della R. Statione chimico-agraria sperimentale di Palermo* 1881–84, p. 58; H. W. VOGEL, *Practische Spectralanalyse* 2nd ed., p. 441.
13. H. BISCHOFF, *Inaug. Diss.* Tübingen 1876.
14. A. HILGER, *Landwirtsch. Versuchsstationen* 1879, **23**, 456.
15. O. GERTZ, *Studier övfer Anthocyan*, Diss., Lund 1906.
16. See for instance: A. EICHLER, *Blütendiagramme* II, Leipzig, 1878.
17. A. ENGLER, Führer durch den Botanischen Garten Breslau, Breslau, 1886.
18. A. HASTERLICK, *Mitt. Pharm. Inst. Univ. Erlangen* von A. HILGER, 1889, Heft II, 84.
19. F. HAVERLAND, Inaug. Diss. Erlangen, 1892.
20. A. HILGER and C. MAI, *Forsch Ber. über Lebensmitt. Beziehung Hyg.* 1895, **2**, 343; (*Zentralbl.* 1895, II, 1083).
21. L. WEIGERT, *Jahresber. u. Programm d. k.-k. önol.-pomol. Lehranstalt Klosterneuburg* Wien, 1894.
22. G. SCHUDEL, Diss. Zürich-ETH, 1918.
23. E. OVERTON, *Pringsheim's Jahrb. Wiss. Bot.* 1899, **33**, 171.
24. F. KRYZ, *Oestr. Chem. Ztg.* 1926, **23**, 55.
25. T. W. J. TAYLOR, *Proc. Roy. Soc.*, 1940, **129B**, 230.
26. R. D. GIBBS, *Trans. Roy. Soc. Canad.* 1945, 3/**39**, Sect. V, 71.
27. W. J. C. LAWRENCE, J. R. PRICE, G. M. ROBINSON and R. ROBINSON, *Phil. Trans.* 1939–41, **B230**, 149.
28. J. B. HARBORNE, *Chromatographic Reviews* 1959, **1**, 209.
29. H. REZNIK, *S. B. Heidelberg Akad. Wiss., Math.-Nat. Klasse.* 1956, 125.
30. H. WYLER and A. S. DREIDING, *Helv. Chim. Acta* 1961, **44**, 249.
31. H. DIETRICH, H. WYLER and A. S. DREIDING, unpublished results.
32. H. WYLER and A. S. DREIDING, *Experientia* 1961, **17**, 23.
33. O.TH SCHMIDT and W. SCHÖNLEBEN, *Naturwiss.* 1956, **43**, 159.
34. G. LINSTEAD, *Acta Chem. Scand.* 1956, **10**, 698.
35. H. REZNIK, *Planta* 1957, **49**, 406.
36. R. M. ACHESON, *Proc. Roy. Soc.* 1956, B**145**, 549.
37. H. JACOBSON, *Handbuch der sukkulenten Pflanzen*, Band III, Jena, 1955.
38. H. C. FRIEDRICH, *Phyton* (Graz), 1956, **6**, 220.
39. F. BUXBAUM, *Biol. Pflanzen* 1961, **36**, Heft 1, 1.
40. G. M. ROBINSON and R. ROBINSON, *J. Chem. Soc.* 1932, 1439.
41. A. D. AINLEY and R. ROBINSON, *J. Chem. Soc.* 1937, 446.
42. J. R. PRICE and R. ROBINSON, *J. Chem. Soc.* 1937, 449.
43. G. W. PUCHER, L. C. CURTIS and H. B. VICKERY, *J. Biol. Chem.* 1937, **123**, 61.
44. I. CHMIELEVSKA, *Roczinki. Chim.* 1938, **18**, 1.
45. S. ARONOFF and E. M. ARONOFF, *Food Res.* 1948, **13**, 59.
46. O. TH. SCHMIDT and W. SCHÖNLEBEN, *Z. Naturforsch.* 1957, **12**b, 262.
47. H. WYLER and A. S. DREIDING, *Helv. Chim. Acta* 1957, **40**, 191.
48. H. WYLER, G. VINCENTI, M. MERCIER, G. SASSU and A. S. DREIDING, *Helv. Chim. Acta* 1959, **42**, 1696.
49. O. TH. SCHMIDT, P. BECHER and M. HUEBNER, *Chem. Ber.* 1960, **93**, 1296.
50. H. WYLER and A. S. DREIDING, *Helv. Chim. Acta* 1959, **42**, 1699.

CHAPTER 12

A NEW FAMILY OF ANTIBIOTICS

W. D. OLLIS and I. O. SUTHERLAND

THE University, Bristol

THIS account is concerned with a group of antibiotics which we have been recently investigating in collaboration with our colleagues of the Medical Research Council's Antibiotics Research Station at Clevedon. The story starts with the discovery by I. N. Asheshov[1] of a group of mouid metabolites which were of particular interest since they exhibited a rather unusual activity. These substances showed antiphage activity and because a possible relationship of this activity to antiviral activity could exist, it was decided that their structural study might be rewarding. During this work it became clear that the compounds we were investigating were closely related to substances which were being simultaneously studied by Professor Brockmann (Göttingen) and Professor Prelog (Zürich). The researches at Göttingen, Zürich, and Bristol have shown that various strains of Actinomycetes produce quite a large number of antibiotics whose structures are closely interrelated. It may be mentioned here that modern structural aids such as ultraviolet, infrared, and nuclear magnetic resonance spectroscopy were extensively used during these studies. This chapter describes the progress which has been made towards the determination of the structures of these antibiotics and the similarity between their structures suggests that they are formed by closely related biosynthetic processes.

RUTILANTINONE

The actinomycete A 220[1] produces a mixture of antibiotics, rutilantins A, B, and C, and on mild acidic hydrolysis they each yielded a red crystalline aglycone, rutilantinone, and nitrogen-containing carbohydrates. Our work was initially concerned with the determination of the structure of rutilantinone. It had the molecular formula $C_{22}H_{20}O_9$ and analysis showed the presence of one C-methyl group by Kuhn–Roth determination, and one alkoxyl group by Zeisel determination. Rutilantinone was clearly a saturated ester which showed characteristic carbonyl absorption at 1730 cm^{-1} and we therefore suspected that the alkoxyl group which was present in rutilantinone was part of this saturated ester group. The infrared spectrum of rutilantinone showed conjugated carbonyl absorption (1618 and 1601 cm^{-1}), multiple absorption in the aromatic C=C region ($\sim$1600 cm^{-1}), and complex hydroxyl absorption in the 3500 cm^{-1} region. It was not, of course, possible to determine the nature of an alkoxyl group by a simple Zeisel determination, and further work was necessary to establish its identity. Reaction of rutilantinone with hydrogen iodide under conditions of the Zeisel determination yielded an alkyl iodide characterized as methyl iodide by reaction with dimethyl aniline, when it was transformed into the crystalline PhNMe$_3$}I. This proved that the alkoxyl group was in fact a methoxyl group and suggested that rutilantinone was a methyl ester. Rutilantinone had an acidic function which could be associated with an apparent dissociation constant of 9.9 and an equivalent weight of 435 showing the presence of one such function. The possibility of rutilantinone being an ester was examined by hydrolysis with base. This yielded rutilantinonic acid which, although it was not obtained crystalline, showed a dissociation constant characteristic of a carboxylic acid at 5.7 and the more weakly acidic function was now characterized by a dissociation constant of 10.2. The equivalent weight was approximately half that observed previously. The methanol produced by this hydrolysis was also characterized chemically so there was no doubt whatsoever about the presence of a methoxycarbonyl group.

When rutilantinone was treated with acetic anhydride it was transformed into a tetracetyl derivative, thus demonstrating the presence of four acylatable hydroxyl groups. The infrared spectrum of this tetracetate showed phenolic acetate absorption (1781 cm^{-1}), saturated carbonyl absorption (1743 cm^{-1}) associated with the ester groups, and conjugated carbonyl absorption (1683 cm^{-1}). It also showed some absorption in the hydroxyl region (3630 cm^{-1}) indicating that there is at least one hydroxyl group which is not easily acetylated in rutilantinone. Therefore, in the structure of rutilantinone the presence of four acylatable hydroxyl groups, one hydroxyl group which is not acylatable, and a methoxycarbonyl group has been diagnosed leading to the part structure shown below; the C$_{20}$H$_{12}$O$_2$ residue must contain the conjugated carbonyl function or functions and the C-methyl group.

$$\left[C_{20}H_{12}O_2 \begin{array}{l} -OH \\ -OH \\ -OH \\ -OH \\ -OH \\ -CO_2Me \end{array} \right]$$

The ultraviolet and visible spectra of rutilantinone were particularly informative and were very detailed when determined in cyclohexane solution. They showed that rutilantinone was quinonoid, and comparison with the data collected by Birkinshaw[2] suggested that the four main absorption bands (see Fig. 1) could be attributed to the presence of a 1,4,5-trihydroxyanthra-quinone chromophore in the rutilantinone structure.

λ_{max} (ε_{max}) in Cyclohexane

Rutilantinone　　　　　　　　486 (13,000); 498 (14,400); 520 (12,000); 534 (11.700).

1,4,5-Trihydroxyanthra-　　　485 (10,000); 495 (11,000); 517 (9,000); 530 (9,000).
　quinone

FIG. 1. Visible spectra of rutilantinone and 1,4,5-trihydroxyanthraquinone.

The infrared spectra of polyhydroxyanthraquinones are also of consider-able value in structural diagnosis, and in Fig. 2 the infrared carbonyl absorptions are listed for various polyhydroxy-derivatives of anthraquinone which have been studied by Bloom et al.[3]

Anthraquinone itself contains two identically placed carbonyl groups and shows carbonyl absorption as one main band. If, however, a hydroxyl group is situated in the peri-position to one of the carbonyl groups, then one carbonyl group is internally hydrogen bonded and the other is not. We therefore have absorption of the unperturbed carbonyl group of the anthra-quinone at 1675–1647 cm^{-1} and a second carbonyl absorption appears at a lower frequency (1637–1621 cm^{-1}). For 1,4- or 1,5-dihydroxyanthraquinones the position of the carbonyl groups is such that they are both hydrogen bonded and show a single carbonyl band at 1645–1608 cm^{-1}. Similarly, the 1,8-dihydroxyanthraquinones show two carbonyl bands whereas the 1,4,5-trihydroxy- and the 1,4,5,8-tetrahydroxyanthraquinones show only one band. Comparison of the infrared spectrum of rutilantinone with these model anthraquinones confirmed the earlier diagnosis that rutilantinone was possibly a 1,4,5-trihydroxyanthraquinone derivative and the original mole-cular formula, $C_{22}H_{20}O_9$, may be expanded as indicated (2).

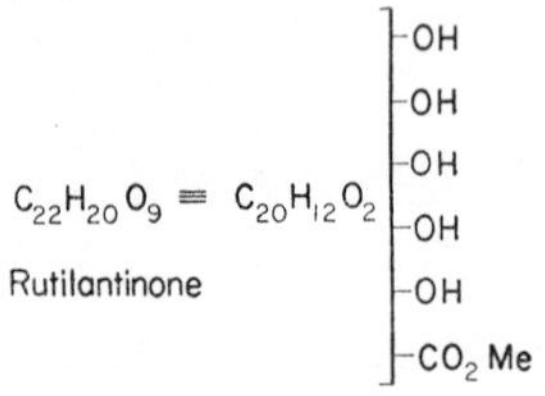

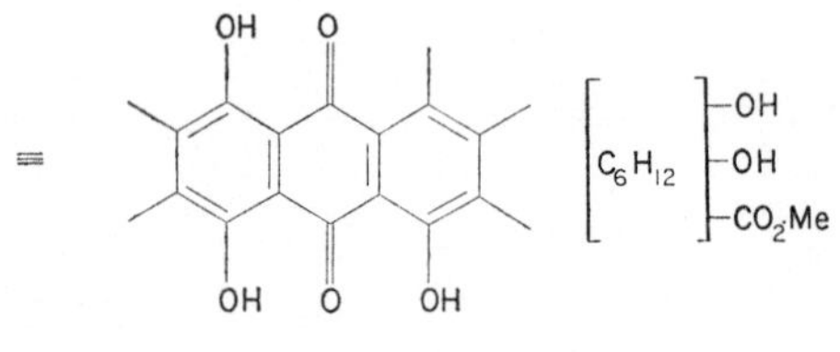

In order to determine something further about the environment of the C-methyl group which had to be contained in the C_6H_{12} residue (see 2), rutilantinone was subjected to a Kuhn–Roth oxidation. This yielded a mixture of carboxylic acids which were separated by chromatography on silica and identified as acetic acid and propionic acid. The isolation of

Position of hydroxyl groups	Structural formula		ν_{max} (C=O) in Nujol, cm^{-1}
			1678 – 1653
1-			1675–1647 1637–1621
1,4- or 1,5-			1645 –1608
1,8-			1678–1661 1626–1616
1,4,5-			1616 – 1592
1,4,5,8-			1592–1572
Rutilantinone			(1618) 1601

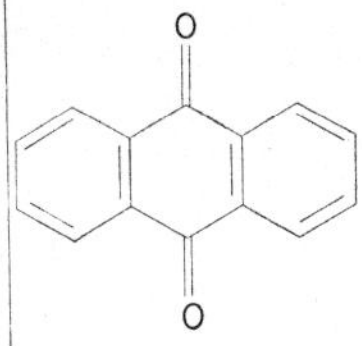

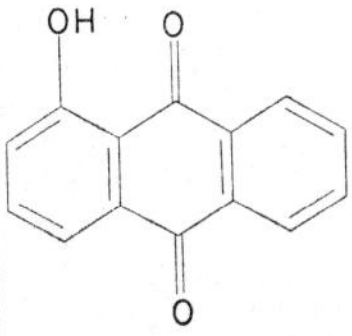

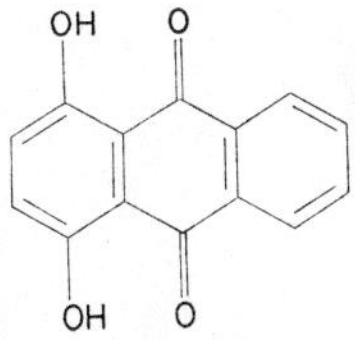

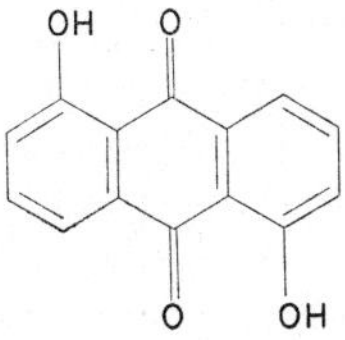

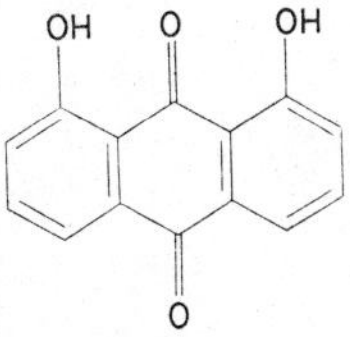

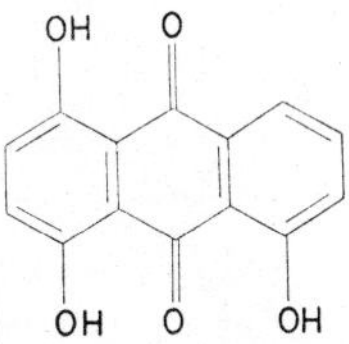

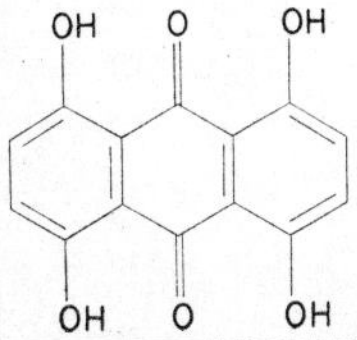

FIG. 2. Infrared carbonyl absorption of rutilantinone and related polyhydroxy-anthraquinones[3].

propionic acid, characterized as its crystalline *p*-bromophenacyl derivative, was important because this established quite certainly that a methylene group was adjacent to the methyl group and proved that rutilantinone contained an ethyl group, thus leading to the part structure (3) for rutilantinone.

(3)

When rutilantinone was subjected to the action of alkali, we isolated a substance, rutilantinonic acid, produced by hydrolysis of the ester group to a carboxylic acid function. We also obtained another product which was a neutral compound and its infrared spectrum showed that it still contained an ester group (1724 cm^{-1}) but there was no alcoholic hydroxyl absorption. The isolation of this neutral compound was particularly intriguing and quite unexpected.

The attempted methylation of rutilantinone with dimethyl sulphate under mildly basic conditions (potassium carbonate–acetone) yielded an unresolved mixture of products which also lacked alcoholic hydroxyl absorption in its infrared spectrum. These base-catalysed dehydrations of rutilantinone presumably involved its alcoholic hydroxyl groups and if these hydroxyl groups were eliminated under basic conditions, it was considered probable that they would also be eliminated under acidic conditions. This suggestion was rewarded by the observation that rutilantinone, $C_{22}H_{20}O_9$, when refluxed in xylene containing a trace of toluenesulphonic acid, was transformed into a bisanhydro derivative, $C_{22}H_{16}O_7$. This bisanhydrorutilantinone was identical with the neutral compound which was a byproduct in the alkaline hydrolysis of rutilantinone, and we later found that it could be formed very easily by just warming a pyridine solution of rutilantinone. Bisanhydrorutilantinone clearly contains the ester group (ν_{max} 1724 cm^{-1}) originally present in rutilantinone (ν_{max} 1730 cm^{-1}) and it forms a triacetate, showing that two of the hydroxyl groups initially present in rutilantinone have now been removed by the extrusion of the elements of two molecules of water.

The formation of bisanhydrorutilantinone from rutilantinone was associated with a dramatic change in the ultraviolet spectra. Bisanhydrorutilantinone shows considerable detail in its ultraviolet and visible spectra which were characterized by seven maxima (see Fig. 3). At this stage a publication by Brockman and Müller on the synthesis of tetracenequinones[4] was of very great assistance to us. We noticed that the ultraviolet and visible spectra of bisanhydrorutilantinone were strikingly similar to those of 1,4,6-trihydroxy-tetracenequinone, and yet were significantly different from the spectra of 1,6,11-trihydroxytetracenequinone (see Fig. 3). It was therefore suggested that bisanhydrorutilantinone contained a fourth carbocyclic ring and was a derivative of 1,4,6-trihydroxytetracenequinone.

Bisanhydro— rutilantinone	1,4,6–Trihydroxytetracene - quinone	1,6,11 –Trihydroxytetracene– quinone
	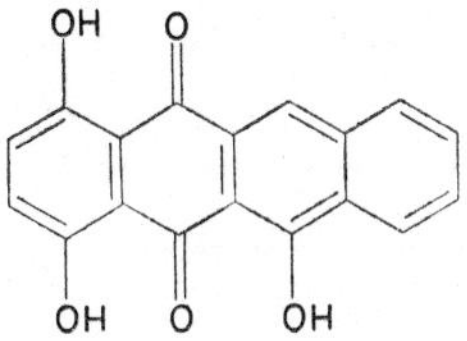	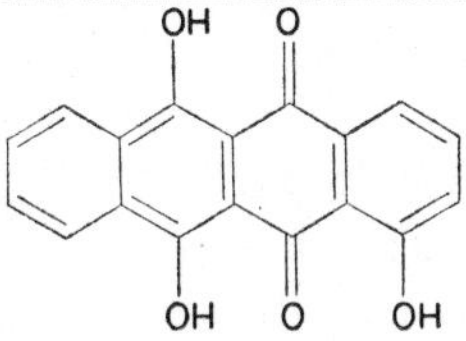
252 (62,500)		
275 (36,700)		
486 (22,600)	483 (20,500)	463 (13,000)
496 (24,200)	493 (22,000)	495 (24,500)
508 (20,800)	505 (18,000)	
519 (25,500)	515 (23,000)	519 (24,500)
530 (21,800)	530 (20,500)	530 (27,500)

FIG. 3. Ultraviolet spectra [λ_{max} (ε_{max})] in cyclohexane.

This suggestion coupled with the part structure (3) considered for rutil-antinone led to the part structure (4) for bisanhydrorutilantinone. This is in accord with the similarity of the ultraviolet spectra of bisanhydro-rutilantinone triacetate [λ_{max} (ε_{max}) 248 mμ (49,500), 299 mμ (28,500), 391 mμ (6,800), 396 mμ (6,860) in methanol] and 1,4,6-triacetoxytetracenequinone [λ_{max} (ε_{max}) 247 mμ (40,000), 295 mμ (22,000), 392 mμ (5,500)][4]. The problem of determining the structure of bisanhydrorutilantinone was now reduced to locating the methoxycarbonyl group and the ethyl group in the part structure (4).

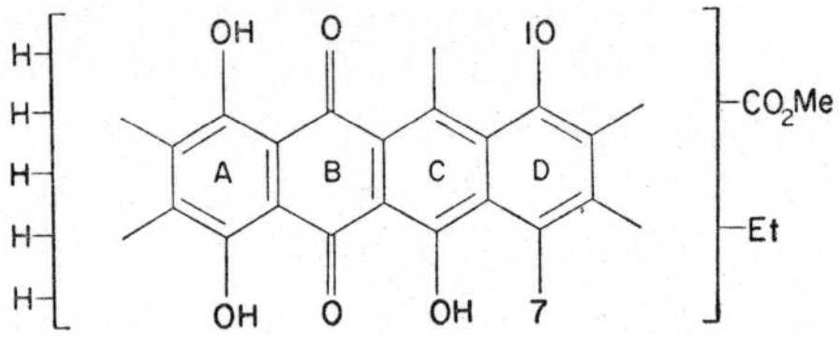

(4)

The acidic or basic conditions under which bisanhydrorutilantinone was formed from rutilantinone were quite mild so it was most unlikely that a fourth carbocyclic ring had been generated during this dehydration. It could therefore be argued that the rings A, B, C, and D were also present in rutilantinone. Clearly it was ring D which had to be hydroaromatic and rutilantinone could be formulated by the part structure (5) which required the location of four functional groups: two alcoholic hydroxyl groups, the methoxycarbonyl group, and the ethyl group.

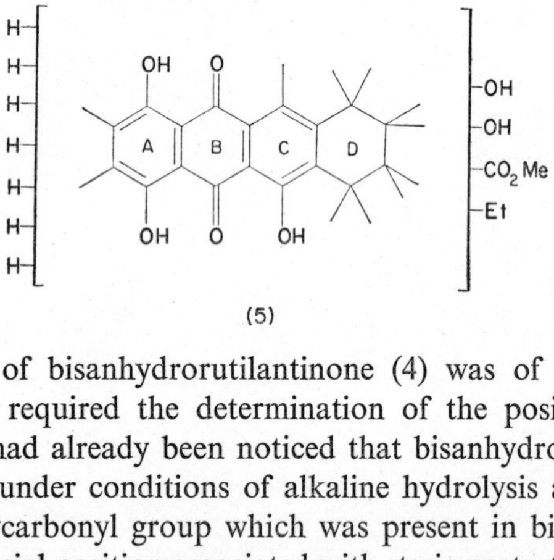

(5)

The structure of bisanhydrorutilantinone (4) was of assistance in this connection as it required the determination of the position of only two substituents. It had already been noticed that bisanhydrorutilantinone was extremely stable under conditions of alkaline hydrolysis and this indicated that the methoxycarbonyl group which was present in bisanhydrorutilantinone was in a special position associated with steric protection. As the infrared spectrum of bisanhydrorutilantinone showed ester absorption at 1724 cm^{-1} the ester group could not be placed in a position where it could form a hydrogen bond with any one of the three phenolic hydroxyl groups; this would have caused a shift of the carbonyl band to a lower frequency. In addition the ester groups in bisanhydrorutilantinone and in rutilantinone must be in equivalent positions and, since the alkaline hydrolysis of rutilantinone could be achieved comparatively easily, it followed that the ester group must be located on the aliphatic portion of the rutilantinone molecule, that is, on ring D. There are therefore only two positions, 7 or 10, in structure (4) where the ester group can be given steric protection, and in each case the ethyl group must be adjacent to it. Of the two possible structures (6) and (7) for bisanhydrorutilantinone, (7) was preferred since the infrared spectral characteristics of the methoxycarbonyl group indicated that it was not hydrogen bonded as it would have been if it were in position 7. The fact that bisanhydrorutilantinone could not be converted into a lactone was also evidence against structure (6). Structure (7) for bisanhydrorutilantinone was supported by the formation of a triacetate which showed phenolic acetate absorption (1776 cm^{-1}), ester absorption (1730 cm^{-1}), and conjugated carbonyl absorption (1681 cm^{-1}) in its infrared spectrum.

(6)   (7)

It was now necessary to propose a structure for rutilantinone. The further development of the part structure (8) for rutilantinone required the placing of the two hydroxyl groups so that one was secondary and the other tertiary. Their positions also had to be compatible with their easy elimination under conditions of acidic or basic catalysis.

(8)

Guidance in the placing of the hydroxyl groups in rutilantinone was also provided by applying the principles of biosynthesis discussed by R. W. Rickards (Chapter 1). There are two ways in which structure (8) can be derived from a poly-β-keto-acid precursor. In one scheme (9), a C_1 unit is introduced into the acetate-derived precursor, and this is followed by a cleavage of the β-diketonic function which had permitted the introduction of the C_1-unit. Cyclizations involving appositely placed and suitably activated positions would then lead to a tetracyclic skeleton bearing oxygen at various positions. Alternatively, it was possible that the biosynthesis of rutilantinone might involve a poly-β-keto-acid precursor which was terminated by a propionate-derived residue [see (10)]. This could provide the ethyl group in rutilantinone directly, and recalls the earlier suggestion made by Woodward that propionate may be involved in some biosyntheses.[5] These considerations led to the structural proposal (11) for rutilantinone.[6]

This structure (11) accounted satisfactorily for the properties of rutilanti-none which have already been discussed and, in particular, the formation of bisanhydrorutilantinone under *basic* conditions is easily rationalized as one

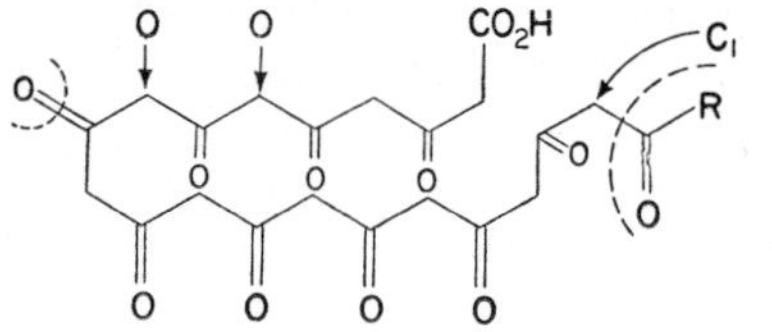

(9)

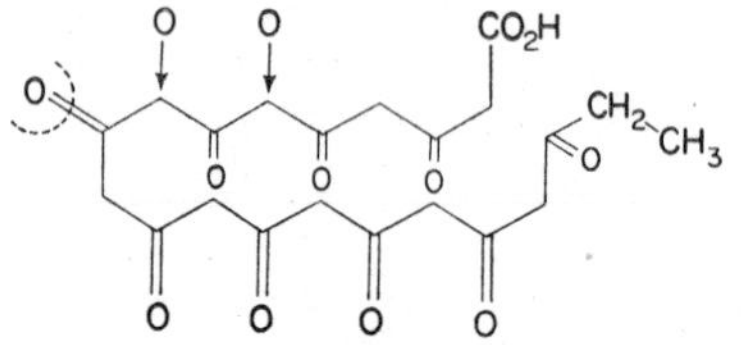

(10)

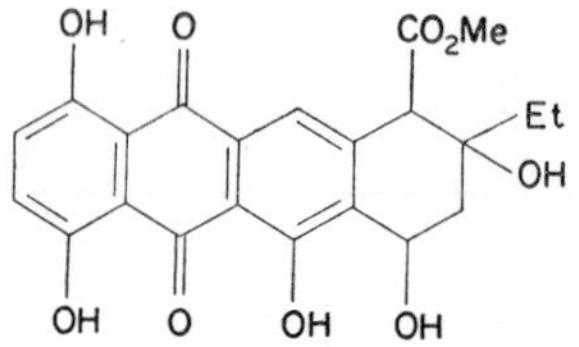

(11)

hydroxyl group is in the β-relationship to the methoxycarbonyl group. It was appreciated, however, that this structural proposal required some definite confirmation and the experiment which was designed in order to prove the positions of the methoxycarbonyl and ethyl groups relative to the

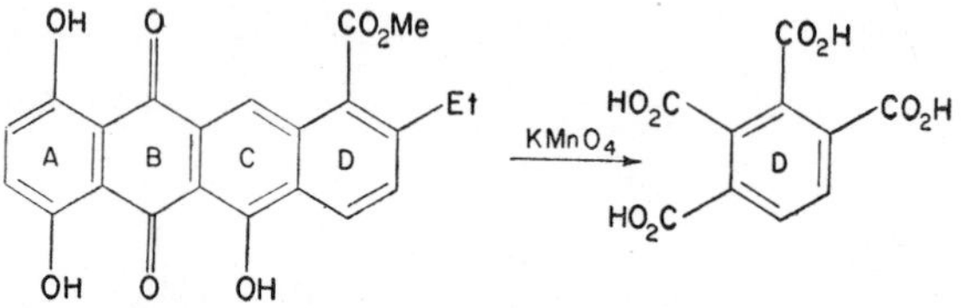

(7)

trihydroxyanthraquinone part of the bisanhydro-structure (7) was its oxida-tion with potassium permanganate. This yielded benzene-1,2,3,4-tetra-carboxylic acid, characterized by comparison of its tetramethyl ester with an authentic specimen. This result confirmed structure (11) for rutilantinone.

THE PYRROMYCINONES, PYRROMYCIN, AND CINERUBINS A AND B

Several weeks after the completion of our work on rutilantinone, three papers appeared describing the very extensive studies by Prelog,[7] Brockmann[8,9] and their collaborators on a number of substances which were obviously closely related to rutilantinone (see Fig. 4).

Brockmann and Lenk[8,9] had shown that a particular strain of Streptomyces produced four metabolites: ε-pyrromycinone, $C_{22}H_{20}O_9$, which had the same molecular formula as rutilantinone; ζ-pyrromycinone, $C_{22}H_{20}O_8$, which lacked one oxygen atom, η-pyrromycinone, $C_{22}H_{16}O_7$, which had the same formula as bisanhydrorutilantinone, and a nitrogenous glycoside pyrromycin having the molecular formula $C_{30}H_{35}NO_{11}$. The relationship between pyrromycin and ε-pyrromycinone was a simple one in that ε-pyrromycinone was the aglycone of pyrromycin; the other eight carbon atoms were accommodated in a nitrogenous sugar, $C_8H_{17}NO_3$, called rhodosamine whose structure had been investigated by Brockmann and Spohler in 1955.[10] They have proposed two structures (12) or (13) for rhodosamine and the structure (12) is considered to be more likely.

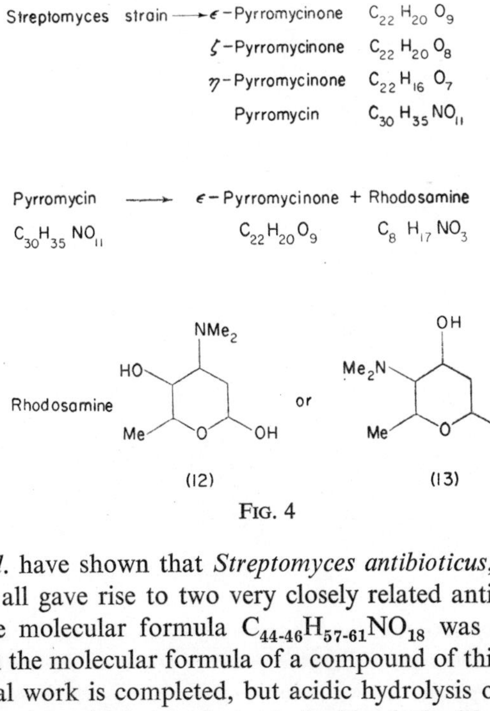

Streptomyces strain ⟶ ε-Pyrromycinone $C_{22}H_{20}O_9$
ζ-Pyrromycinone $C_{22}H_{20}O_8$
η-Pyrromycinone $C_{22}H_{16}O_7$
Pyrromycin $C_{30}H_{35}NO_{11}$

Pyrromycin ⟶ ε-Pyrromycinone + Rhodosamine
$C_{30}H_{35}NO_{11}$ $C_{22}H_{20}O_9$ $C_8H_{17}NO_3$

Rhodosamine (12) or (13)

FIG. 4

Prelog *et al.* have shown that *Streptomyces antibioticus*, *S. galilaeus*, and *S. niveoruber* all gave rise to two very closely related antibiotic substances, for which the molecular formula $C_{44-46}H_{57-61}NO_{18}$ was proposed. Some uncertainty in the molecular formula of a compound of this size is inevitable until structural work is completed, but acidic hydrolysis of cinerubins A or B gave an aglycone which was shown to be identical with ε-pyrromycinone.

ε-Pyrromycinone

Prelog,[7] Brockmann,[8] and their co-workers conducted independent investigations on the structure of ε-pyrromycinone before they discovered that they were working with the same compound. They proposed for ε-pyrromycinone the structure (14) and the methods and arguments which they used were very similar to those which we had independently used in our investigation of rutilantinone. They showed that, like rutilantinone, ε-pyrromycinone also formed a bisanhydro-derivative for which they proposed the structure (15);

this bisanhydro-compound was identical with η-pyrromycinone. It can be seen that the structures proposed for ε-pyrromycinone (14) and η-pyrromycinone (15) bore a striking relationship to the structures which we had deduced for rutilantinone (17) and bisanhydrorutilantinone (18). The interest of these relationships was also amplified when it was recognized that the biosynthesis of compounds with the structures (14) and (15) could clearly

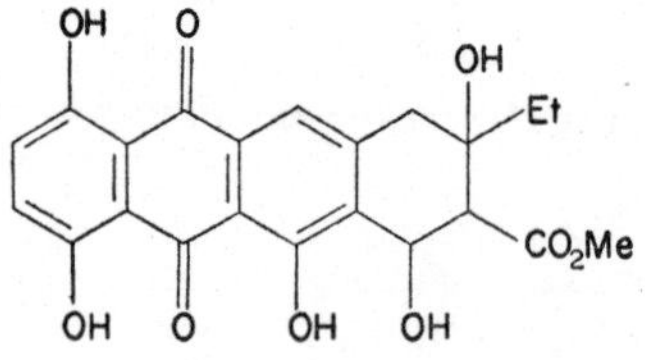

(14)

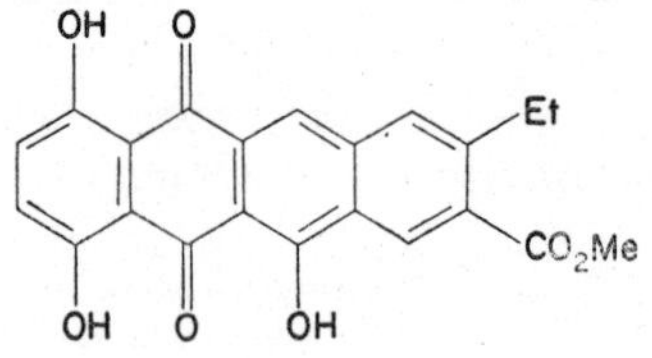

(15)

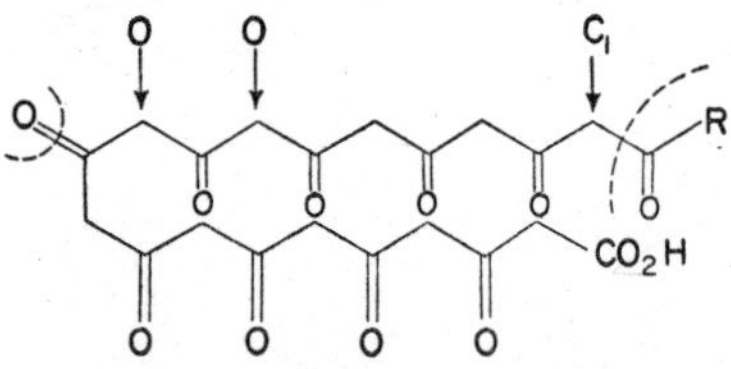

(16)

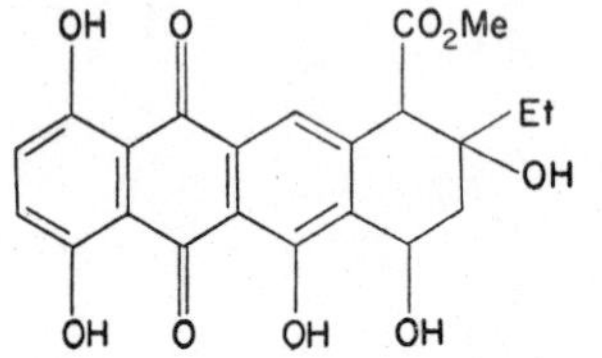

(17)   Rutilantinone

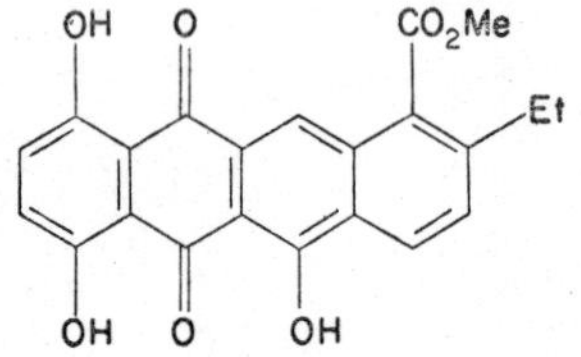

(18)   Bisanhydrorutilantinone

involve a precursor (16) identical with that proposed for the biosynthesis (9) of rutilantinone. The only difference between the two biosynthetic processes was the course taken by condensation reactions.

At this stage in our investigations, we corresponded with Professor Brockmann and Professor Prelog and exchanged specimens of rutilantinone, bisanhydrorutilantinone, ε-pyrromycinone, and η-pyrromycinone when it became clear that ε-pyrromycinone and rutilantinone were identical, as were η-pyrromycinone and bisanhydrorutilantinone. This was established by comparison of their infrared spectra and was placed beyond doubt by the observation that oxidation of η-pyrromycinone gave benzene-1,2,3,4-tetracarboxylic acid. These results required a revision of the structures of the pyrromycinones, and we should like to thank Professor Brockmann and Professor Prelog most warmly for their collaboration which settled this point.[11]

As Brockmann and his colleagues[12] named two of their compounds pyrromycinones in 1957, it is clear that this name should take precedence over rutilantinone. However, the latter name has been retained in the first part of this account for ease of presentation. Where necessary in the rest of this chapter the equivalence of the names will be indicated.

η-Pyrromycinone

As already indicated, the structure (15) first proposed for η-pyrromycinone required revision when it was shown to be identical with bisanhydrorutilantinone (18). Brockmann and Brockmann[13] have recently carried out a very interesting experiment in which they hydrolysed η-pyrromycinone (18) under very vigorous conditions and decarboxylated the η-pyrromycinonic

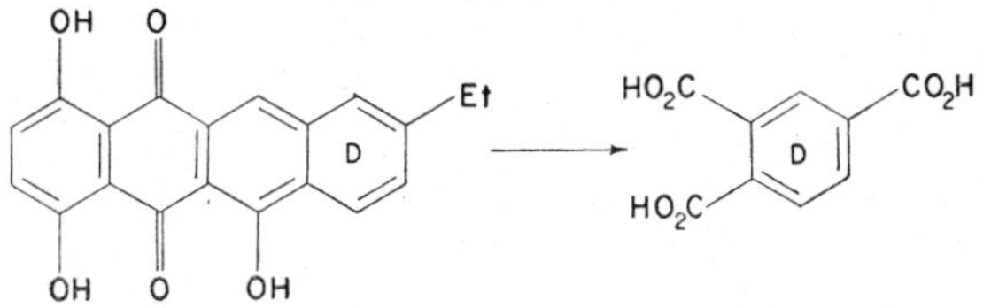

(19)   (20)

acid giving desmethoxycarbonyl-η-pyrromycinone (19). This substance on nitric acid oxidation gave benzene-1,2,4-tricarboxylic acid (20). This is an important result and establishes beyond all doubt the position of the methoxycarbonyl group.

ζ-Pyrromycinone

This substance, $C_{22}H_{20}O_8$, which is a congener of ε- and η-pyrromycinone (see Fig. 4), was first investigated by Brockmann and Lenk[12] who recognized that it contained an alcoholic hydroxyl group and an ester group, and that it was a derivative of 1,4,5-trihydroxyanthraquinone. The structure (21)

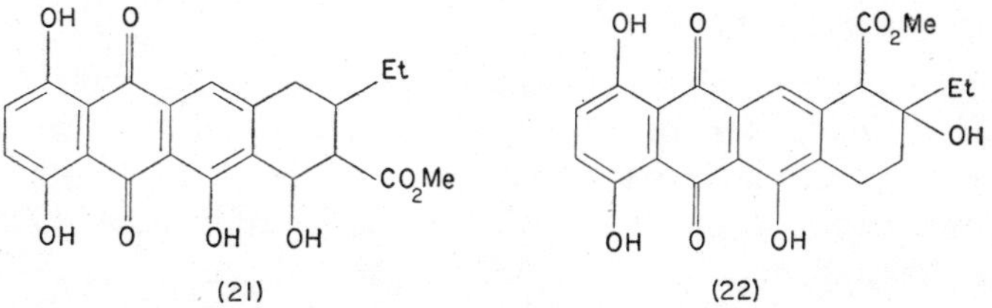

(21)   (22)

which was first proposed by Brockmann and Lenk[8] for ζ-pyrromycinone was later amended by them[14] to the structure (22).

The structure of ζ-pyrromycinone (22) is proved by the catalytic hydrogenation of ε-pyrromycinone (17) to ζ-pyrromycinone (22),[13] a transformation which would involve the hydrogenolysis of a benzylic hydroxyl group. The structure (22) therefore follows from the structure of ε-pyrromycinone (17). It is confirmed by the formation by heating with palladium-charcoal of η-pyrromycinone (18) from ζ-pyrromycinone.

When ζ-pyrromycinone is heated it gives an anhydro-compound and an isomeric keto-ester which probably has the constitution (23). This keto-ester

(23)

(23) is transformed back to ζ-pyrromycinone (22) by heating with pyridine-triethylamine; this product is presumably a racemate. This is a reaction which is related to one of the steps envisaged in the biosynthesis (9) or (10).

RHODOMYCINONES AND RHODOMYCINS

For some years Brockmann and his colleagues[15-21] have been interested in the mould products produced by *Streptomyces purpurascens* and an interesting account of this work is available.[22] This mould produces a complex mixture of metabolites including β-rhodomycinone, γ-rhodomycinone, ε-rhodomycinone, ζ-isorhodomycinone, ε-isorhodomycinone, and the rhodomycins which are nitrogenous glycosides in which some of the rhodomycinones are the aglycones. Acidic hydrolysis of rhodomycins A and B gave rhodosamine (12) or (13).[10] A considerable amount of work on the rhodomycinones has been done, particularly on β-rhodomycinone,[20] but it is not yet possible to make complete structural proposals for them, although β- and ε-rhodomycinone appear to be derivatives of 1,4,5-trihydroxyanthraquinone.[19]

ε-Isorhodomycinone

Brockmann and Frank[19] investigated ε-isorhodomycinone for which they proposed the molecular formula, $C_{20}H_{20}O_9$. It was shown that oxidation gave propionic acid and that it contained an ester group. Furthermore, it was recognized that it showed the chromophoric properties of 1,4,5,8-tetra-hydroxyanthraquinone.

When the structure of ε-pyrromycinone (rutilantinone) had been established, it was clear that the similarity between ε-isorhodomycinone and ε-pyrromycinone was so close that ε-isorhodomycinone could be the 11-hydroxy-derivative (25) of ε-pyrromycinone (24). This position for the additional oxygen atom in the ε-isorhodomycinone structure would be biochemically acceptable.

This structural proposal for ε-isorhodomycinone has been elegantly confirmed by Brockmann and Boldt[21] very recently. They showed that its molecular formula had to be amended to $C_{22}H_{20}O_{10}$ and that it formed a pentaacetate which still contained a hydroxyl group resistant to acetylation. η-Pyrromycinone (27) was oxidized with manganese dioxide when hydroxylation at the one available p-position occurred giving the compound (26) which

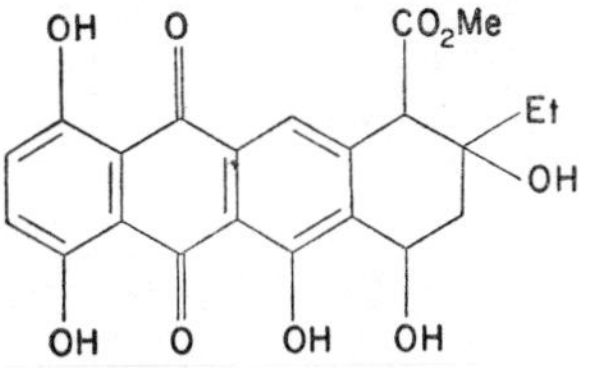

(24) ε—Pyrromycinone

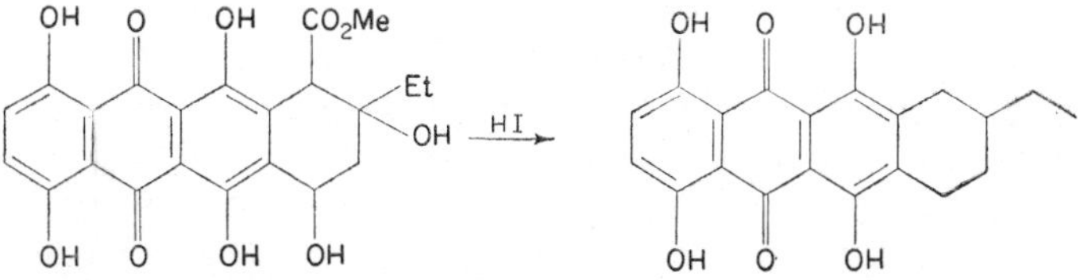

(25) ε—Isorhodomycinone

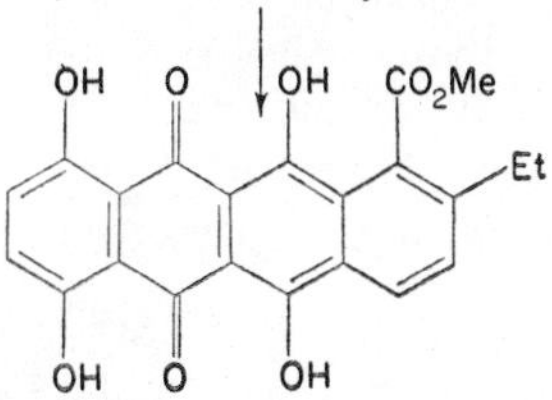

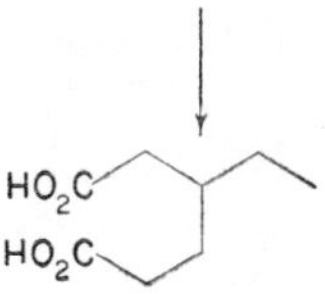

(26)

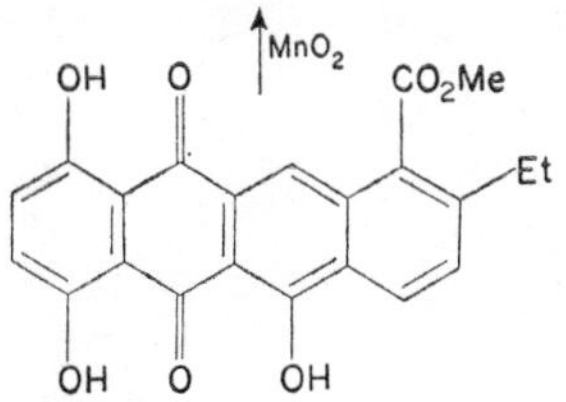

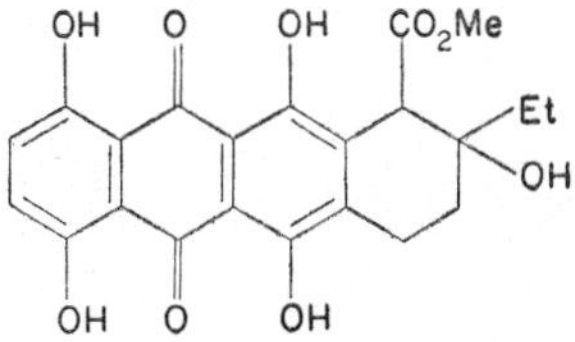

(27) η—Pyrromycinone

(28)

(29)

(30)

was identical with the bisanhydro-derivative (26) of ε-isorhodomycinone. The structure (25) for ε-isorhodomycinone has therefore been confirmed. Furthermore, the chemical study of ε-isorhodomycinone has provided a very satisfying demonstration of the position of the ethyl group in these compounds. ε-Isorhodomycinone on treatment with hydrogen iodide and phenol gave a compound, $C_{20}H_{18}O_6$, with the constitution (28) which on oxidation gave β-ethyl adipic acid (29), thus establishing the position of the ethyl group.

15

ζ-Isorhodomycinone

ζ-Isorhodomycinone, $C_{22}H_{20}O_9$, is a congener of ε-isorhodomycinone and is isomeric with ε-pyrromycinone. Since it is a derivative of 1,4,5,8-tetra-hydroxyanthraquinone it is likely that it lacks one of the two alcoholic hydroxyl groups present in ε-isorhodomycinone (25). Catalytic hydrogenation of ε-isorhodomycinone (25) in ethanol-triethanolamine with a palladium–barium sulphate catalyst gave a deoxy-derivative identical with ζ-isorhodomycinone from which it may be deduced that ζ-isorhodomycinone has the structure (30).[21]

AKLAVIN AND AKLAVINONE

The antibiotic aklavin is another substance which shows antiphage activity and on mild acidic hydrolysis it gave a yellow, crystalline aglycone, aklavinone, whose structure has been recently determined.[24]

The molecular formula of aklavinone, $C_{22}H_{20}O_8$, suggested that it could be a deoxy-ε-pyrromycinone (deoxy-rutilantinone), so when it was shown to contain a 1,8-dihydroxyanthraquinone chromophore, it was considered possible on biogenetic grounds that aklavinone had the structure (31). The biosynthetic processes (9) or (10) leading to the members of the group of antibiotics which has been discussed require the introduction of one or more oxygen atoms in the positions para to phenolic hydroxyl groups; in ε-pyrromycinone (24) one oxygen atom is introduced and in ε-isorhodomycinone (25) two such oxygen atoms are introduced. Therefore, if the suggestion could be made that aklavinone lacked hydroxyl groups which were introduced in this way, structure (31) could be proposed.

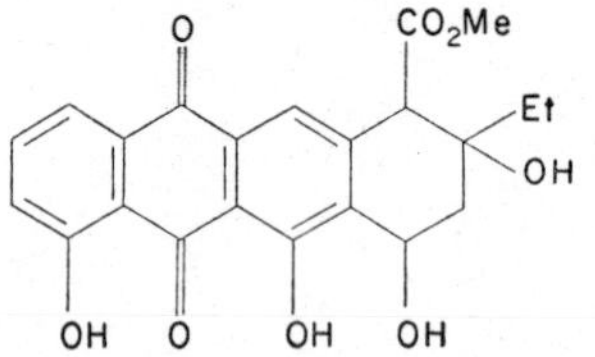

(31) 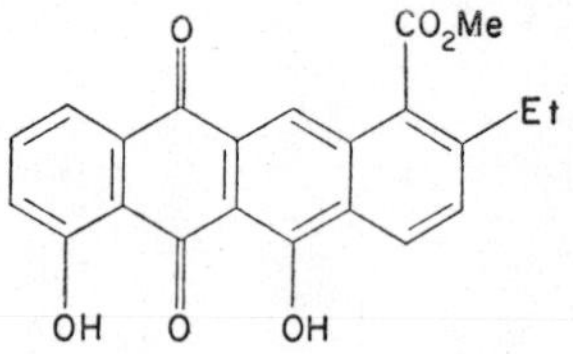　　　　　(32)

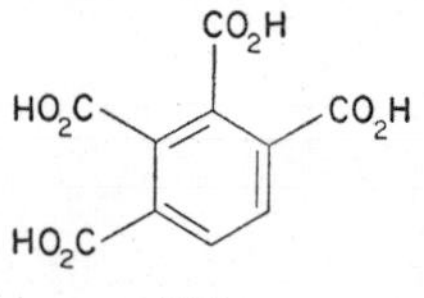

(33)

Structure (31) for aklavinone was confirmed using methods which were analogous to those which we had used previously for rutilantinone (ε-pyrromycinone). Aklavinone formed a triacetate which still contained a hydroxyl group and when heated with toluene containing toluene sulphonic acid it gave a bisanhydro-derivative (32) which formed a diacetate. Oxidation of this bisanhydro-derivative (32) gave benzene-1,2,3,4-tetracarboxylic acid (33), thereby substantiating its structure.

There is one feature of the structure (31) for aklavinone which is not settled and this is characteristic of all aglycones which have been discussed. This uncertainty concerns the position of the secondary hydroxyl group, which was placed originally on proposals for the biosynthesis of aglycones. The hydrogenolysis of the secondary hydroxyl group in ε-pyrromycinone and ε-isorhodomycinone is evidence in support of its benzylic location, but it is not definitive.

The one method which is now available to the organic chemist for providing the solution to this type of structural problem is nuclear magnetic resonance spectroscopy and Dr. L. M. Jackman[24] very kindly examined the nuclear magnetic resonance spectrum of aklavinone and was able to provide information about the environment of practically all the hydrogen atoms.

The nuclear magnetic resonance spectrum of aklavinone ($CHCl_3$, 56.4 Mc) exhibited bands with the following τ values with relative integrated intensities corresponding to the indicated number of protons.

τ values	8.90	8.43	7.66	6.30	5.70	4.67
Number of protons	3	2	2	3	1	1

The bands at 8.90 and 8.43 were characteristic of an isolated ethyl group, the first band being associated with the terminal CH_3—group and the second band with the adjacent—CH_2—group. The band at 7.66 is due to a methylene group which is not benzylic and that at 6.30 is sharp and is characteristic of an ester methyl group. The absorption at 4.67 gives a broad band and must be assigned to the proton attached to a carbon atom which is itself attached to a benzene ring and a hydroxyl group. This proves that aklavinone contains a secondary benzylic hydroxyl group.

The remaining band (5.70) is assignable to a proton which is simultaneously benzylic and α to a methoxycarbonyl group. The lack of fine structure in this group indicates the absence of protons on the two carbon atoms to which the —CH— group is attached. This proves the presence of an CO₂—Me group where C_A bears no hydrogen atoms. Ar—CH—C_A

Thus, the nuclear magnetic resonance spectrum of aklavinone is compatible only with the arrangement of substituents on ring D as shown in formula (31). This is direct proof of the position of the secondary hydroxyl group in aklavinone and it may be presumed that the secondary hydroxyl groups of ε-pyrromycinone and ε-isorhodomycinone are similarly located.

STRUCTURAL RELATIONSHIPS

The current situation regarding the members of this new family of anti-biotics is indicated in Fig. 5. In some cases these compounds occur in the free state and in others they are glycosidically combined with nitrogenous sugars, and possibly other types of compounds. Those compounds which exist as glycosides are indicated in Fig. 5.

There is included in Fig. 5 a substance which has been isolated since this paper was given. In a further examination of the quinonoid compounds which are produced with aklavin we have isolated a compound with the molecular formula $C_{22}H_{20}O_7$ which is a deoxyaklavinone lacking the benzylic hydroxyl group.[25] It is therefore the 1,8-dihydroxyanthraquinone analogue of ζ-pyrromycinone and ζ-isorhodomycinone.

GLYCOSIDES

Several known glycosides are listed in Fig. 5, but the detailed investigation of their structures has been mainly limited to their aglycones. The one glycoside whose structure has been determined is pyrromycin (34). Brock-mann and Lenk[9] have shown that pyrromycin, $C_{30}H_{35}NO_{11}$, is derived from

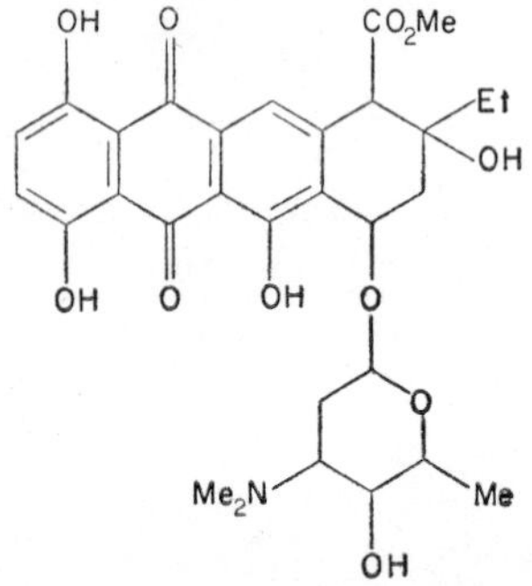

(34)

ε-pyrromycinone and rhodosamine. Comparison of the ultraviolet spectra of pyrromycin and ε-pyrromycinone has shown that none of the three phenolic hydroxyl groups of the aglycone is involved in glycoside formation and since pyrromycin forms a tetra-acetate hydrochloride it follows that it has the constitution (34).

BIOSYNTHESIS

The variety of structures shown by the compounds in Fig. 5 is a particularly good example of the operation of the principles of biosynthesis as discussed by R. W. Rickards (Chapter 1) and by W. B. Whalley (Chapter 2). The molecular formulae of the members of this group range from $C_{22}H_{20}O_7$ to $C_{22}H_{20}O_{10}$, and if we disregard for the moment the details of the process

Compound	Molecular formula	Structure	Glycoside
Aklavinone	$C_{22}H_{20}O_8$	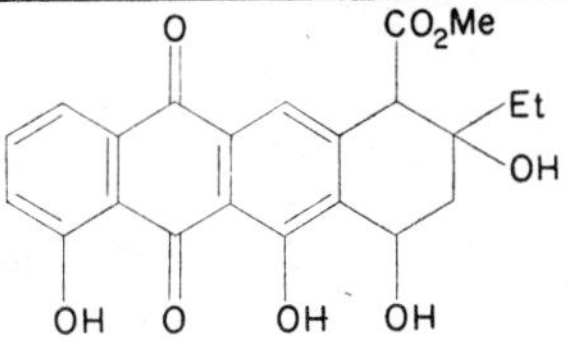	Aklavin
7 – Deoxyaklavinone	$C_{22}H_{20}O_7$	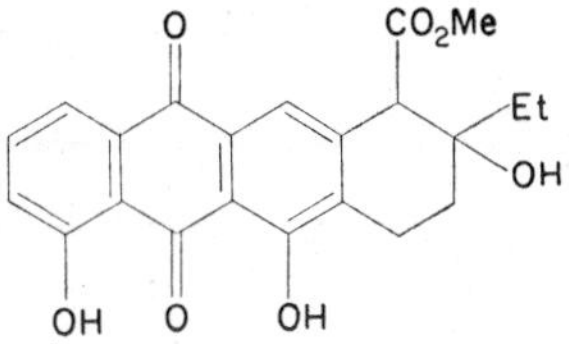	
Rutilantinone (ϵ – Pyrromycinone)	$C_{22}H_{20}O_9$	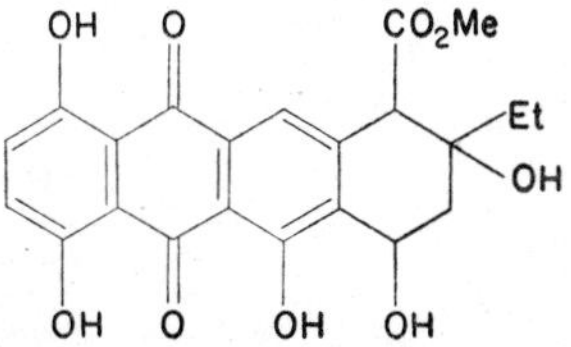	Rutilantins A,B,C Cinerubins A and B Pyrromycin
ζ – Pyrromycinone	$C_{22}H_{20}O_8$	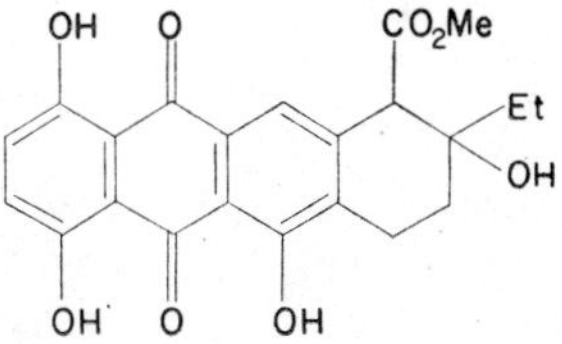	
ϵ – Isorhodomycinone	$C_{22}H_{20}O_{10}$	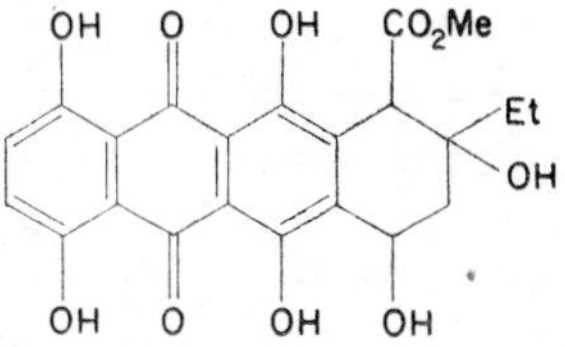	
ζ – Isorhodomycinone	$C_{22}H_{20}O_9$	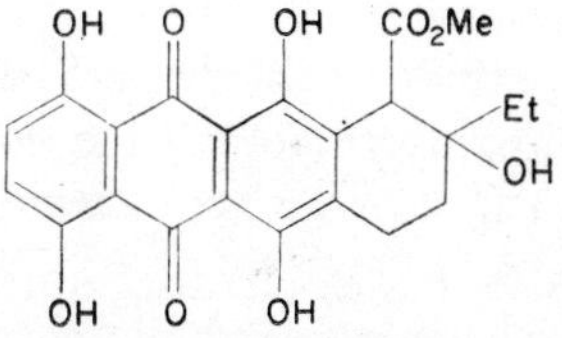	

FIG. 5. A new family of antibiotics.

leading to the ethyl group (see formulae 9 or 10) then the general features of the biosynthesis of these compounds can be summarized by the scheme shown in Fig. 6.

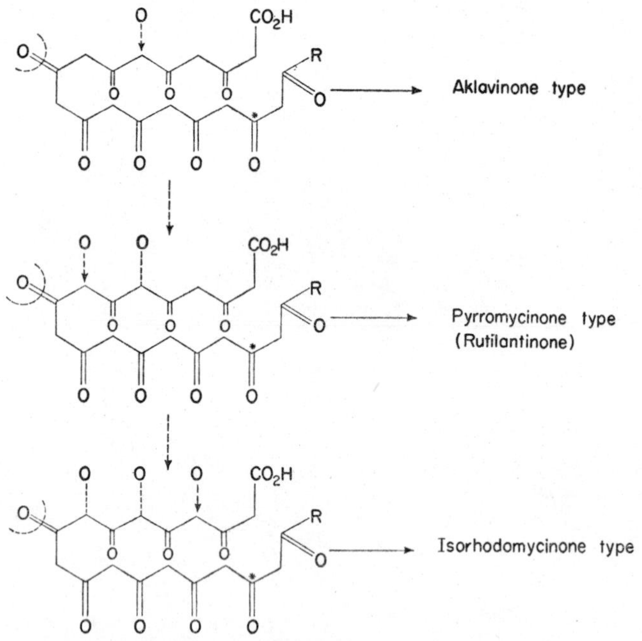

Fig. 6. Biosynthetic relationships.

The asterisked carbonyl group in the three precursors formally represented in Fig. 6 provides a methylene group in one of the representatives of the three types and the secondary hydroxyl function in each partner. It would appear that further structural variation in compounds of this class is limited. For this reason it will be particularly interesting to await further results from Professor Brockmann's group on the chemistry of β-rhodomycinone and related compounds which may well indicate a further variation on the structural theme provided by the biosynthetic reactions indicated in Fig. 6.

Since the lecture on which this chapter is based was given it has been established that the biosynthesis of ε-pyrromycinone follows route (10) rather than route (9).[26] Thus it has been demonstrated that propionic acid is directly involved as a precursor and this is the first case where it has been shown that the biosynthesis involves both acetate and propionate.† It is probable that the biosyntheses of all the compounds listed in Fig. 5 are closely related. The variation among these structures is a good example of

† Added in proof: Since this chapter was written further examples of propionate incorporation have been reported. They are a-methylbutyric acid,[27] erythromycin,[28] and methymycin.[29]

the consequences of the operation of secondary reductive and oxidative processes on an acetate–propionate derived precursor.

Acknowledgement.—We should like to thank Mr. B. K. Kelly, the Director, Dr. J. J. Gordon and Mr. R. C. Codner of the Medical Research Council's Antibiotic Research Station, Clevedon, for their collaboration.

REFERENCES

1. I. N. ASHESHOV. Private communication.
2. J. H. BIRKINSHAW, *Biochem. J.* 1955, **59**, 485.
3. H. BLOOM, L. H. BRIGGS and B. CLEVERLEY, *J. Chem. Soc.* 1959, 178.
4. H. BROCKMANN and W. MÜLLER, *Chem. Ber.* 1959, **92**, 1164.
5. R. B. WOODWARD, *Angew. Chem.* 1956, **68**, 13.
6. W. D. OLLIS, I. O. SUTHERLAND and J. J. GORDON, *Tetrahedron Letters* 1959, **16**, 17.
7. L. ETTLINGER, E. GÄUMANN, R. HÜTTER, W. KELLER-SCHIERLEIN, F. KRADOLFER, L. NEIPP, V. PRELOG, P. REUSSER and H. ZÄHNER, *Chem. Ber.* 1959, **92**, 1867.
8. H. BROCKMANN and W. LENK, *Chem. Ber.* 1959, **92**, 1880.
9. H. BROCKMANN and W. LENK, *Chem. Ber.* 1959, **92**, 1904.
10. H. BROCKMANN and E. SPOHLER, *Naturwiss.* 1955, **42**, 154.
11. H. BROCKMANN, H. BROCKMANN, Jr., J. J. GORDON, W. KELLER-SCHIERLEIN, W. LENK, W. D. OLLIS, V. PRELOG and I. O. SUTHERLAND, *Tetrahedron Letters* 1960, **8**, 25.
12. H. BROCKMANN, L. COSTA PLÀ and W. LENK, *Angew. Chem.* 1957, **69**, 477.
13. H. BROCKMANN and H. BROCKMANN, Jr., *Naturwiss.* 1960, **47**, 135.
14. H. BROCKMANN and W. LENK, *Naturwiss.* 1960, **47**, 135.
15. H. BROCKMANN, K. BAUER and I. BORCHERS, *Naturwiss.* 1950, **37**, 492.
16. H. BROCKMANN, K. BAUER and I. BORCHERS, *Chem. Ber.* 1951, **84**, 700.
17. H. BROCKMANN and I. BORCHERS, *Chem. Ber.* 1953, **86**, 261.
18. H. BROCKMANN and B. PATT, *Chem. Ber.* 1955, **88**, 1455.
19. H. BROCKMANN and B. FRANK, *Chem. Ber.* 1955, **88**, 1792.
20. H. BROCKMANN and P. BOLDT, *Naturwiss.* 1957, **44**, 616.
21. H. BROCKMANN and P. BOLDT, *Naturwiss.* 1960, **47**, 134.
22. R. H. THOMPSON, *Naturally Occurring Quinones*, Butterworths, London, 1957.
23. F. STRELITZ, H. FLON, U. WEISS and I. N. ASHESHOV, *J. Bacteriol.* 1956, **72**, 90.
24. J. J. GORDON, L. M. JACKMAN, W. D. OLLIS and I. O. SUTHERLAND, *Tetrahedron Letters* 1960, **8**, 28.
25. W. D. OLLIS, I. O. SUTHERLAND and J. J. GORDON, unpublished observations.
26. W. D. OLLIS, I. O. SUTHERLAND, R. C. CODNER, J. J. GORDON and G. A. MILLER, *Proc. Chem. Soc.* 1960, 347.
    W. D. OLLIS, I. O. SUTHERLAND and P. L. VEAL, *Proc. Chem. Soc.* 1960, 349.
27. H. J. SAZ and A. WEIL, *J. Biol. Chem.* 1960, **235**, 914.
28. H. GRISEBACH, H. ACHENBACH and U. C. GRISEBACH, *Naturwiss.* 1960, **47**, 206.
    J. W. CORCORAN, T. KANEDA and J. C. BUTTE, *J. Biol. Chem.* 1960, **235**, P.C. 29.
    H. GRISEBACH, H. ACHENBACH and W. HORHEINZ, *Z. Naturforschg.* 1960, **15b**, 560.
29. A. J. BIRCH, E. PRIDE, R. W. RICKARDS. P. J. THOMSON, J. D. DUTCHER, D. PERLMAN and C. DJERASSI, *Chem. and Ind.* 1960. 1245.

INDEX

233